The World Food Problem

The Crowell Economics Series

Willard W. Cochrane
UNIVERSITY OF MINNESOTA

The
World Food Problem

A Guardedly Optimistic View

THOMAS Y. CROWELL COMPANY, INC.

NEW YORK · *Established 1834*

*This book is part of the Crowell/Challenge Series,
prepared in cooperation with Challenge Communications, Inc.,
New York, Haig Babian, Editor.*

Library of Congress Catalog Card Number: 78–87151

Series design by Klaus Gemming
Manufactured in the United States of America

TO MY MOTHER

Preface

THIS IS A BOOK about a problem whose outward appearance seems to change dramatically every few years. In the 1950's it appeared that the world community was slowly but surely solving the problem of raising enough food to feed an ever-increasing population. By the early 1960's the future looked less bright: rates of population growth were reaching frightening levels, and rates of increase in food production gave some evidence of slowing down. A partial failure of the monsoon in South Asia in 1965–66 and continued poor weather in 1966–67 turned the earlier uneasiness into dark despair, and talk of widespread famine in the developing world became commonplace. Now with some startling technological developments in the production of wheat, rice, and other grains, the outlook has turned bright once again.

This book attempts to build an understanding of the nature of the *world food problem* and its solution by diverting the discussion away from the hopes and fears of the moment to a consideration of the basic forces involved, the interaction of those forces, and the consumption-production product of those forces. We do this, first, by defining and describing the world food problem in historical perspective; second, by analyzing the problem in the context of the basic forces involved—political, social, economic, technological, and demographic; and third, by discussing the kinds of action required by both the developed and the developing countries to solve the problem permanently.

This book attempts to delve below the froth of popular discussions. It is not, however, a technical book intended for technical readers alone. It is designed to reach interested and informed laymen—businessmen, teachers, students, politicians, and internationalists—who are concerned with the problem and may in some way contribute to its solution. It is the hope of the author that the ideas and materials presented in this book will help many people in many walks of life think and act more constructively with regard to the world food problem.

The ideas developed and the materials presented in this volume come from four principal sources: (1) the work and findings of professionals in the U.S. Department of Agriculture who specialize in world food and agricultural development problems, (2) the published documents of the Food and Agricultural Organization and other specialized agencies of the United Nations, (3) the writings of economists at home and abroad specializing in economic development problems, and (4) the overseas experience of the author while working on food and agricultural problems. Of course, the way in which these ideas and materials have been used and developed in this book is the responsibility of the author alone.

Two men read all of the manuscript and made many valuable suggestions for its improvement: Martin E. Abel, formerly Deputy Assistant Secretary, U.S. Department of Agriculture and now Professor of Agricultural Economics at the University of Minnesota, and Lee R. Martin, Professor of Agricultural Economics at the University of Minnesota. Dr. Abel and his many colleagues in the U.S. Department of Agriculture also provided vital estimates of food consumption, production and trade, and data breakdowns required in this analysis, but not regularly published; this assistance was most helpful in presenting evidence in support of the lines of reasoning developed in this study. I should like to thank the two men named above, and the many unnamed others in the U.S. Department of Agriculture who contributed to the writing of this book.

Dudley Kirk, formerly Director of the Population Council and now a member of the Food Research Institute, Stanford University, read Chapters 2 and 6 dealing with population problems, and is the author of the article on national population policies quoted extensively in Chapter 6.

A word should be said at this point with regard to the data problem. Anyone who attempts to deal seriously with the world food problem is confronted immediately by one huge difficulty—the lack of reliable data on food consumption and production for the developing countries. Much of the data presented as evidence in this volume will probably undergo important revisions in the years ahead as the methods for collecting data and making estimates in the developing countries are improved and become more inclusive. But the following can be said about the food consumption and production data presented in this volume: Based on the work of professionals in the U.S. Department of Agriculture and FAO, they are the best data currently available, and they are probably representative of major trends and developments, even though particular estimates could turn out to be wide of the true mark.

Special thanks are due my secretary, Miss Donna Jamesgaard, who typed the many drafts of the manuscript. She contributed importantly to the production of this book. My wife, Mary, contributed to the readability of the text by reading the manuscript in its many different versions. Lastly, I should like to thank the administration of the University of Minnesota for helping this administrator find the time to write this book.

Minneapolis, Minn.   *Willard W. Cochrane*
January 1969

Contents

Tables and Figures

Tables

Figures

I

The Setting

1

The Revolution
in Expectations

THE COMMON MAN throughout the less developed world has come to believe in, indeed to expect, economic progress for himself, his family, his community, and his nation. The shopkeeper in Tunisia, the government clerk in India, the farm cultivator in Pakistan and Taiwan, the factory worker in Singapore and Bangalore, the college student in Korea and Chile, the farm market woman in Nigeria, and the plantation worker in Malaysia and Central America—all expect a higher material level of living for themselves and their families in the years immediately ahead. Particular expectations, of course, differ from man to man and from country to country; but the expectation of an important improvement in levels of living is fairly general throughout the world.

These people want and expect to receive this year, not next, improved medical services, a richer and more healthful diet, an improved mechanical means of transportation, a transistor radio, schooling for their children, and such frivolities as soft drinks. All this they have learned about, come to believe is possible for them, and built into their regular demands in the two short decades between 1948 and 1968. This is the revolution in expectations that has swept over the developing world.

How did this happen? How did the common man in Asia, Africa, the Middle East, and Latin America become aware of these material things and come to believe that he would have them? There are many facets to the explanation. First, he experienced some of these material things as national and international agencies

3

brought him pills to cool his fevers and school feeding programs to help his children grow strong bodies. Second, he has seen in movies how the other half of the world lives; he has seen modern gadgets on garish billboards, and he has heard about these things on the radio and at government information meetings. Third, his children have learned about the essentials of modern life in public schools. Fourth, local and national politicians have told him that he could have these things if he would vote for them, or help throw out the foreign colonial power. Fifth, the great statesmen of the Western world have declared on numerous occasions that it is the responsibility of the developed countries to help free the developing nations from poverty.

The first of these momentous statements was the Atlantic Charter, August 14, 1941, in which Prime Minister Churchill and President Roosevelt, on behalf of their respective countries, jointly declared:[1]

> After the final destruction of Nazi tyranny, they hope to see established a peace which will afford to all nations the means of dwelling in safety within their own boundaries, and which will afford assurance that all the men in all the lands may live out their lives in freedom from fear and want.

The Atlantic Charter statement was followed shortly after by a declaration of the United Nations Conference on Food and Agriculture, June 3, 1943, which said:[2]

> Thereafter we must equally concert our efforts to win and maintain freedom from fear and freedom from want. The one cannot be achieved without the other.
>
> There has never been enough food for the health of all people. This is justified neither by ignorance nor by the harshness of nature. Production of food must be greatly expanded; we now have knowledge of the means by which this can be done. It requires imagination and firm will on the part of each government and people to make use of that knowledge.

[1] This particular point and all others in the Atlantic Charter were adopted by the United Nations on January 1, 1942. See W. Arnold-Forster, *Charters of the Peace* (London: Camelot Press Ltd., 1944), pp. 9–10, 96, a commentary on the Atlantic Charter and the Declarations of Moscow, Cairo, and Teheran.

[2] *Department of State Bulletin*, Vol. VIII, No. 208, June 19, 1943, p. 552.

This statement was given additional support by the reviewing panel of the Conference in a report entitled *The Work of FAO,* which stated:[3]

> The Food and Agriculture Organization is born out of the idea of freedom from want. This is not one man's fortunate phrase; it expresses an aspiration as old as mankind. Whenever primitive men tried to imagine paradise in concrete terms, they pictured it as a place where food was plentiful and want no longer existed. Every utopia man has conceived has been such a place. But in this generation freedom from want has come to have a different meaning. It has been taken out of the realm of utopian ideas. The conviction has spread that it can be achieved; indeed, this is one of the convictions most characteristic of the thinking and the mood of this generation.

More recently, Pope Paul VI has argued with all the persuasiveness at his command that every man has a responsibility for assisting in the development process:[4]

A Task for All

> (86) All of you who have heard the appeal of suffering peoples, all of you who are working to answer their cries, you are the apostles of a development which is good and genuine, which is not wealth that is self-centered and sought for its own sake, but rather an economy which is put at the service of man, the bread which is daily distributed to all, as a source of brotherhood and a sign of Providence.

Blessing

> (87) With a full heart We bless you, and We appeal to all men of good will to join you in a spirit of brotherhood. For, if the new name for peace is development, who would not wish to labour for it with all his powers? Yes, We ask you, all of you, to heed Our cry of anguish, in the name of the Lord.

In the other great ideological camp—the Communist camp—the leaders, great and small, are also telling the people of the developing world that increased production, a fairer distribution of income, and a higher level of living can be achieved in their lifetimes,

[3] Gove Hambidge, *The Story of FAO* (Princeton, N. J.: D. Van Nostrand Co., Inc., 1955), p. 54.
[4] Encyclical Letter of Pope Paul VI *On the Development of Peoples,* The Vatican, Rome, March 26, 1967.

if they will follow the Communist path. So, through personal experience, advertising and propaganda, education, local political action, and the world struggle for his political allegiance, the common man has first learned about the new products, new gadgets, and new services; second, come to want them; and third, come to expect them.

It is difficult to say which facet of the explanation above has been the most important, and it is really fruitless to pursue such an inquiry. The different strands have played different roles, but their overall effect has been to support the revolution in expectations. The common man has learned about Coca-Cola and transistor radios from advertising and about birth control practices and school feeding programs from government propaganda. He has come to want these new goods and services from personal experiences within the context of his own country's development. And he has come to expect them from being told in the political process that they are commonplace in the developed world and that he, too, can have them if he makes the right political decision (e.g., joins the Communist Party, joins a party to throw out the foreign imperialists, supports a particular local political leader). The struggle for the political allegiance of the common man in the less developed countries (LDC's)—in the context of a certain amount of development and a vision of what is commonplace in the developed countries—has led to extravagant claims regarding production and distribution possibilities in those same countries, and so to a revolution in consumer expectations.

It is probably correct to say that this revolution in expectations has been most intense in urban areas where the causative forces have been the strongest, and least intense in rural areas where such forces have been weak or nonexistent. Similarly, it is likely to be strongest among young people and weakest among the elderly. Thus, there is an unevenness in the expectations of consumers for material progress throughout the developing world. But by this same line of reasoning, we should recognize that the expectations of young people in urban areas of the developing world for the fruits of material progress are at white heat. This group of people, visible and articulate, expects to reap for itself significant material gains in the immediate years ahead. These people have been told in many ways that they can and should share in the bounty of modern, scientific production; they know that the new goods and services are widely available in the developed world; and they expect them to become commonplace in their societies in their lifetimes.

What Are the Facts?

The total annual production of goods and services, or gross national product (GNP), is increasing at a moderate to rapid rate in almost all of the less developed countries. Even on a per capita basis, which takes into account the effects of population increases, the GNP data continue to show substantial rates of growth for most countries in the developing world—that is, the total production of goods and services per person grew a few percentage points per year over the period 1955–66 in most areas of the developing world (see Table 1.1). Furthermore, the growth in per capita gross national product has been remarkable for a good number of LDC's in the first half of the 1960's (Table 1.1 shows the rapid rates of growth of Israel, Korea, Taiwan, and Thailand). In almost every part of the developing world there was real material progress, measured on a per capita basis, from 1955 through 1966. And there is every reason to believe that these rates of growth can be maintained and increased overall in the decades ahead.

But—and this is a big but—the GNP levels from which these rates of growth take off are very low in most developing countries (see Table 1.1, column 3). The total per capita production of goods and services in Kenya in 1966 was $116; in Pakistan, $113; in India, $74; in Korea, $131; and in Sudan, $106. And the per capita GNP for all the less developed countries averaged $184 in 1966, as compared with $2,280 for all the developed countries—a striking difference. From these low product bases, even with good rates of economic growth, it will take many years, even decades, to produce a GNP in which the average person can command a level of living equal to, say, that of Mexico in 1966.[5] More specifically, with average rates of growth in gross national product, countries like India, Korea, or Kenya must expect to go through a long period of devel-

[5] A developing country with a per capita gross national product of $100 and a growth rate of 2 percent per year, compounded annually, would require about 81 years to reach the Mexican level of $493 per capita. At a growth rate of 3 percent, it would require about 54 years, and with a growth rate of 4 percent, about 41 years.

TABLE 1.1

Per Capita Gross National Product, Annual Growth Rates, 1955–66, and Estimate for 1966, for the Developed and Less Developed Countries

Region and Country	Percent Change Per Year 1955–60	Percent Change Per Year 1960–66	Estimate for 1966 in U. S. Dollars
Less Developed Countries			
Total [1]	2.1	2.3	184 [2]
Latin America	2.0	1.6	407
Brazil	2.8	1.2	310
Chile	1.6	2.1	556
Mexico	2.8	2.7	493
Peru	1.6	3.4	295
Near East	3.3	3.9	283
Israel	5.1	4.5	1,454
Turkey	2.3	2.4	296
Iraq	3.6	3.1	268
South Asia	2.1	1.4	82 [2]
India	2.3	1.1	74 [2]
Pakistan	1.3	2.9	113
East Asia [4]	1.3	2.3	[3]
Korea	1.8	4.7	131
Philippines	1.5	1.4	171
Taiwan	[3]	6.8	235
Thailand	[3]	4.1	141
Africa	[3]	1.1	164
Kenya	[3]	1.6	116
Nigeria	[3]	2.9	125
Sudan	[3]	0.8	106
Tunisia	[3]	2.4	209
Developed Countries			
Total	2.2	3.8	2,280
Canada	0.8	3.8	2,660
Europe [5]	4.4	3.8	1,756
Japan	8.9	8.3	986
United States	0.5	3.4	3,797

[1] Excludes Mainland China.
[2] Includes India converted at the new devalued rate of 7.50 rupees per dollar.
[3] Not available.
[4] Excludes Japan, includes Indonesia.
[5] Includes only the EEC countries of Belgium, Luxembourg, France, Germany, Italy, and The Netherlands.
SOURCE: *Gross National Product: Growth Rates and Trend Data*, AID, U. S. Government, RC-W-138, March 31, 1967, pp. 1–5; *ibid.*, July 25, 1968, pp. 8–14; and *Reports Control*, No. 137, July 25, 1968.

opment, perhaps 50 to 100 years, before their populations, on an average, can expect to live as well as the average person in Mexico in 1966. With good to exceptional rates of growth in GNP, the period of development to reach the Mexican level for these countries will approach 30 to 50 years.

Herein lies the problem. Economic progress is, or has been, a slow process. Even with rates of growth in per capita gross national product of 3 to 4 percent, which are very good rates, it is a long, drawn-out process.

Food Production and Consumption

As is often the case, the issues for food and agriculture differ somewhat from those for the total product, or nonfood products. A 2.5 percent annual increase in *total* food production isn't bad in any country, developing or developed. And certainly most people concerned about the world food problem would be happy to see an increase of 4.0 per year in *total* food production in each developing country; for with a 2.5 percent rate of population increase per year, this means that the increase in per capita food production is 1.5 percent per year. With such a rate of increase in per capita food production, the dietary deficiencies in calories and proteins of most consumers in developing countries could be eradicated in a decade or so. This is true because the average consumer does not in the consumption of food go from no consumption to full consumption, as he must in the consumption of a transistor radio or motor scooter. In food consumption, the average consumer may be 10 percent deficient in calories and perhaps 20 percent deficient in protein. Such an average deficiency would be made up, or nearly so, in a single decade (possibly with some dietary changes and food fortification) with an annual increase in per capita food production of 1.5 percent.[6] So the absolute increases in food production do not need to be so great, or sustained so long, as for all nonfood products, to realize the expectations of present-day consumers in the developing countries.

[6] If the caloric deficiency is made up with increased grain consumption, the protein deficiency would be reduced, if not eliminated, by the increased grain products intake.

But in the short run, the failure to meet the consumers' expectations of food and nutrition may be more demoralizing, and more explosive, than the failure to meet nonfood consumption goals. First, it hurts to go hungry. Second, it hurts more to see your children going hungry. Third, malnutrition and hunger increase man's susceptibility to infectious diseases and hence the incidence of sickness and death. Fourth, it is extremely difficult, as we shall see, to increase agricultural production quickly. It takes time to put together the pieces of the production puzzle in agriculture that lead to large increases in food production.

Because hunger and malnutrition call for urgent corrective action, and because corrective action to increase production is complex and slow going, the food and agricultural sector presents a stubborn and explosive problem. The incidence of hunger and malnutrition is so widespread in the developing countries that the seriousness of the situation cannot be doubted. The desire for, and expectation of, improved diets is so general and strong that the problem is highly explosive. And the production reorganizations that must be undertaken to increase food production are so complex and time-consuming that many people are inclined to throw up their hands in despair. These are the attitudes, fears, and thoughts that overlay the food problem in the developing countries in the late 1960's.

The Dilemma

The expectations of the common man in the developing countries have, through the interaction of numerous forces, been built up to a point where he looks forward to significant gains in his material level of living in the years immediately ahead. The economies of most developing countries are making good progress; but they take off from such a low product level that they cannot possibly produce the bill of goods expected of them by their populations in the next decade or even several decades. There is a wide gap between what the average urban consumer in a developing country expects to have in the way of a level of living in the next 5 to 10 years, and what his economy can possibly produce in that period of time. This gap has resulted from the revolution in expectations among the populations of the developing countries.

If the common man in the less developed countries were willing to live with, participate in, and accept the material progress that a 2 or 3 percent rate of growth in per capita gross national product would yield, the expectation gap would recede and some of the politically explosive aspects of the problem would disappear. This is in essence what happened in the United States and in Japan during the long period from 1870 to 1930; the populations in both countries accepted sustained, but reasonable rates of growth in gross national product, which in turn produced high levels of living in those countries in the 1950's and 1960's.[7] This is not to say that these two countries did not encounter problems and suffer reverses during this long period; both ran into deep economic troubles at different times. But neither experienced serious political upheavals or social unrest as the result of an expectation gap. The common man in these two countries was content to see his level of living grow with the national economy; money panics, economic recessions, and unemployment were the crosses that the common man had to bear in Japan and the United States.

But the common man in the developing world of the 1960's gives no evidence that he is willing to wait 50 or 100 years to enjoy the fruits of the modern industrial world. He has seen how his counterpart lives in the developed world, and he has been told by his leaders at home and by world political leaders abroad that he does not have to accept poverty as his lot. So he wants and expects to escape from the chains of poverty in this decade and start living like a farmer, factory worker, or clerk in Western Europe, Japan, or the United States. But economic growth rates in the developing countries cannot support such a leap in this or the next decade. Thus, the expectations of the common man are presently colliding with economic reality, and the crunch will come with greater force in the 1970's. The outcome will vary from country to country and by specific events, but certainly it will involve disillusionment, demoralization, and political upheavals in the developing world.

The gap between expectations and fulfillment is narrower for

[7] Bruce F. Johnston reports in his monograph, "Agriculture and Economic Development: The Relevance of the Japanese Experience," *Food Research Institute Studies*, Vol. VI, No. 3, 1966, Stanford University, Stanford, Calif., that the rate of growth in per capita GNP for Japan over the period 1879–1964 was 2.7 percent per year, and the figure for the United States for the period 1871–1964 was 1.9 percent per year.

food than for total level of living. And the time span required to
eradicate food and nutrition deficiencies in most developing countries is probably much shorter than for total level of living. But
the food problem is more acute and more urgent of solution than
the level of living problem. Hunger and malnutrition cannot wait;
their crippling effects are immediate and direct. Thus, the common
man wants and expects to consume an improved diet, and he demands that he be freed of the fear of hunger and famine. But once
again the production possibilities within most developing countries
do not admit of an out-turn of food products that will meet current expectations. Some gains in per capita availability of food supplies have been made in the 1950's and 1960's,[8] and more gains will
be made in the 1970's and 1980's. But food supplies will not reach
the level of wants and expectations in many, if not most, developing countries in this or the next decade.

This is the expectations problem that colors and influences every
political and economic decision in the less developed countries. It
makes rapid economic development and agricultural development
national imperatives; but it also leads to despair on the part of those
deeply involved in the development process. What kinds of political and economic decisions should be made regarding the development process, when it is recognized that nothing that will be
achieved will match the expectations of the average citizen? And
how can the development process in the general economy and
agriculture be supported and sustained when it continuously fails
to meet the expectations of the average citizen?

This is the situation in which the man with a responsibility for
economic development and agricultural development finds himself,
whether he be a national leader or foreign expert. And it is the
climate of social and political thought in which realistic discussions
of the world food problem and agricultural development must take
place. It is not enough to make some economic progress in the developing countries these days: the revolution in expectations demands that the gains be large and rapid.

[8] These gains are described in Chapters 2 and 3.

2

Population Growth and Agricultural Production

IN THIS CHAPTER we shall be concerned with the race between population growth and agricultural production. Since the end of World War II, it has been a real race. In the 1950's, food production gained on population growth in most parts of the developing world; in other words, food production on a per capita basis increased. But in the 1960's, population growth has gained on food production in some important parts of the developing world, and per capita food production has declined in those places. This latter development has caused some analysts and most of the Cassandras to conclude that the race is over—that population growth in the developing world is running, and will continue to run, away from food production. In this view, we have a population explosion in the developing world and no possibility of a food production explosion.

No one, either optimist or pessimist, can read the future with certainty. But, as we shall demonstrate in this chapter with the best data available, the race in the late 1960's has by no means been won by population growth, and there have been some remarkable production achievements in the developing world, as well as some failures. Further, we will discuss possible developments in population growth and agricultural production between 1970 and 2000 and suggest how the race may still be won by agricultural production, if we get the proper inputs of wisdom, hard work, and discipline on the part of peoples and leaders in both the developed and the developing worlds. In fact, most of this book is concerned with this same theme.

Population Growth

It is popular these days to talk and write about the "population explosion" in the less developed countries, and the phrase is not an improper one, for the populations of those countries are increasing dramatically. With sharply declining death rates and relatively constant birth rates, the rate of population increase for the less developed areas of the world went up from 12 percent in the 1940's to 22 percent in the 1950's (see Table 2.1). Stated differently, the rate of population growth in the less developed world increased from 1.2 percent per year, noncompounded, in the decade of the 1940's, to 2.2 percent per year, noncompounded, in the decade of the 1950's. This is indeed a big jump.

Further, the demographers are unanimous in their view that these high rates of population increase will not decline significantly for a long time to come. The medium variant population projection of the United Nations experts, which most demographers consider the most plausible for the long-run period 1960–2000, suggests that the rate of population growth for the less developed areas of the world will increase to 2.4 percent per year, noncompounded, for the decade of the 1960's, rise to 2.5 percent per year for the decade of the 1970's, and then begin to decline slowly in the decade of the 1980's (see Table 2.2). With these rapid rates of population growth in the developing regions, the total world population will increase to just over 6 billion in the year 2000, or more than double the 1960 figure.

Population experts in the U. S. Department of Agriculture are of the opinion that rates of population growth in the less developed areas of the world, *excluding Communist Asia*, were running at 2.5 percent per year for the period 1960–65, and are running at a rate of 2.6 percent per year for the period 1965–70.[1] And this rate of increase of 2.6 percent per year is projected to run through the decade of the 1970's.

---

[1] Martin E. Abel and Anthony S. Rojko, *The World Food Situation: Prospects for World Grain Production, Consumption, and Trade*, Economic Research Service (ERS), U. S. Dept. of Agriculture (USDA), Foreign Agricultural Economic Report No. 35 (August 1967), p. 9.

TABLE 2.1
World Population Growth, 1920–60

Area Category	1920		1930		1940		1950		1960	
	Population in Millions	Decennial Increase in Percent	Population in Millions	Decennial Increase in Percent	Population in Millions	Decennial Increase in Percent	Population in Millions	Decennial Increase in Percent	Population in Millions	Decennial Increase in Percent
World Total	1,861	—	2,070	11	2,296	11	2,516	10	2,998	19
Developed Areas	674	—	759	13	822	8	858	4	976	14
Less Developed Areas	1,187	—	1,311	10	1,474	12	1,658	12	2,022	22

SOURCE: *World Population Prospects, As Assessed in 1963*, United Nations, New York (Sales No. 66.XIII.2, 1966), p. 23.

TABLE 2.2

World Population Growth, Medium Variant Projection to the Year 2000

Area Category	1960 Population in Millions	1960 Decennial Increase in Percent	1970 Population in Millions	1970 Decennial Increase in Percent	1980 Population in Millions	1980 Decennial Increase in Percent	1990 Population in Millions	1990 Decennial Increase in Percent	2000 Population in Millions	2000 Decennial Increase in Percent
World Total	2,998	—	3,592	20	4,330	21	5,187	20	6,129	18
Developed Areas	976	—	1,082	11	1,194	10	1,318	10	1,441	9
Less Developed Areas	2,022	—	2,510	24	3,136	25	3,869	23	4,688	21

SOURCE: *World Population Prospects, As Assessed in 1963*, p. 23.

Thus, in this volume we shall assume that the rate of population increase for the developing world (excluding Communist Asia) is 2.6 percent per year in the second half of the 1960's, will continue at this rate throughout the 1970's, and will begin to decline thereafter. There are, however, some important variations to this overall average. The estimated annual rate of population increase for Latin America as a whole in the late 1960's is 2.9 percent per year, with the rate running as high as 3.4 percent per year for Venezuela and 3.8 for Costa Rica. These latter rates are exceptionally high, approaching the maximum for a society with a normal age distribution and a zero immigration. Offsetting the very high rates in Latin America is an estimated rate of 2.4 percent per year for India, which helps produce an overall average of 2.6 percent per year.

As is generally recognized, the high rates of population increase in the less developed areas have not been brought about by increases in the birth rate; birth rates have held constant at a level around 40 per thousand persons. But death rates have been cut in half or more by improved public health measures and the presence of modern medical services. And death rates in the less developed countries are expected to decline still further in the 1970's and 1980's as modern medical services reach more and more people. This by itself will, of course, have the effect of further increasing the rate of population growth.

The great unknown in the field of demography is: When will birth rates begin to decline significantly in the developing world? When will the influences of rising income and urbanization, together with new and improved birth control techniques, begin to cut the number of births per thousand significantly? Professor M. A. El-Badry seems to reflect the prevailing opinion among demographers when he projects that the birth rate for the developing world as a whole will decline to 37 per thousand in the decade of the 1970's and then fall to 33 per thousand in the 1980's.[2] But such a decline yields only a very modest decline in the overall rate of population increase in the 1980's, because the death rate continues to fall in the developing world.

[2] "Population Projections for the World, 1965–2000," *Annals of the American Academy of Political and Social Science: World Population* (January 1967), p. 11.

In sum, the rate of population increase is going to remain high in the developing regions in the 1970's and 1980's—probably at or near 2.6 and 2.4 percent per year respectively. A great deal more could be written about the current population explosion and prospective growth rates—individual country estimates, projections under different assumptions, and methodological problems—but the reader interested in greater detail or in methodology can begin his intensive look with the citations provided in this section. The data presented above describe the population growth problem for the developing world as it is understood in the late 1960's. And we are not inclined to minimize the problem; it is one of the great problems confronting the developing world. But neither are we inclined to believe that it will destroy us.

Agricultural Production

Since the end of World War II agriculture has not been standing still—either in the developed areas or in the less developed areas. The world output of food products increased about 2.7 percent per year between 1956 and 1967. And this rate of increase was about the same in the developed areas and the less developed areas (see the indices of total production in Table 2.3).

Food production in the developed countries could have increased more rapidly than it did from 1961 to 1967; over 50 million acres were held out of production in the United States during most of those years to reduce surplus stocks and to bring production more nearly in line with commercial demand. The agricultural production plant in the United States was certainly operating under wraps in the period 1961–67.

Some of the increases in food production in the less developed countries during the 1950's resulted from bringing new land under cultivation. But most of the production increases noted in Table 2.3 for the developing countries in the early 1960's resulted from the modernization of their agricultural plants—from the application of new technologies and modern production methods. Moreover, it will be noted that the less developed countries as a whole were making excellent production gains until India ran into two serious droughts in a row—1965 and 1966—causing the index of total agricultural production in the developing nations to fall mod-

TABLE 2.3

Indices of Total World Food Production, Excluding Communist Asia, 1956–67
(1957–59 = 100)

Region	1956	1957	1958	1959	1960	1961	1962	1963	1964	1965	1966	1967
World[1]	96	95	102	103	107	108	111	114	118	118	124	128
Developed Countries	96	96	102	102	106	107	110	112	116	117	126	128
Less Developed Countries[1]	94	95	101	103	108	110	112	118	121	120	120	130

[1] Excludes Communist Asia.
SOURCE: *The World Food Situation: Prospects for World Grain Production, Consumption, and Trade*, ERS, USDA, Foreign Agricultural Economic Report No. 35 (August 1967), p. 8, as revised by the Division of Foreign Regional Analysis.

estly from 121 in 1964 to 120 in 1965 and to hold constant at 120 in 1966. (India's production bulks so large in the less developed countries aggregate that an important reduction in its output visibly influenced the index for all the developing nations.) It simply is not true, as some observers imply and others state outright, that the agricultures of the developing countries have been stagnant during the 1950's and 1960's. A rate of increase in total food production in excess of 2.7 percent per year for the period 1956–67 for the less developed world as a whole is a far cry from agricultural stagnation.

Among the developing countries there have been some outstanding agricultural production success stories. Over the period 1948–63, the rate of increase in crop production on a compound basis exceeded 5 percent per year in seven countries—Israel, Sudan, Mexico, Costa Rica, the Philippines, Tanganyika, and Yugoslavia; and production increases varied between 4 and 5 percent per year for Taiwan, Turkey, Venezuela, and Thailand.[3] These are outstanding rates of increase in crop production for any country; a good deal higher, for example, than was achieved in the United States and Canada during the same period or comparable periods of development.

How, it may be asked, did these substantial increases in crop production come about? It would be comforting to say that the increases occurred as the result of some specific causative element or pattern of events. But that does not happen to be so. The explanations for the increases seem to be as varied as the countries themselves. In some cases, increases in production seem to be associated chiefly with increased acres under cultivation; in other cases, with increasing rates of fertilizer application; in others, with improved roads and other social overhead services; and in still others, with various combinations of these elements. So we have our first introduction to the problem of development: to increase agricultural production, and thus effect agricultural development, is a highly complex and frustrating task, and one that must vary with the resource base, the state of technology, the social attitudes and goals, and the effectiveness of government of the countries involved. But

[3] See *Changes in Agriculture in 26 Developing Nations, 1948–63*, ERS, USDA, Foreign Agric. Econ. Report No. 27 (November 1965), pp. 6, 7.

agricultural development can take place in the most economically backward countries; this has been demonstrated in the 1950's and 1960's.

In a recent study of world grain prospects, Martin Abel and Anthony Rojko have appraised grain production possibilities for different groups of developing countries under three assumptions: historical trends, moderate improvements in production, and rapid improvements in production.[4] Abel and Rojko conclude in this study that, with a continuation of the trends and developments of the period 1954-66, the production of grain for all the less developed countries (excluding Communist Asia) would increase 2.6 percent per year through 1980 (see Table 2.4), and grain production in the grain-exporting developing countries (Argentina, Mexico, Burma, Cambodia, and Thailand) would increase 3.1 percent per year. These are impressive figures. In other words, if the developing countries as a whole continue doing the things they were doing during the period 1954-66, and historical trends are maintained, then grain production for the whole developing world can be expected to increase 2.6 percent per year through 1980.

If the LDC's effect modest improvements in agricultural production, then grain production for the developing world can be expected to increase to 3.1 percent per year through 1980. If, however, the LDC's make major efforts in the agricultural sector and effect rapid improvements in agricultural production, then grain production could be expected to increase 3.9 percent per year. These are even more impressive figures, since they indicate rates of increase in grain production that are consistent with the needs and aspirations of the countries involved and are realistic and feasible in the opinion of technical experts in the U. S. Department of Agriculture.

The rates of increase presented in Table 2.4 are not estimates of what will happen in the future; since *alternative* rates of increase in grain production are being presented, the rate data cannot take the form of estimates. The rates of production increase in Table 2.4 represent projections under alternative, but realistic sets of con-

[4] Abel and Rojko, *The World Food Situation: Prospects for World Grain Production, Consumption, and Trade*, ERS, USDA, Foreign Agric. Econ. Report No. 35 (August 1967).

TABLE 2.4

Annual Rates of Growth in Grain Production for the Less Developed Countries[1] Projected to 1980 under Alternative Assumptions

Country or Region	Historical Trends (percent)	Moderate Improvement in Production (percent)	Rapid Improvement in Production (percent)
India	2.0	2.8	3.8
Pakistan	2.9	3.2	3.9
Other Nonexporting Developing Countries	2.7	3.0	3.9
Grain-Exporting Developing Countries[2]	3.1	3.6	3.6
Total, All Less Developed Countries	2.6	3.1	3.9

[1] Excluding Communist Asia.
[2] Argentina, Mexico, Burma, Cambodia, and Thailand.
SOURCE: *The World Food Situation: Prospects for World Grain Production, Consumption, and Trade*, ERS, USDA, Foreign Agric. Econ. Report No. 35 (August 1967), p. 17.

ditions: (1) a rate of increase in grain production in the 1970's equal to the historical trend for the period 1954–66; (2) a situation in which the less developed countries place greater emphasis on agricultural development in the future, but not implying "crash" programs for production, and; (3) a situation in which programs and efforts leading to agricultural development are greatly accelerated.

The rates of increase presented in Table 2.4 indicate what can be done, not necessarily what will be done. What will be done depends upon the efforts made and the wisdom exercised in the decades ahead, which is the subject of much of this book. But the projections presented in Table 2.4 are technically feasible; that is the main point of this discussion.

The Race

When we put world food production on a per capita basis and thereby take account of the world population growth for the period

1956–67, we discover that per capita food production has been increasing over that period. The index of per capita food production rose from 100 in 1956 to 107 in 1967 (see Table 2.5). Thus, in the race between population growth and food production, for the world as a whole, production has not been losing. It has been winning.

But there was an imbalance in per capita food production between the developed world and the less developed world over the period 1956–67. Per capita food production in the developed world increased about 20 percent between 1956 and 1967, while it increased only about 5 percent for the same period in the less developed world. And the potential imbalance was much greater, since the United States was effectively controlling food production in the latter part of this period.

But let us look at the less developed countries production aggregate more closely. Only in the case of India do we find a sharp and significant decrease in per capita food production, and that decrease is limited to two years: 1965 and 1966. We know that 1965 and 1966 were serious drought years for India.[5] Thus we discover that the explanation for the dip in the index of per capita food production for the less developed world as a whole is in fact the serious drought in India in 1965 and 1966. If India had experienced more normal weather in those two years, its index of per capita food production, in all likelihood, would have stood at 105 or 106 in 1965 and 1966; this, in turn, would have represented a 4 or 5 percent increase in per capita food production for the less developed countries as a whole for the period 1956–66.

In sum, the historical data in Table 2.5 do not suggest that population was running away from production in the less developed countries. Except for the special case of India, the race between food production and population growth was either a draw or running in favor of production throughout the less developed world in the period 1956–67.

In fact, much of the recent interest by laymen of the Western world in "the world food problem" stems from two bad crop years

---

[5] The Indian droughts of 1965–66 and 1966–67 were reported repeatedly by the press and popular journals during those years, but a good brief description of them in historical context may be found in William E. Hendrix, James J. Naive, and Warren E. Adams, *Accelerating India's Food Grain Production, 1967–68 to 1970–71*, ERS, USDA, Foreign Agric. Econ. Report No. 40 (March 1968), pp. 2–4.

TABLE 2.5
Indices of Per Capita World Food Production, 1956–67, Excluding Communist Asia
(1957–59 = 100)

Country or Region	1956	1957	1958	1959	1960	1961	1962	1963	1964	1965	1966	1967
Less Developed Countries	99	97	101	101	103	102	101	104	104	101	98	104
India	101	96	102	103	106	108	100	104	105	92	88	103
Pakistan	104	99	95	106	108	106	101	111	108	108	100	108
Other Asia[1]	98	96	102	100	99	101	102	104	104	102	105	105
Africa[2]	102	100	100	101	103	98	104	103	102	100	97	98
Latin America	101	100	102	100	100	101	102	103	103	107	102	105
Developed Countries[3]	98	97	102	101	103	103	105	105	108	107	114	117
The World[4]	100	97	102	101	103	102	103	103	105	103	106	107

[1] Excluding India, Pakistan, Communist Asia, and Japan.
[2] Excluding Republic of South Africa.
[3] United States, Canada, Europe, U.S.S.R., Japan, Republic of South Africa, Australia, and New Zealand.
[4] Excluding Communist Asia.
SOURCE: *The World Food Situation: Prospects for World Grain Production, Consumption, and Trade*, ERS, USDA, Foreign Agric. Econ. Report No. 35 (August 1967), p. 8, as revised by the Division of Foreign Regional Analysis.

in one very large country—India. The continuing problem of achieving satisfactory rates of agricultural production in the less developed countries has not challenged the man in the street in North America or Europe. But the possibility of widespread famine in India in 1965 and 1966 (which did not occur because of large-scale grain shipments from the United States) raised first the fear of mass starvation and second predictions of the Malthusian prophecy stalking the less developed world. Two bad crop years in a row in India shot the thinking of comfortable Americans past the difficult, chronic problem of agricultural development, which begged for attention, to the immediate question of mass starvation and on without a pause to the Malthusian specter of population outrunning the food production base on this planet. Fortunately, the facts do not support such grandiose fears.

But what of the future? What is likely to be the outcome of the race between population growth and food production in the 1980's? Here we must again limit the analysis to grain production, since the best available production data, projected to 1980, are limited to the grains. This does not, however, seriously weaken the analysis since the grains alone (rice, wheat, corn, sorghums, and millets) provide over 50 percent of mankind's total caloric intake, and in South and East Asia these grains provide up to two-thirds of man's caloric intake. Thus, in much of the developing world food grain production is synonymous with food production.

If we look at the per capita production of grain for the period 1959–61 and a probable projection to 1970, we see that the per capita production of grain for the less developed world as a whole (excluding Communist Asia) increases from 163 kilograms to 170 kilograms (see Table 2.6). This is progress. And the per capita production of grain for India increases modestly from 156 kgs. to 159 kgs. At least this is not retrogression. In short, the experts in the U. S. Department of Agriculture are of the opinion that the per capita production of grain will increase modestly in the grain deficit regions of the developing world in the 1960's, and increase importantly in the grain-exporting countries of the developing world— Argentina, Mexico, Burma, Thailand, and Cambodia.

In the decade of the 1970's, the outcome of the race depends upon the assumptions used. But no reasonable set of assumptions leads to a decline in per capita grain production. If we assume a continuation of the grain production trends of the period 1954–66, the race is essentially a draw; per capita grain production holds constant at 170 kgs. for the less developed world as a whole, with minor deviations for different countries or regions within the whole (see Table 2.6).

If, however, we assume a moderate improvement in grain production technology, then we get an 8 kg. increase in per capita production for the less developed world as a whole between 1970 and 1980, with comparable increases for countries and regions within it. And if we assume a rapid increase in grain production technology, then we get a significant further increase in per capita grain production. In sum, it is reasonable and realistic to project significant gains in per capita grain production throughout the developing world during the 1970's, even with the expected high rates of population increase. This is true because most countries in the less developed world in the last half of the 1960's are, in fact, achieving rates of increase in grain production that parallel population increases. And agricultural production specialists can see developments under way, and developments that could be undertaken, to lift rates of grain production above the population growth rates in the 1970's.

All, then, is not despair in the race between population growth and food production in the years ahead. Given the will and the wisdom, the resources and the technology are available to push rates of increase in food production ahead of population growth in the developing world.

The FAO Analysis[6]

The analysis of the race between population growth and food production to this point has made exclusive use of production data developed and published by the U. S. Department of Agriculture. The use of United Nations food production data would not significantly change the conclusions of the foregoing analysis, though interpretations do vary somewhat.

[6] See *The State of Food and Agriculture 1967*, The Food and Agricultural Organization of the United Nations (Rome, 1967), pp. 11–23.

TABLE 2.6

Per Capita Grain Production, Less Developed Countries and Regions,[1] Estimates for 1959–61 and 1964–65, and Projections to 1980

(Kilograms)

Country or Region	1959–61 Average	1964–65	1970[2]	1980[3] Historical Trend	1980[3] Moderate Improvement	1980[3] Rapid Improvement
India	156	155	159	155	167	184
Pakistan	155	158	159	167	171	184
Other Less Developed Countries, Excluding Grain Exporters	148	149	150	149	154	168
Net Grain Exporters[4]	297	364	343	355	373	373
Total, All Less Developed Countries	163	169	170	170	178	192

[1] Excluding Communist Asia.
[2] Refer to pp. 11–14 in source.
[3] Refer to pp. 15–21 in source.
[4] Argentina, Mexico, Burma, Cambodia, and Thailand.
SOURCE: *The World Food Situation: Prospects for World Grain Production, Consumption, and Trade*, ERS, USDA, Foreign Agric. Econ. Report No. 35 (August 1967); derived from data presented in Tables 3, 5, and 9 on pp. 9, 12, and 19.

The Food and Agricultural Organization of the United Nations estimates that food production *for the world as a whole* increased about 30 percent between 1956 and 1966; the percentage increase for the less developed regions for the same time period was somewhat less—approximately 26 percent. These percentage increases are very close to the estimated increases in total food production for comparable areas for the period 1956–66 published by the U. S. Department of Agriculture (see Table 2.3). Since the food production data generated by the FAO and the USDA tell essentially the same story for the world and for the principal regions within it, and since both agencies rely upon the same United Nations population estimates, it necessarily follows that the per capita food production estimates for the period 1956–66 are highly similar.

The FAO position is summarized as follows:[7]

> . . . it appears that until 1964 there had for some years been a slow but definite upward movement in per caput food production in the developing countries. Between 1953 and 1964 their per caput food production is estimated to have increased by about 9 percent. As a result of the setback to production in 1965 and the incomplete recovery in 1966, however, much of this progress has been lost. Per caput food production in the developing countries is estimated as more than 4 percent less in 1966 than in the peak year of 1964 and lower than in any year since 1957.

This description closely parallels the conclusions reached earlier based upon data from the U. S. Department of Agriculture, with one exception. The final sentence above implies that the world food situation deteriorated badly in 1965 and 1966. And other statements in the document *The State of Food and Agriculture 1967* suggest that the years 1965–66 may represent a turning point in the race between population growth and food production, with food production beginning to fall behind at that point.

The point at issue is thus as follows: Is the decline in per capita production in 1965 and 1966 a general phenomenon with basic roots, or is it a special phenomenon in an isolated context? We are too close to the production developments of 1965 and 1966 at the present writing (early 1968) to place those developments in proper perspective and hence to generalize about the per capita

[7] *Ibid.*, p. 13.

food production decline in 1965 and 1966. The FAO experts seem to believe that the developing world generally may be entering a production slowdown phase. The reasons for this slowdown are not articulated and its duration is not discussed. But there is a strong expression of pessimism regarding the trend in per capita output of food in the less developed regions of the world for the late 1960's.

It may turn out that the FAO viewpoint of per capita food production in the developing world in the late 1960's is the correct one —namely, that per capita food production has fallen sharply and generally throughout the developing world and that it will be some time before the per capita food production high of 1964 is regained. But the per capita data for 1967 do not support that view; the index of per capita food production for the less developed world moves back to 104 in 1967, to regain the level achieved in 1964 (see Table 2.5). And this development reflects the bountiful harvest in South Asia in 1967. Thus, for this writer the FAO interpretation of the events of 1965 and 1966 is misleading. The really overriding events of those two years were two consecutive droughts in India, which led to two disastrous crop years for that country, and a downturn in the index of food production for the overall aggregate of the developing countries. This is not to say that India, or other parts of the globe, will not suffer from droughts, floods, and bad crop years in the future, because so long as agriculture is to depend on the weather they will. But we should not conclude that *agricultural production throughout the developing world* is on the decline because India suffered two bad crop years. Two years of drought in India do not presage worldwide agricultural failure and a long-run decline in per capita food production. On the contrary, technological developments in agriculture in both the developed and the developing worlds over the period 1956–67 suggest the continuance of significant increases in agricultural production in the 1960's and 1970's.

The Case of India

Because of the vast size of India's population, the ubiquity of its poverty, and the desire of its people to maintain an open society with viable democratic institutions, there is great interest in the West in the economic development of India. Will India be able to raise the level of living of its people significantly and throw off the chains of poverty? Will it escape the threat of communism? Will it succeed in modernizing its primitive agriculture, and thereby enable food production to meet the growing demand for food? These are questions that men of good will in the West are forever asking about India.

Nathan Koffsky, a former chief economist of the U. S. Department of Agriculture and more recently a Ford Foundation staff member in India, provides an excellent analysis and answer to the last question. Let us therefore consider the Koffsky analysis of the race between the expanding demand for food and increases in food production by means of agricultural development in India.[8]

> In India, the pattern of converging food-population trends, foreshadowed for the LDC's as a group, has more or less occurred. The high growth rate of food output in the early 1950's of over 3 percent a year had moved down toward 2½ percent a year by the early 1960's. At the same time, population growth, which was only a little more than 2 percent a year in the early 1950's, rose to about 2½ percent.
>
> This balance was upset by recent drought years. Compared with 1964–65, food-grain production (the dominant food) was 19 percent lower in 1965–66 and 15 percent lower in 1966–67. Even with a large increase in imports (mostly P.L. 480) to the rate of 10–11 million tons a year, per capita consumption in the last two years has been reduced to the levels of the early 1950's. While this adds to the strain and emphasizes the need to develop a buffer stock for such contingencies, there is no evidence that a new and lower trend has been established.
>
> Sir John Crawford, a really astute observer of Indian agriculture, projects the demand for food in the next 4–5 years to rise about 4 percent a year (assuming population growth of 2.6 percent and per capita income growth of 2.4 percent, with an income elasticity for food of 0.6).*
>
> In addition, India, even under normal conditions, has been importing about 7 percent of its grain requirements. If the target for

---

* John Crawford, "Planning Under Difficulties," *Australian J. Pol. and Hist.*, Vol. 12 (August 1966), pp. 155–176.

[8] "The Food Potential of Developing Nations," *Journal of Farm Economics*, Vol. XLIX, No. 5 (December 1967), pp. 1108–1113. Koffsky shifts the analysis from population growth above to *demand*, taking into account key *income* factors, as we too shall do in later chapters.

India is to be self-sufficient over a reasonable period of time, say 10–15 years, the growth rate in food output will need to be about 4½ percent.

Does India have the capacity to make the quantum jump to a 4–4½ percent rate of increase in food output from the recent trend of 2½ percent a year?

It will have to come from increasing yields and greater crop intensity on existing cultivated land rather than from the possibility that much more land can be brought under cultivation. The land area factor, which contributed almost half of the gains in production recorded in the 1950's, has not increased in the 1960's.

Although only a few developing nations have achieved this rate of increase in yields—notably Taiwan, Sudan, and Yugoslavia—it is not at all out of the question for India. First, India starts from a very low base, reflecting the traditional agriculture of the past. Yields of rice in India are less than one-third of those in Japan and less than two-fifths of those in the United States. Wheat yields in India are one-half those in the United States and one-third those in Japan. Corn yields are only one-fourth those in the United States.*

The comparison with Japan is particularly meaningful in that population density in Japan is about three-fourths greater than in India and the average size of holding less than one-third as large. This shows that the shortcomings of crowded lands and small, fragmented holdings need not be a barrier to much higher yields.

Second, India has moved to give agricultural development the resources and policies needed for faster growth. The drought emergencies of the past few years have brought a redirection of national priorities. The emphasis on heavy industry has been muted and in the past few years public outlays directed toward agriculture and associated industries have been doubled. Even within the austere budget for 1967–68, in which total outlays, in real terms, will be reduced from last year, outlays for agricultural development have been increased.

Equally important, there has been recognition, in the last few years, that price policies must provide incentives to cultivators if they are to adopt new practices and new technology, considering the added risks and costs involved. In the last three years, prices of food grains relative to other prices have risen about 15 percent. But policy rarely moves in a straight line. It should be admitted that as food

---

* U. S. Department of Agriculture, *Changes in Agriculture in 26 Developing Nations, 1948–63*, ERS, Foreign Agric. Econ. Report No. 27 (November 1965).

supplies tightened the establishment of internal food zones which prevent the free movement of grain from surplus to deficit areas and the practice of mandatory procurement at relatively low prices by the government have penalized cultivators in the best producing areas.

Finally, India now has the scientific and resource base for much more rapid growth in agriculture. This is the main factor that suggests quite strongly that the trend of the future will show a sharp upturn from the past. In fact, there is enough evidence to indicate that the rate of growth since 1964, had it not been obscured by the droughts, is about 3 percent a year. Real progress has been made in the last few years in assembling the ingredients which make for increased food output.

To summarize, the evidence suggests that the rate of growth in food production will run about 3½ percent a year in the immediate years ahead. This is based on programs and technology in hand.

While this rate is substantially ahead of population growth and shows an increasing capacity to pull away from the hunger line, it still falls short of the 4- to 4½-percent annual rate required to meet all the demands of population and income growth and a phasing out of food assistance from abroad.

India could do better if additional resources were put in. By and large, cultivators' demands for inputs such as fertilizer, improved seeds, and water are substantially ahead of the government's ability to supply. If, for example, fertilizer availability were to increase at the rate of 500,000 tons a year instead of the 300,000 tons now planned, the rate of growth could be raised to over 5 percent—a safe margin over the demands arising from population and income growth. Consumption of fertilizer per acre in India is only 10 percent of that in the United States and only 1 percent of consumption in Japan. Over the longer run, it is also evident that exploitation of India's water resources for intensive agriculture will be necessary to sustain a high rate.

But it will be difficult for India to do more, especially in the next few years. Economic growth has been interrupted, largely as a result of the drought disaster. Resources are thin and priority for those resources has been given to agricultural development. If there is to be an additional push given to agriculture, it will have to come mostly from outside resources.

Much occurred in agriculture in India between the spring of 1967, when Koffsky made his analysis, and the spring of 1968. India harvested its largest food grain crop in history in 1967–68; the crop is estimated at 97 million tons—some 22 million tons above the 1966–67 crop. The new, high-yielding varieties of wheat swept across northern India, as millions of farmers participated in an agricultural production revolution by putting those new varieties into production. And we obtained for the first time, from William Hendrix and his associates, a comprehensive analysis of India's grain production potential.[9]

Just as the poor crops of 1965 and 1966 are attributable to poor-to-bad weather, the bountiful crop of 1967 is attributable in large measure to good-to-excellent weather. But underlying these wide fluctuations in crop production, there has been a continuous improvement in the state of the arts in Indian agriculture: new and improved varieties of rice, wheat, and other grains have been developed, replicated, and the seeds made available to farmers; increased quantities of fertilizer have been produced, imported, and made available to farmers; water management has improved; and many other production items have been produced and made available to farmers. Thus, Hendrix and his associates conclude that food grain production in India in 1967–68 should have been 94 million tons given average weather, the technological developments that had already occurred, and the productive resources available to farmers in 1967–68.

This estimate rests on the following combination of inputs:

117.5 million hectares sowed to grain—up only 1 million hectares from the 1959–62 base

32 million hectares of gross irrigated grain area—up 10 million hectares from the 1959–62 base

1.6 million tons of fertilizer in terms of plant nutrients applied to grains—up 1.4 million tons from the 1959–62 base

6.1 million hectares sown to new, high-yielding varieties—up 6.1 million hectares from the 1959–62 base.

So the bountiful harvest of 97 million tons of food grains in 1967–68 is not greatly in excess of the expected production of 94

[9] Hendrix, Naive, and Adams, *Accelerating India's Food Grain Production, 1967–68 to 1970–71*, Foreign Agric. Econ. Report No. 40 (March 1968).

million tons—expected on the basis of existing technological developments and available production inputs.

Hendrix and his associates then ask: What resource base would be required in 1970–71 to make possible an annual rate of increase in food grain production of 5 percent from 1967–68 to 1970–71? They conclude that one such base would include:

121 million hectares sown to food grains
38 million hectares irrigated for food grains
2.7 million tons of fertilizer in terms of plant nutrients
13.2 million hectares sown with high-yielding varieties.

They do not argue that a 5 percent rate of increase in food grain production *will* be achieved. But they do argue that: "These levels of inputs could be attained and, in fact, could be exceeded. So, the 5-percent growth objective is well within reach."[10]

In the light of food grain production developments in 1967–68 and the production potential analysis of Hendrix and his associates, the goal of a rate of growth in food output of 4.5 percent per year, which would make India self-sufficient in food within a decade, no longer seems far away or impossible to attain. Given normal weather and political stability, India should not find it unduly difficult to achieve a 4 to 4.5 percent annual growth rate in food production; it is moving toward that rate of growth in the late 1960's.

Some Concluding Thoughts

The evidence presented in this chapter on population growth and agricultural production for the past decades of the 1950's and 1960's and the future decades of the 1970's and 1980's leads to the following conclusions. First, for the world as a whole, and for the less developed countries as a whole, increases in food production have held even with, or outpaced, population growth in the past two decades. Within these aggregates, food production in the developed regions of the world has increased slightly faster than in the less developed regions, and within the less developed regions some countries have met with great success in increasing food output and some with failure. But per capita food production for the world as a whole has been on the increase in the recent past.

[10] *Ibid.*, p. iv.

Second, in the decades ahead, it is technically feasible and economically possible for the less developed countries of the world to increase their food production sufficiently, through agricultural development, to increase per capita supplies of food. In other words, the technology is known and the resources are available to push food production ahead of population growth in the less developed countries—if that technology and those resources are combined in more efficient producing units. The recent historical record suggests that they will be; but the task is not an easy one. Further, the rate of population growth in the 1970's is likely to be slightly more rapid than that of the 1960's.

The outcome of the race between population growth and agricultural production in the less developed world in the 1970's and 1980's is certainly not settled. It depends on what world leaders, national leaders, the technically skilled, businessmen, farmers, and all the ordinary people do over the next 25 years. Will population control through birth control become a reality in peasant societies? Will the farm-producing units in economically backward societies be modernized and so become more productive? And at what rates will these developments take place? The victor in the race between population growth and agricultural production will in fact emerge from these developments.

But since the recent historical record is one of food production progress, not failure, and the technology and resources are available to increase significantly the per capita production of food in the developing world in the decades ahead, the message here is not one of dark despair and prediction of mass famine. This book is concerned with finding ways and means of using modern technology and world productive resources to increase per capita supplies of food in the developing countries. This is critically important in the 1970's, since rates of population growth are already largely fixed for that period. In the 1970's, the outcome of the population-food race will turn on agricultural developments in both the developed and the developing countries.

But it is the view of this writer that agricultural production can win the race, if presently available knowledge and resources are applied wisely and diligently. It is the purpose of this volume to make some contribution to that application, however modest.

3

Food Balances
and Imbalances:
By Countries and Regions

TWO-THIRDS of the world's people live in countries where diets
on a national average are nutritionally inadequate. The diet deficit
regions of the world include all of Asia except Japan and Israel, all
but the southern tip of Africa, parts of South America, and almost
all of Central America and the Caribbean (see Fig. 3.1). But, as
we shall discover, the really great food deficit of the world is centered in the Far East.

However, before we can describe the nature of dietary inadequacies and delineate them around the world, we must define our
concepts and terms. There is much fuzzy thinking about the incidence of hunger, the inadequacy of diets, and food deficits in this
"old world."

The term "food balance" as used in this chapter refers to an
estimate of food available for consumption on a national average,
or per capita, basis derived through an accounting procedure;[1] such
an estimate of per capita food consumption is then commonly compared with an accepted nutritional standard to attain a measure of
the adequacy of the national average diet. The estimate of the food

----

[1] This is the technical meaning of the term "food balance." For a good
discussion of food consumption data derived by the balance sheet approach,
see Helen Farnsworth, "Defects, Uses, and Abuses of National Food Supply
and Consumption Data," *Food Research Institute Studies*, Vol. II, No. 3
(November 1961), Stanford University, Stanford, Calif.

FIGURE 3.1 Diet Deficit Regions and Subregions of the World, 1970

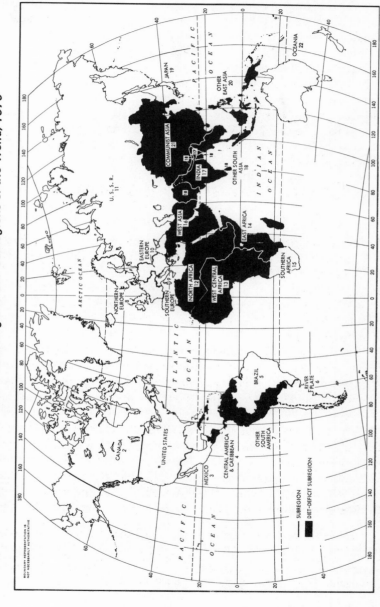

SOURCE: U.S. Department of Agriculture, Economic Research Service, Neg ERS 3084–64 (9).

37

available for consumption may exceed or fall below the nutritional reference standard. If the per capita estimate exceeds the nutritional reference standard, the country is defined as a "food surplus country"; if it falls below the reference standard, the country is defined as a "deficit country."

It would be helpful to have estimates of food consumption based upon family surveys or clinical findings; but because such data are expensive to collect, they are very scarce. Estimates of food consumption are thus typically derived by an accounting procedure on balance sheets (hence the name food balance), starting with estimates of domestic production, then taking into account in turn imports and exports, increases and decreases in national stocks, quantities used for seed and livestock feed, and various kinds of food losses due to pests, spoilage, and processing, to yield a total food availability figure for a country. This figure is next divided by an estimate of the national population for the year involved; the final result—the estimate of national average per capita food consumption—is then compared with a nutritional reference standard for a population of the age and composition of that national society to derive a measure of the adequacy of the *national average diet*.

The dietary data presented and discussed in this chapter were constructed by the balance sheet approach and are valid only in a national average sense. They don't and can't describe how good or how bad the diet of a particular person may be. The data describe the diet for a *national average person*.

The term "imbalance" as used in this chapter refers to a situation wherein one region typically produces a surplus of food and has difficulty disposing of it through commercial channels, and another region chronically runs a food deficit and has difficulty acquiring needed supplies.

"Undernutrition," or "undernourishment," refers to an inadequacy in the quantity of the diet—that is, to an inadequacy of calories.

"Malnutrition," or "malnourishment," refers to an inadequacy in the quality of the diet. More precisely, it denotes the inadequacy of one or more essential nutrients in the diet (e.g., protein, calcium, or vitamin C).

By "hunger" we mean a state of undernourishment acute and persistent enough to cause physical discomfort or pain to the individual.

"Dietary inadequacy," or "deficiency," are general terms that denote that something is lacking in the diet; they may refer to undernourishment or malnutrition or some combination of both.

We shall try to hold to these usages in the remainder of this study, and it is important to remember that the per capita food consumption data, including measures of dietary deficiencies, are national average data unless otherwise specified. Some persons will be better off, and some worse off, in a particular country than is implied by the estimate of national average food consumption. But these national averages indicate levels of food consumption, country by country, and are useful in comparing food consumption developments over time and among countries. They also happen to be the best food consumption data that we have.

Food Consumption Patterns, 1959–61 [2]

Most of the world's population relies upon foods high in carbohydrates—grains, sugar, roots, tubers, and plantains—for a high percentage of its diet. In this carbohydrate grouping, grains are the major food staple. In the Far East, which accounts for well over half of the world's population, grains provide more than two-thirds of the total energy, or calorie value, of the diet. The people of North Africa, West Asia, and East Europe acquire more than half of their calories from grains.[3] Of all regions in the world, North America is the least dependent upon the direct consumption of grains.

Rice and wheat are the dominant food grains. In the Far East, the major rice-producing and consuming region, rice accounts for 42 percent of the total caloric intake. The consumption of wheat varies greatly among the regions of the world—from a low of 1.2

---

[2] The material and data presented in this and the following two sections come primarily from the study *The World Food Budget, 1970*, ERS, USDA, Foreign Agric. Econ. Report No. 19 (October 1964).

[3] See Figure 3.1 and Appendix A for definitions of the regions and subregions used in this study.

percent of the calories consumed for West Central Africa to a high of 48 percent for West Asia.

The consumption of other starchy crops, such as cassava, potatoes, sweet potatoes, yams, and plantains, varies widely from region to region. Such crops are most important in West Central Africa, where they account for more than 45 percent of the caloric intake.

The consumption of pulses and nuts is relatively unimportant in most of the world. The proportion of total calories derived from pulses and nuts ranges from a high of over 13 percent in India, where utilization of animal products is the lowest and pulse protein must substitute for animal protein, to a low of 1 percent in the River Plate countries of South America.

Sugar consumption is important in the Western Hemisphere and in Oceania. Consumption ranges from a high of more than 16 percent of the total caloric intake in Canada to a low of 1.2 percent in Communist Asia.

The high-protein, low-carbohydrate foods—meat, fish, and eggs, and milk products (excluding butter)—account for a minor part of total protein, as well as calorie, consumption in most of the world. The animal protein foods contribute less than 10 percent of the total calorie value and only one-fourth of the protein content of the food supply in the low income, densely populated countries of Asia. Consumption of these foods is lowest in Communist Asia and West Central Africa and highest in Oceania, Canada, and the United States.

Fruits and vegetables, another group of foods high in quality but low in calories, make a limited contribution to the energy value of the food supply of all regions of the world. Their share in total calories ranges from a high of 7.5 percent in West Asia and Southern Europe to a low of less than 1 percent in East Africa.

Even the low cost, high-calorie fats and oils provide only a small share of the energy value of the diet in most less developed countries. In East Africa and Communist Asia, this share is only about 3 percent. In the United States, by contrast, the share of fats and oils exceeds 20 percent of total calorie consumption.

For those persons not bored by tabular material, a wealth of information describing the composition of diets—as measured by calories provided—may be gleaned from Table 3.1. Certainly, the data in this table dramatize the differences in the composition of

TABLE 3.1

Calorie Levels Per Capita and Percentage of Calories from Food Groups by Subregion in Ascending Order of Percent of Calories from High-Carbohydrate Foods, Average 1959–61[1]

(In percent)

Subregion	Calorie Level (Number)	High-Carbohydrate Foods	Wheat	Rice	Other Grains	Other Starchy Crops	Pulses and Nuts	Sugar	Vegetables and Fruits	Fats and Oils	Meat, Fish, and Eggs	Milk Products
United States	3,190	40	17.4	0.9	2.5	3.1	3.3	15.7	6.2	20.5	16.9	13.5
Canada	3,100	42	18.8	0.6	1.9	4.5	1.9	16.3	4.8	15.1	22.0	14.1
Oceania	3,260	43	25.2	0.6	1.3	2.7	1.3	13.4	4.7	14.3	24.8	11.7
Northern Europe	3,060	48	23.4	0.6	4.0	6.9	1.7	13.4	4.5	17.8	16.4	11.3
River Plate	3,200	56	33.2	1.7	2.3	6.0	1.0	12.4	3.3	12.5	21.0	6.6
Southern Europe	2,720	60	40.1	2.4	3.8	6.0	4.4	7.6	7.4	15.6	6.9	5.8
Eastern Europe	3,000	66	32.1	1.0	16.5	7.8	1.3	8.5	2.9	11.4	11.9	6.6
Central America and Caribbean	2,240	69	8.8	9.4	23.0	12.7	5.9	15.0	4.2	8.6	7.4	5.0
Mexico	2,580	70	11.1	1.6	42.2	1.8	8.0	13.0	2.8	8.1	6.1	5.3
Other South America	2,260	70	16.9	5.9	16.0	15.5	3.9	15.9	3.9	7.5	9.0	5.5
Brazil	2,710	71	8.6	14.5	11.2	20.9	8.9	15.4	2.3	5.9	8.4	3.9
Southern Africa	2,670	72	14.0	1.1	41.6	1.1	1.7	14.0	2.4	5.3	12.4	6.4
West Asia	2,350	72	48.0	4.2	8.8	1.6	4.1	9.4	7.6	8.1	4.0	4.2
U.S.S.R.	3,040	73	35.7	0.8	16.9	9.9	1.4	9.8	1.9	8.9	8.1	6.6
North Africa	2,210	73	26.4	3.1	36.2	1.3	5.7	6.1	6.1	6.0	4.3	4.8
India	2,060	74	11.3	33.1	19.0	2.6	13.2	8.2	2.0	4.2	0.9	5.5
Japan	2,360	78	11.7	46.9	4.6	7.7	5.9	6.7	4.2	5.0	5.9	1.4
Other East Asia	2,150	78	1.8	50.1	7.7	12.7	6.6	5.2	5.4	5.7	4.1	0.7
Other South Asia	2,120	79	19.4	47.1	4.9	1.0	5.9	6.7	3.6	4.0	3.0	4.4
West Central Africa	2,460	81	1.2	5.7	27.2	45.3	6.5	1.5	1.0	9.0	2.0	0.6
East Africa	2,390	83	2.3	8.4	55.9	12.4	6.5	4.3	0.8	3.4	3.6	2.4
Communist Asia	1,790	87	12.2	44.3	18.1	11.1	5.9	1.2	1.7	3.1	2.3	0.1

[1] Definitions of the geographic regions and subregions and the food groups may be found in Appendices A and B.
SOURCE: The World Food Budget, 1970, ERS, USDA, Foreign Agric. Econ. Report No. 19 (October 1964), p. 4.

diets between the opulent West and the struggling, less developed regions. The low-cost, high carbohydrate foods provide the bulk of the calories in the diets of the peoples living in Communist Asia, East and West Africa, and the remainder of Asia; and the high-cost, high-protein foods—meat, fish, eggs, and milk products—are almost absent from the diets of the populations of these regions. On the other hand, fats and oils, meat, fish, and eggs, and milk products bulk large in the diets of people living in the United States, Canada, Oceania, and Northern Europe, and the high-carbohydrate foods are relatively less important in these countries. In short, the composition of diets is highly correlated with the level of economic development.

The Adequacy of Diets

A comparison of national food consumption data with relevant nutritional standards, country by country, for the period 1959–61 shows that, on the average, the populations of much of Africa, Central America, and the Caribbean, and all of northern South America and Asia (except Japan) suffer from undernourishment (see Table 3.2). In most instances, this national average caloric deficiency does not exceed 10 percent, but for Communist Asia in the period 1959–61 it is estimated to have been as great as 24 percent (Table 3.2). Stated differently, in 1959–61 about 60 percent of the world's population lived in countries where the average person suffered from undernourishment. But most of these 1.8 billion people were in fact concentrated in Communist Asia, South Asia, and East Asia (excluding Japan).

Seven geographic subregions were deficient in total protein in the period 1959–61 (see Table 3.3). But the most serious protein deficiencies were found in four subregions: Central America and Caribbean, West Central Africa, Communist Asia, and Other East Asia. In these last two regions the diet of the average person was more than 20 percent deficient in protein.

Except for Japan, in 1959–61 all the subregions with adequate supplies of calories and protein also had adequate supplies of fat (see Table 3.4). The subregions with serious fat deficits were Communist Asia, Other South Asia, India, Japan, Other East Asia, and East Africa.

TABLE 3.2

Calorie Level, by Subregion in Descending Order of Adequacy, Average 1959–61

Region	Calorie Level (Number)	Calorie Standard[1] (Number)	Level as Percentage of Standard
Oceania	3,260	2,650	123
United States	3,190	2,650	120
River Plate	3,200	2,700	119
Northern Europe	3,060	2,650	115
Canada	3,100	2,700	115
Eastern Europe	3,000	2,650	113
U.S.S.R.	3,040	2,700	112
Southern Africa	2,670	2,450	109
Southern Europe	2,720	2,500	109
Mexico	2,580	2,450	105
West Central Africa	2,460	2,400	102
Brazil	2,710	2,650	102
Japan	2,360	2,350	100
East Africa	2,390	2,450	97
West Asia	2,350	2,450	96
North Africa	2,210	2,350	95
Other South Asia	2,120	2,300	92
Other East Asia	2,150	2,350	92
Central America and Caribbean	2,240	2,450	91
Other South America	2,260	2,500	90
India	2,060	2,300	90
Communist Asia	1,790	2,350	76
World	2,360	2,440	97

[1] The calorie standards used in the table were developed by the Food and Agricultural Organization of the U.N.; these standards represent physiological requirements for normal activity and health, taking account of environmental temperature, body weights, and distribution by age and sex of national populations.
SOURCE: *The World Food Budget, 1970*, ERS, USDA, Foreign Agric. Econ. Report No. 19 (October 1964), p. 25.

In summary, undernourishment and malnutrition tend to be found together and both are concentrated in Asia. The six subregions with the lowest levels of calorie consumption also had national average diets that were deficient in protein. These subregions comprised Other South Asia, Other East Asia, Central America and Caribbean, Other South America, India, and Communist Asia.

To repeat, national average dietary data do not tell us the proportion of people in each region who may be undernourished or malnourished. These data simply describe the average level of diets;

TABLE 3.3

Protein Consumption Per Capita Per Day, by Subregion in Descending Order of Adequacy of Total Protein, Average 1959–61

Region	Protein Consumption, in Grams		Protein Consumption as Percentage of Standard[1]	
	Total	Animal	Total	Animal
Oceania	101	68.6	169	686
River Plate	101	54.3	168	543
Canada	96	64.3	159	643
United States	95	63.8	159	638
Northern Europe	88	52.0	147	520
U.S.S.R.	87	29.5	145	295
Southern Africa	84	35.3	140	353
Southern Europe	79	26.5	131	265
Eastern Europe	77	28.0	129	280
Japan	70	18.0	117	180
West Asia	69	13.1	115	131
North Africa	68	17.0	113	170
Mexico	68	17.2	113	172
East Africa	65	11.5	109	115
Brazil	65	20.4	108	204
Other South America	57	20.6	96	206
India	56	7.2	93	72
Other South Asia	55	11.0	92	110
Central America and Caribbean	54	17.0	90	170
West Central Africa	52	5.7	86	57
Communist Asia	48	3.2	79	32
Other East Asia	45	7.3	75	73
World	64	18.6	107	186

[1] The same standard is used for all countries in this table. It provides for a minimum allowance of 60 grams of total protein per capita per day, of which 10 grams should be animal protein.
SOURCE: *The World Food Budget, 1970*, ERS, USDA, Foreign Agric. Econ. Report No. 19 (October 1964), p. 26.

but they are useful in comparing one country, or region, with another. And certainly it follows that, if the national average level of consumption is below the nutritional reference standard for a country, a high proportion of the people must be suffering from an inadequate diet.

Writing in 1964, the authors of the *World Food Budget, 1970* had this to say about progress in improving national diets.[4]

[4] See p. 29.

TABLE 3.4

Fat Consumption Per Capita Per Day, by Subregion in Descending Order of Adequacy, Average 1959–61

Region	Fat Consumption, in Grams	Fat Standard,[1] in Grams	Fat Consumption as Percentage of Standard
United States	146	45	325
Oceania	146	45	324
Canada	140	46	305
Northern Europe	129	45	286
River Plate	117	46	255
Eastern Europe	89	45	197
Southern Europe	81	42	192
Southern Africa	67	42	158
U.S.S.R.	67	46	145
Mexico	60	42	143
Central America and Caribbean	52	42	143
Other South America	51	42	121
Brazil	52	45	116
West Central Africa	46	41	111
West Asia	46	42	108
North Africa	41	40	102
East Africa	37	42	89
Other East Asia	36	42	89
Japan	32	40	79
India	30	39	78
Other South Asia	29	39	74
Communist Asia	20	39	51
World	53	41	129

[1] The reference standards for fat used in this table are expressed in terms of the amount that would provide 15 percent of the reference standard for calories.
SOURCE: *The World Food Budget, 1970*, ERS, USDA, Foreign Agric. Econ. Report No. 19 (October 1964), p. 28.

Supplies of calories, total protein, and fat will improve in all of the diet-deficient subregions by 1970, with many approaching or exceeding the established reference standards. Except Other South Asia, every subregion deficient in combined animal and pulse protein and animal protein in 1959–61 will have increased supplies by 1970. However, this subregion had adequate supplies of animal protein and is projected to have adequate supplies in 1970.

Other ways in which diets could be improved would not be shown in national food balance data. For example, improvements in food storage and preparation, and the use of additives—such as synthetic vitamins and amino acids—would not be reflected. Also, changes in the combination of food consumed because of better food distribution would do much to improve diets. Some of these developments will be fostered by better education, higher incomes, and more rapid economic development as well as by national and international programs for improving diets. In some cases, such developments probably will bring about important improvements in the diet by 1970 which will be in addition to those projected by this study.

Measuring the Food Deficit

The authors of the *World Food Budget, 1970* firmly believe that, on the average, diets will improve in the food deficit areas of the world in the 1960's. Writing in 1964 and again in 1966,[5] they argued that by 1970 the level of calorie consumption is likely to be 8 percent above the base period 1959–61. And they expect the consumption of protein and fat to be up overall by 10 and 16 percent respectively. In other words, they expect an improvement not only in the quantity of food available per person, but also in the quality of diets in the food deficit areas by 1970.

In their view, however, a large food deficit would still exist in 1970. The calorie gap in the food deficit areas of the world is estimated to be equal to 54 million metric tons of grain. The deficit in animal protein is expected to be equivalent to 6.5 million tons of nonfat dry milk. Some 3.2 million tons of soy grits would be required to fill the pulse and other protein deficit. And 3.1 million tons of vegetable oil would be needed to satisfy the fat deficit.

The total cost of the world food deficit in 1970 is projected to run to about $6.8 billion. Because of dietary improvements in the food deficit regions of the world in the 1960's, the projected total figure of $6.8 billion is about one-third below the cost of the food deficit during the base period 1959–61.

About 93 percent of the food deficit is accounted for by countries in the Far East; Communist Asia alone is responsible for 62

[5] Quentin M. West, *World Food Needs*, an address given at Utah's Tenth Annual Agricultural and Industry Conference, Salt Lake City, Utah, February 1966.

percent. The distribution of the food deficit among the regions of the world with inadequate diets is as follows:

	Share of Deficit (Percent)
Central America and Caribbean	1.3
South America (excl. Brazil, Argentina, and Uruguay)	1.0
North Africa	1.0
West Central Africa	2.1
East Africa	0.3
West Asia	1.7
India	13.2
Other South Asia	5.0
East Asia (excl. Japan)	12.0
Communist Asia	62.4

The world food deficit, as of 1970, constitutes a very great problem. This is particularly true for Communist Asia. But the problem does not seem insurmountable for most of the other regions when the per capita food deficit measured in value terms is related to per capita food consumption measured in value terms. The ratio of the estimated per capita deficit to estimated per capita food consumption for the various regions as of 1970 is:

Region	Percent
Central America and Caribbean	4.3
Other South America	1.9
North Africa	1.6
West Central Africa	3.2
East Africa	2.6
India	5.3
Other South Asia	5.3
Other East Asia	6.1
Communist Asia	16.6

For example, to bring the average per capita level of food consumption to an adequate level in India in 1970, it is estimated that food consumption would have to increase 5.3 percent. In most other diet

deficit areas (excluding Communist Asia), the percentage increases
in food consumption needed to achieve adequacy are of the magnitude for India or less. These represent significant per capita increases; but they do not seem impossible to achieve. In sum, we
are talking about a large problem, but not a *hopelessly* large problem.[6]

Third World Food Survey

The Food and Agricultural Organization of the U.N. produced the
first *World Food Survey* in 1946, only a few months after its establishment. In 1952, FAO produced a more detailed and reliable picture of the world food situation in the *Second World Food Survey*.
Then, in 1963, FAO produced the most comprehensive extant survey of the world food situation in the *Third World Food Survey*.

The broad conclusions of the *Third World Food Survey* are as
follows:[7]

1. The world food supply available per caput, though higher than
   in the postwar years, is only slightly above the prewar level.
   The progress over the last decade has mainly taken place in
   the developed areas with the result that the gap between the
   developed and the less developed areas has tended to increase
   rather than to decrease.
2. The calorie content of the diet has generally regained the prewar level in both the developed and the less developed areas.
   Nevertheless, the current calorie supply per caput in the less
   developed areas falls short of the corresponding requirement
   and it is estimated that at least 20% of the population in
   these areas is undernourished.
3. The nutritional quality of the diet has shown a distinct though
   small improvement over the prewar level. However, this improvement has again mainly taken place in the developed
   areas, while in the less developed areas the quality of diets has
   barely regained the unsatisfactory prewar level. Reports of dietary and clinical surveys show that nutritional deficiency dis-

---

[6] This is precisely the same conclusion that D. Gale Johnson reaches in the
pamphlet *The Struggle Against World Hunger*, Headline Series No. 184
(August 1967), Foreign Policy Association, New York City, N.Y., pp. 10, 18.

[7] The Food and Agricultural Organization of the United Nations (Rome,
1963), pp. 8–9.

eases are still common in large parts of the world. Retarded growth of children, poor physique and health of adults, low resistance to disease, particularly in children below 5 years and low working efficiency together with high mortality rates among young children and low expectations of life are an indication of widespread malnutrition in the less developed areas. This is not surprising, since in these areas the level of animal protein intake is only one fifth of that in the more developed areas.

4. It is generally agreed that if more than about 80% of the calories in a diet are derived from cereals, starchy roots, and sugar, there is a risk that the nutritional quality of diet is inadequate. If this percentage is less than about 80, the diet is likely to be adequate. In well-fed countries like the United Kingdom and France hardly any households derive more than 80% of their calories from cereals, starchy roots, and sugar, whereas some 60% of the households in the less developed countries have a proportion exceeding 80%. In other words, it appears probable that some 60% of the households in the less developed areas live on diets which are inadequate in nutritional quality.

5. Presenting the results of undernutrition and malnutrition for the world as a whole, the survey concludes that 10 to 15% of its people are undernourished and up to a half suffer from hunger or malnutrition or both.

The World Food Budget, 1970 states that "two-thirds of the world's people live in countries with nutritionally inadequate national average diets" and the *Third World Food Survey* that up to one-half of the world's people "suffer from hunger or malnutrition or both." Neither statement, because of their reliance on average national data, is too precise; but worded as they are, they are not necessarily inconsistent with one another. Both tell a story of millions and millions of people suffering from undernourishment, or malnutrition, or both; both find the great food deficits to be centered in the Far East; and both find a high correlation between the quality of food consumption and average per capita incomes. High-quality diets and nutritional adequacy are commonplace in the developed countries of the Western world; diets heavily weighted with low-cost, high-carbohydrate foods and nutritional inadequacy are commonplace in the less developed countries.

Thus, neither survey describes in detail the incidence of under-nourishment and malnutrition in national populations, or the numbers of persons involved. But each tells the same story of a general pattern and magnitude of nutritional inadequacy. It is a huge problem and it is correlated inversely with economic development.

The Basic World Imbalance

There is a basic imbalance in the production and availability of food between the developed and the developing nations. This imbalance is inseparable from the development gap between the rich and the poor nations.

It is highly probable that the developed nations of the Western world will be plagued by food and fiber surpluses during the 1970's, at the very time that the developing nations are suffering from food shortages. How can this be? How can there be food surpluses in the developed world at the same time there are undernourished and hungry people in the less developed world? The answer, of course, has many facets, but there are two main elements to it. First, at prevailing prices and returns, farmers in the Western world can produce much more food and fiber than consumers and manufacturing users in the Western world want to buy at prevailing prices. Second, the less developed countries, because of their low economic productivity, lack the foreign exchange to purchase the food surpluses of the West and distribute that food to their undernourished and hungry populations. True, food aid can bridge this gap to some degree. But, as we shall discover later, there are difficult problems to be overcome on both the importing and exporting sides with regard to food aid. Thus, the probability remains that actual surpluses or potential surpluses (idle acres) will exist in the West in the 1970's while consumers in the developing world suffer from food shortages, undernourishment, and hunger.

This phenomenon can best be illustrated and explained in terms of world grain production and the international trade in grains. We turn to the grains, first, because (as already noted) they are the primary source of calories for mankind and second, because grains are far and away the most important foodstuff moving in international trade. Food and grains are almost synonymous to those dealing with the world food problem.

The data presented in Table 3.5 on the production, trade, and consumption of grains by categories of countries may appear formidable, even at a first glance confusing. But they tell a most important story.

Assuming moderate improvement in production in the less developed countries, these less developed countries in total (excluding Communist Asia) will produce 399 million metric tons of grain in 1980. For this production projection, the experts in the U. S. Department of Agriculture reviewed the production possibilities in the more important LDC's and arrived at production estimates that could be achieved with modest improvements in production practices—improvements that appear to be feasible in terms of both technological developments and investment requirements. In other words, this projection is realistic and possible under the conditions that will prevail in these countries.

From the production total of 399.3 million tons must be subtracted 22.5 million tons of grains exported to the developed world; and 52.2 million tons imported into the LDC's must be added to yield a total available for consumption of 429.0 million tons. This total yields a per capita grain consumption figure of 191 kgs. for the total developing world (excluding Communist China) as of 1980. The projected per capita consumption figure of 191 kgs. is 21 kgs. larger than the estimated figure of 170 in 1959–61, and 3 kgs. larger than a minimum requirement figure of 188 kgs. per capita specified by the U. S. Department of Agriculture. So the data in Table 3.5 suggest clear progress with respect to per capita food consumption for the developing world generally as of 1980, and also by categories of countries.

But this is not the end of the story. The developed countries are projected to produce 767 million tons of grain in 1980. Of this total, 77.6 million tons *would be available for export from the developed countries.* It is estimated that 9.0 million would be exported to Communist Asia; and, as we have already observed, 29.7 million tons would be exported to the less developed countries in total. This means that 38.9 million tons of grain produced in the Western world would be surplus—could not, in the year 1980, find an export home.

We need to consider this 38.9 million tons surplus figure more closely. If this grain were in fact produced, it would, like many mil-

TABLE 3.5

World Production, Trade, and Consumption of Grains by Regions; Projections to 1980 under the Assumption of Moderate Improvement in Production in the Less Developed Countries (Excluding Communist Asia)

Country or Region	Production	Net Imports	Total Consumption	Per Capita Consumption	Minimum Requirements[1]
	Million Metric Tons			Kilograms	
Less Developed Countries					
India	114.7	10.3	125.0	182	186
Pakistan	28.1	2.9	31.0	189	199
Other Less Developed Countries, Excluding Grain Exporters	185.0	39.0	224.0	186	188
Subtotal	327.8	52.2	380.0	185	—
Net Grain Exporters	71.5	−22.5	49.0	255	216
Total, Less Developed Countries	399.3	29.7	429.0	191	188
Developed Countries					
United States	315.0	−109.5	205.5	—	—
Developed Exporters (less U. S.)	115.0	−42.5	72.5	—	—
Other Developed Free World	106.8	73.2	180.0	—	—
Eastern Europe (incl. U.S.S.R.)	230.2	1.2	231.4	—	—
Total, Developed Countries	767.0	−77.6	689.4	—	—
Communist Asia	183.5	9.0	192.5	—	—
World Total	1,349.8	−38.9	1,310.9	—	—

[1] Specified by the USDA.
SOURCE: *The World Food Situation: Prospects for World Grain Production, Consumption, and Trade*, ERS, USDA, Foreign Agric. Econ. Report No. 35 (August 1967), pp. 19, 20.

lions of tons of grain produced in the United States in the 1950's, move into surplus stocks. But it might not be produced; the resources that could be used to produce it could be held idle by means of production controls. However, whether actually produced or not, the 38.9 million tons represent the estimated excess grain production capacity of the developed world as of 1980; in grain actually produced, or grain that could be produced, this figure represents the surplus-producing capacity of the developed West in 1980.

But there would still be unmet needs for grain in the developing world in 1980 for human and animal feed. Why then would not these 38.9 million tons of grain flow to the less developed countries that need them? They do not move in Table 3.5, and they would not move in international trade, first, because the less developed countries lack the foreign exchange to purchase those tons of grain and, second, because it is judged that the donor countries and the recipient countries could not for one reason or another (e.g., program costs, port and storage facilities in the recipient countries, and politics) mount larger food aid programs.

Net imports of grain into the less developed countries of 29.7 million tons in 1980 (see Table 3.5) represent a great increase over the 1964–65 level of 13.7 million tons. Built into the net import figure of 29.7 million tons are large increases in both commercial imports and food aid imports over the levels of the mid-1960's. In sum, the figure represents all that is believed could be realistically moved into the less developed countries in 1980 via both commercial and aid channels.

The data in Table 3.5 describe the nature of the fundamental imbalance in food production between the developing and the developed worlds as of 1980. The countries of the developed West, because of their great producing capacity, are likely to be grappling with grain surpluses at the same time that unmet needs are creating problems in the less developed countries. The 1970's may well repeat the incongruous situation of the 1950's in which the developing countries made significant gains in increasing their food production, but an important share of the increased grain production in the United States and Canada accumulated in huge surplus stocks while millions of people in the less developed regions were both undernourished and malnourished. The food-producing plant of the developed countries has too great a capacity in relation to the effective demands made upon it, while the food-producing plant of the less developed countries has too little capacity; and the means have not yet been developed to solve these disproportionate situations simultaneously.

The Nature of the Solution

The general nature of the solution to the world food problem is clear to all who have studied it seriously. It is economic development—a maintenance of rapid rates of development for those countries that have already achieved satisfactory rates, and increased rates for those countries that are in the economic doldrums. Increasing per capita food consumption requires, it is true, a series of specific developments, which might be listed as follows: increasing total production per farm, increasing the production of resources required in turn to increase farm production (e.g. fertilizer, tube well equipment, and pesticides), increasing the real incomes of consumers to enable them to purchase the increased farm output at satisfactory prices, and increasing the production of farm and nonfarm commodities for sale in world markets to earn foreign change and so import more food and farm production supplies (e.g., fertilizer, improved seeds). But any one of these developments, or all of them in combination, could no more take place in isolation from the general operating economy than a man's arm could increase in length in isolation from the rest of his body.

Each of the specific activities listed above is an integral and component part of a general economic process. As such, each must be developed in relation to the other in a systematic and balanced manner. But each must also be developed in a proper functional, as well as quantitative, relation to other sectors of the general economy. For example, increasing the real incomes of consumers to enable them to purchase the increased farm output at satisfactory prices is directly related to and dependent upon the increased productivity of those consumer-workers in nonfarm enterprises. And agricultural production cannot be increased in a vacuum; it can be increased only to the extent that a whole set of production practices and resources are made available to farmers in the necessary price relationships. Agricultural production will increase and be sustained only as functionally related activities and processes outside agriculture achieve a parallel development.

The actions of the developed countries facing the world food problem will be many and varied (they are the subject of much of the remainder of this volume), but food shipments from the developed countries to the less developed countries will depend in part upon the policies of the less developed countries. If the less developed countries decide to emphasize food production, it is possible that food exports to those countries will decline over the long run. But if they emphasize such nonfarm enterprises as ore production and processing, cotton and hard fiber production and processing, and tourism, for example, the "export" of such items might be used to pay for the increased importation of grains and animal products. It is then impossible to foresee specific long-term enterprise developments, but the commodity structure of such developments will have important implications for the commercial agriculture of the developed countries in the temperate zone.

On the basis of past experience, however, this observer is inclined to guess that total exports of grains and animal products from the developed countries to the developing countries will continue to increase absolutely, but that such rates of export expansion—together with the slow rates of growth in food demand in the domestic markets in the developed countries—will not serve to expand the total demand for farm products in the developed countries as rapidly as total output will seek to expand in those countries. Thus, there will be a continuous pressure of food supplies on demand in the developed countries, with a consequent downward pressure on farm prices.

This is simply another way of repeating what the USDA economists and technologists have said in their study of *The World Food Situation: Prospects for World Grain Production, Consumption, and Trade*.[8] Their projections to 1980 involve increases in grain production in the developing countries and increased grain exports from the developed countries to the developing countries. But even

[8] Foreign Agric. Econ. Report No. 35 (August 1967).

with such favorable developments, grain production is likely to increase so substantially in the developed countries in the 1970's that those countries will end up with a sizeable grain surplus.

And this set of developments may be generalized even further to include the 1980's. Thus it seems probable that the agricultural production plants of the developed countries will be plagued with excess productive capacity, physical surpluses, and downward pressures on farm prices for a long time to come. All this, even if the developing countries generally are highly successful in developing the productivity of their economies over the next two decades.

4

Toward
an Understanding of
the Problem

WE NOW KNOW a good deal about the world food situation: where
the surpluses and deficits are to be found, the approximate magnitude and incidence of undernourishment and malnutrition, past
and prospective food production trends, and rates of population
growth. We also know something about the political and social
milieu in which the problem is to be found. It is time, then, to put
these pieces of information together into an explicit statement,
for it is clear that a worldwide problem, or series of problems, exists.
It is important to do this, because a clear statement, or formulation,
of the problem enables us, first, to discuss the issues with clarity
and, second, to focus on a solution.

But two questions immediately come to mind. Is not the problem obvious—simply a very large number of hungry people? Or,
are there not hundreds, or thousands, of particular food problems in
the world? In a sense, the problem is obvious and it is hungry people. But there have been millions of hungry people for thousands
of years in this world, and there will be millions more for many
years to come. Thus, stating the problem in this form does not
help us to analyze the situation or correct it. And, of course, there
are thousands of specific food problems in the world. In one locale,
it is a crop shortage resulting from drought; in another, a faulty
distribution system; in still another, a protein deficiency; and so on
around the world. But again, listing these many and varied specific

food problems does not help us to think creatively or effectively about the widespread hunger and malnutrition that exists in the world.

It seems reasonable to conclude that any statement of the world food problem will be complex because the world is diverse and complex. But this is not the important point. The important point is that the problem be stated in a form that lends itself to purposeful discussion, rational analysis, and ultimate solution. And that is the goal of this chapter—to develop a formulation of the world food problem that contributes first to discussion and analysis in the remainder of this book and second to productive discussion and decision making on farms, in educational institutions, and in businesses and governments in the wide world outside the pages of this book.

The World Food Problem before 1750

In the millennia that preceded the scientific and industrial revolutions of the Western world (i.e., before 1750), birth rates were high (at about 35 per 1,000 population), agricultural productivity was low and virtually stagnant, and there was a persistent pressure of population on the available and limited food supplies in all regions of the world. Except for the very few who lived in relative luxury, malnutrition, hunger, and disease were commonplace; they were everyday occurrences everywhere. Given this state of mankind, death rates were also high (approaching 35 per 1,000). A high death rate, particularly a high infant mortality rate, resulting from starvation and disease in the context of limited and inadequate food supplies, roughly balanced the high birth rate for thousands of years and held the growth of population in check. For example, the population of Europe grew very little, if any, from A.D. 1 to 1500 —probably fluctuating severely with famine, wars, and plagues between 40 and 70 million persons over that long period. And what did the common man eat during this period, when he did eat? According to M. K. Bennett ". . . it is probably true that the main dish of practically every meal was a grain product. . . . [w]e can think of a heap of mush, a pile of flatcakes, or loaves of leavened bread as the central calorie-providing dishes of the great masses of

eleventh-century populations, aside from herdsmen and hunters."[1]
It was a grim existence in which the weak perished from starvation
and diseases related to malnutrition. Through the variable of death,
the population was held in balance with the food supply.
Writing in the year 1798, Thomas Robert Malthus concluded
that this was the necessary state and inevitable fate of mankind.
He argued in his *First Essay on Population* as follows:[2]

> I think I may fairly make two postulata.
> First, that food is necessary to the existence of man.
> Secondly, that the passion between the sexes is necessary, and
> will remain nearly in its present state . . .
> Assuming then, my postulata as granted, I say, that the power
> of population is indefinitely greater than the power in the earth to
> produce subsistence for man.
> Population, when unchecked, increases in a geometrical ratio.
> Subsistence increases only in an arithmetical ratio. A slight acquain-
> tance with numbers will shew the immensity of the first power as
> compared with the second.
> By that law of our nature which makes food necessary to the life
> of man, the effects of these two unequal powers must be kept equal.
> This implies a strong and constantly operating check on popula-
> tion from the difficulty of subsistence. . . . The race of plants, and
> the race of animals shrink under this great restrictive law. And the
> race of man cannot, by any efforts of reason, escape from it. Among
> plants and animals its effects are waste of seed, sickness, and pre-
> mature death. Among mankind, misery and vice. The former, mis-
> ery, is an absolutely necessary consequence of it. Vice is a highly
> probable consequence . . . I see no way by which man can escape
> from the weight of this law which pervades all animated nature . . .

Whether these relationships must necessarily be the true relationships between population growth and food supply has been
hotly debated ever since 1798. But the situation wherein population growth is controlled by a limited food supply—hence through

---

[1] *The World's Food* (New York: Harper and Brothers, 1954), pp. 34, 35.
[2] These statements, taken from *An Essay on the Principle of Population as
It Affects the Future Improvement of Society* (reprinted by Macmillan & Company, London, 1926, and reissued in 1966 under the title, *First Essay on
Population 1798*), represent the core of the Malthusian argument. See Chapter 1, pp. 11–17.

hunger, misery, disease, and death—is everywhere known and described now as "Malthusian."

It is interesting to speculate why someone other than Malthus did not formulate his celebrated proposition on the relationship between human population and food supply in 1698, say, or 1498. The situation in England and Europe in those earlier periods was truly Malthusian, in that population was held in check by a limited food supply through high death rates. Malthus wrote in 1798, some 50 years after death rates in England had begun to fall for a variety of reasons: improved medicine, improved sanitation, a more stable and responsible government, the beginning of improved agricultural practices and increased agricultural productivity, and the introduction of important new products from the New World (e.g., the potato, maize). What Malthus must have seen in 1798 were the effects of declining death rates—a significant decline in infant mortality and more children reaching adulthood—as well as some of the reasons for those declining rates, namely, no great famines or plagues during the period 1750–1800.

Certainly he had no world population statistics with which to work, and few reliable statistics for his own tight little isle. But what he saw in the way of falling death rates and an expanding population for England must have made a great impression on him, perhaps even frightened him as many people are frightened today. (See the falling death rate for England and Wales after 1750 in Fig. 4.1, but no decline in the birth rate up to 1880.)

But Malthus did not see agriculture emerging from a thousand years of stagnation in Western Europe during his lifetime, nor could he envisage the flood of imports to come from the New World during the next two centuries. He saw a falling death rate, a high and stable birth rate, and a trebling of population in England and Wales between 1750 and 1880, but he missed the dramatic changes in the state of the agricultural arts in England and on the European continent at this time and the rising tide of food imports from the New World. So he postulated a population growth–food supply relationship for the world, which we now call Malthusian after him, *at the very time the Western world was breaking out of that kind of relationship.* The control of population growth through hunger, misery, disease, and death, which had reigned supreme for

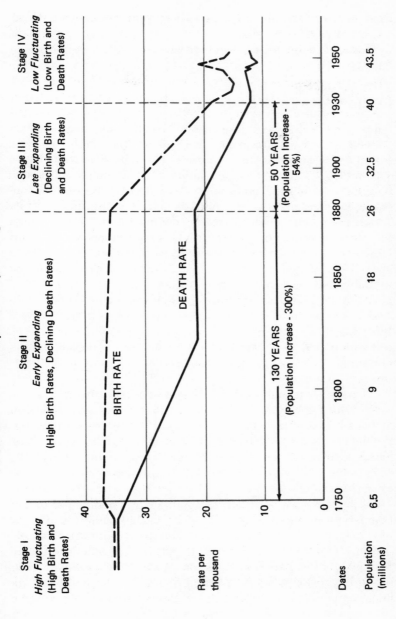

*FIGURE 4.1 *The Population Cycle: England and Wales*

| Stage I
High Fluctuating
(High Birth and
Death Rates) | Stage II
Early Expanding
(High Birth Rates, Declining Death Rates) | Stage III
Late Expanding
(Declining Birth
and Death Rates) | Stage IV
Low Fluctuating
(Low Birth and
Death Rates) |

130 YEARS
(Population Increase - 300%)

50 YEARS
(Population Increase -
54%)

BIRTH RATE

DEATH RATE

Rate per
thousand

Dates	1750	1800	1850	1880	1900	1930	1950
Population (millions)	6.5	9	18	26	32.5	40	43.5

SOURCE: *World Population and Resources* (London: Political and Economic Planning, September 1955), fig. III, p. 10.

61

thousands of years, was in the process of being lifted for the Western world at the very time he wrote. He caught one part of the dynamic scene; he missed the other part.

The Situation after 1750 in the Western World

During the century and a half from 1750 to 1900, birth rates remained high, death rates fell to about 20 per 1,000, and population soared in Europe; it increased from about 100 million in 1750 to 400 million in 1900 (this population phenomenon is illustrated in Fig. 4.1). But the burgeoning population of Europe did not starve; on the contrary, per capita diets improved both in quality and quantity. The rapidly increasing population of Europe did not starve for two important reasons: (1) improved agricultural technology in Europe, and (2) new lands in the Americas. Improved agricultural technology—involving new plants, improved tillage and rotation practices, and improved livestock breeds—greatly increased agricultural production and thus the food supply in Europe itself. And the new lands of the Americas, particularly the Mississippi River Basin of North America, produced a surplus of grain, which was transported to Western Europe. This was to become an important and sustained source of food supply to Europe for two centuries.

The soaring populations of Europe and North America did not press against a limited food supply, with hunger, misery, disease, and death as the consequence. Except in a few dramatic cases (e.g., the potato famine in Ireland in the late 1840's), food supplies outpaced population growth, with the result that per capita food consumption increased and farm prices in surplus-producing areas were often distressingly low.

In the latter part of the nineteenth century another important population development got under way in the Western world; the birth rate began to fall (see Fig. 4.1). With significant increases in real incomes in the late nineteenth and early twentieth centuries, families began to have fewer children. Without help from, or recognition by, governments, and certainly without the benefit of the Church, family planning became an undiscussed but very real phenomenon. Probably first through abstinence and induced abortion, and later with the aid of various mechanical gadgets, families began to control their size. Thus, the number of births per 1,000 fell from the neighborhood of 35 in 1850 to about 15 in 1930.

With great improvements in medical practice and in public health in this same era, death rates, too, began to decline once again. By the 1930's, the Western world had reached the final stage of the population cycle: low birth rates, low death rates, and a nearly stationary population. Since World War II, the death rate has declined still further in many countries, falling to roughly 10 per 1,000 for Italy, the United Kingdom, and the United States, and as low as 8.6 for Canada. Birth rates, on the other hand, have typically increased: to around 18 per 1,000 for the United States and the U.S.S.R. Thus, the Western world generally has experienced a modest rate of population increase in the post-World War II period, and countries such as Canada and Puerto Rico have experienced a rapid rate of population increase. But, except in time of war or immediately thereafter, peoples of the Western world have enjoyed bountiful food supplies and a steady improvement in diets since the middle of the nineteenth century. In fact, it is probably correct to say that in the past century the age-old pressure of population on food supply has been turned around, so that in the Western world food supplies are now pressing on population.

During this past century, too, a whole new set of attitudes has developed toward food and diets in the West. The new viewpoint holds that hunger and malnutrition are terrible evils which should be eliminated wherever they exist. Where 300 years ago most of the people were hungry most of the time, and were probably malnourished all of the time, we now believe that no one should be hungry any time and that malnutrition should be sought out and eradicated like the plague. The prevailing attitude in the West with respect to food is now very much like that for the element air—it is necessary; it is abundant; hence no one should be in want.

The New Popular Conception of the World Food Problem

As the average American sits in his warm, comfortable home, eating expensive but not always nutritious foods, he is greatly troubled by what he reads about population developments in South America, the Middle East, South Asia, and East Asia. He reads scare headlines that tell him: "At present rates of increase, the population of tropical Latin America will double in 19 years, West Africa in 21 years, South East Asia in 23," and so on. He reads further that the population of India alone could be 1.2 billion by the year 2000, and that of the world 7.5 billion. At this point he begins to worry about standing room in the world, let alone enough food. Then he reads interviews, articles, and books by such experts as Harrison Brown,[3] Lester Brown,[4] Georg Borgstrom,[5] and Gunnar Myrdal,[6] describing the world population explosion and the very great difficulties that must be overcome if these added millions are to avoid serious undernourishment, malnutrition, hunger, and perhaps death from starvation. And finally he reads *Famine 1975*, which asserts categorically that "The exploding populations in the hungry nations combined with their static agricultures make famines, in many [countries], inevitable." By 1975, "the Time of Famines will have begun."[7] At this point he panics and starts worrying about how long he and his children can hang onto their comfortable surroundings.

These are the frightening elements of the new popular conception of the world food problem, seen in the 1960's. And because it is the popular formulation, it has great force in present-day political thought and action. Let us therefore try to state this popular view as precisely as possible.

Because of improved medical practices and public health measures in the developing countries of Asia, the Middle East, Africa, and Latin America, death rates in those regions have been falling rapidly since 1950, with no corresponding decline in birth rates. As a consequence, the populations of those regions are increasing very rapidly—with annual rates of increase running as high as 3.7

[3] "If the World Population Doubles by the Year 2000," *U. S. News and World Report*, January 9, 1967; and with James Bonner and John Weir, *The Next Hundred Years* (New York: The Viking Press, Inc., 1957).

[4] "Giveaway Food Is Giving Out—And Still the World Hungers" *U. S. News and World Report*, January 2, 1967; and *Man, Land and Food*, ERS, USDA, Foreign Agric. Econ. Report No. 11 (November 1963).

[5] *The Hungry Planet* (New York: The Macmillan Company, 1965).

[6] "Will We Prevent Mass Starvation?" *The New Republic*, April 24, 1965.

[7] William and Paul Paddock (Boston: Little, Brown and Company, 1967), p. 205.

or 3.8 per year in some countries. The situation in these regions is analogous to that of England and Wales from 1750 to 1800, but more dramatic because the medical and health practices now being introduced are more powerful in cutting death rates.

As the argument goes, these regions are experiencing a population explosion. Population growth is running away from food production. Food production is not, or cannot, keep up with this rate of population growth; hence, malnutrition, hunger, and death must be the result for the developing world. And when the developing world comes tumbling down as the consequence of widespread misery, vice, hunger, and death, it is implied that somehow those regions will pull the opulent Western world down with them.

But then there is usually a ray of hope included somewhere in the final stages of the argument. It is the following: If we become sufficiently aware of the problem and are willing to take the necessary steps *now*, we may be able to slow down the "runaway" population express, or speed up the modernization of sluggish agricultural plants, and thereby avoid world catastrophe. In other words, there is even a solution to this problem, if we hurry.

The new popular formulation of the world food problem has much in common with the Malthusian formulation. They were both conceived in the same stage of the population cycle, Stage II: during the early period of declining death rates, one for Western Europe in the period 1750–1800, the other for the developing world for the period 1950—. They both lead to the Malthusian conclusion —misery, vice, hunger, and death—although the new, popular formulation usually provides a ray of hope, if we act in time. And they both largely ignore the food production potential of their respective periods. Population is viewed as being out of control and agriculture is viewed as a stagnant, dormant thing. Hence the result must be a control over population growth that takes the form of misery, vice, hunger, and death.

The new, popular conception of the world food problem probably has greater scare potential, and therefore greater political significance, than the older formulation developed by Malthus for two important reasons. First, the average man in the Western world is, by any relative standard, terribly rich and weighted down with physical comforts that he doesn't want to lose through a worldwide

Malthusian upheaval. Second, he has an attitude toward food, evolved over 100 years of food abundance, that makes malnutrition and undernourishment a particular evil—an evil that cannot be countenanced in this modern world. In this view, malnutrition and undernourishment must be banished from the world immediately. Thus, Western men find the new popular conception of the world food problem at once both terrifying and an impossible evil.

A Second View of the World Food Problem, *circa* 1968

It is correct, as we learned in Chapter 2, that the population of the world is increasing at a rapid rate. It was increasing at a rate of 1.9 percent per year in the 1950's and it is generally agreed that it is increasing at a rate of about 2 percent per year in the 1960's.[8] But these rates of increase, which lead to a total world population of 3.6 billion in 1970, do not reflect a "runaway" situation in relation to world food supplies. It is also a recorded fact that the total production of food in the world was increasing at a rate of 2.8 percent per year in the 1950's[9] and is increasing at a rate of about 2.8 percent per year during the 1960's.[10] Thus, in the two decades during which the new, popular conception of the world food problem came into being, *the per capita availability of food in the world actually increased;* total world food supplies increased somewhat faster than total population growth. And as we recall from Chapter 2, the index of per capita food production for the world (exclusive of Communist Asia) edged upward from 103 in 1960 to 107 in 1967.

In Tables 4.1, 4.2, and 4.3, we can compare rates of population growth with rates of increase in cereal production (the principal food staple for the world's population) for the periods 1955–60, 1960–65, and 1965–70 for different regions of the world, and for the world as a whole. Ignoring for the moment the deficit areas of Western Europe and Japan, which traditionally import grain from the Americas and Australia, we observe that cereal production in

[8] *World Population Prospects, as Assessed in 1963*, United Nations, New York (Sales No. 66. XIII. 2, 1966), p. 23.

[9] *The World Food Budget, 1970*, Foreign Agric. Econ. Report No. 19 (October 1964), p. 40.

[10] See Chapter 2, Table 2.3, p. 19.

most regions of the world has increased as rapidly as population growth. There are some notable exceptions, however: cereal production lagged badly behind population growth in Latin America during the years 1955–60; with adverse weather and poor crop conditions in India during the period 1960–65, cereal production ran badly behind population growth for the South and Southeast Asia region (and, of course, for India as well) in 1960–65; and it is anticipated that population growth will outdistance cereal production for the Other East Asia region during the period 1965–70. For the world as a whole, however, we see that the rate of increase in total cereal production exceeds population growth in each of the three periods, 1955–60, 1960–65, and 1965–70. Thus it can be generalized that, for the world as a whole and for most of the regions comprising it, rates of increase in grain production have exceeded rates of population growth during the critical time span 1955–70.

No one knows for certain what will happen to the rates of population growth and food production between the years 1970 and 2000. Hence the outcome of the race between the two is uncertain. But some things we do know.

We know, first, that the developing world has been going through Stage II of the population cycle, which involves high birth rates and declining death rates; if the past is any guide to the future, Stage II should be followed by Stage III, which involves a substantial decline in birth rates. Second, the technologies for preventing births today are infinitely superior to those available to men and women in Western societies during the late nineteenth century when birth rates began to decline. Third, the potential for increasing food production in the developing world is very great indeed when considered in the light of food production developments in some of the developing countries themselves. For example crop production, which is closely associated with food production and more reliably measured, increased 9.7 percent per year in Israel, 6.3 percent in Mexico, 5.2 percent in Taiwan, and 4.4 percent in Thailand during the period 1948–63.[11] These rates of increase in crop production indicate what can be achieved throughout the developing world *if* developing nations take their food production problems seriously, make the investments required to modernize their agri-

[11] *Changes in Agriculture in 26 Developing Nations, 1948–63*, Foreign Agric. Econ. Report No. 27 (November 1965), p. 12.

TABLE 4.1

Average Annual Rate of Growth in Population, Per Capita GNP and Per Capita and Total Demand for Cereals,[1] Compared with Average Annual Rate of Growth in Total Cereal Production, by Regions of the World, for the Period 1955–60

Region	Average Annual Rate of Growth in Population[7] (Percent)	Average Annual Rate of Growth in Per Capita GNP[8] (Percent)	Demand Factors			Average Annual Rate of Growth in Cereal Production[9] (Percent)	Production Surplus over Demand (Percent)
			Income Elasticity for All Cereal (Coefficient)	Average Annual Rate of Growth in Per Capita Demand (Percent)	Average Annual Rate of Growth in Total Demand for Cereal (Percent)		
Canada	2.6	0.8	0.2	0.2	1.8	-3.2	-6.0
United States (50 states)	1.7	0.5	0.2	0.1	2.8	4.6	2.8
Mexico	3.3	3.0	0.4	1.2	4.5	5.1	0.6
Latin America[2]	2.8	1.4	0.5	0.7	3.5	1.4	-2.1
Western Europe	0.8	3.7	0.4	1.5	2.3	1.9	-0.4
Eastern Europe & U.S.S.R.	1.5	4.3	0.5	2.2	3.7	2.3	-1.4
Republic of South Africa	2.5	1.9	0.4	0.8	3.3	3.5	0.2
Africa, excl. South Africa	2.3	NA	0.3	NA	NA	0.7	
West Asia[3]	2.7	NA	0.3	NA	NA	0.8	
South & Southeast Asia[4]	2.2	2.4	0.6	1.4	3.6	2.3	-1.3
India	2.1	2.2	0.5	1.1	3.2	2.9	-0.3
Japan	0.9	8.6	0.5	4.3	5.2	1.7	-3.5
Other East Asia[5]	2.5	NA	0.5	NA	NA	2.6	
Oceania	2.2	1.6	0.2	0.3	2.5	7.2	4.7
The World (less Communist Asia)	1.9	3.0[6]	0.2	1.5[6]	3.3[6]	2.6	-0.7

[1] Includes all cereal grains—wheat, rice, maize, sorghums, millets, barley, oats, and rye.
[2] Excludes Mexico; includes Cuba, Guyana, Jamaica, Trinidad, British Honduras, and Surinam.
[3] Afghanistan, Cyprus, Iran, Iraq, Israel, Jordan, Lebanon, Syria, and Turkey.
[4] India, Pakistan, Ceylon, Burma, Cambodia, Thailand, and South Vietnam.
[5] Korea, Taiwan, Philippines, Malaysia, Singapore, and Indonesia.
[6] Excludes Africa, West Asia, and Other East Asia because of lack of data on grain consumption and GNP.
[7] Based on estimates made by U.N. or AID and projections 1965–70 made by FAO for the Indicative World Plan.
[8] Based on estimates of GNP at constant market prices published by U.N., AID, Joint Economic Committee of Congress, Far East Economic Review, or FAO.
[9] Indices of Agricultural Production, by Region of the World, Foreign Regional Analysis Division, ERS, USDA, and Quentin M. West, Foreign Supply and Demand Projections; Outlook for U. S. Agricultural Exports, AFEA meeting, College Park, Md. August 23, 1966.
SOURCE: Prepared by the Economic Research Service of the U.S. Department of Agriculture at the request of the author from the data compiled by that agency and regularly used by it.

TABLE 4.2

Average Annual Rate of Growth in Population, Per Capita GNP and Per Capita and Total Demand for Cereals, [1] Compared with Average Annual Rate of Growth in Total Cereal Production, by Regions of the World, for the Period 1960–65

Region	Average Annual Rate of Growth in Population[6] (Percent)	Demand Factors			Average Annual Rate of Growth in Total Demand for Cereal (Percent)	Average Annual Rate of Growth in Cereal Production[8] (Percent)	Production Surplus over Demand (Percent)
		Average Annual Rate of Growth in Per Capita GNP[7] (Percent)	Income Elasticity for All Cereal Demand (Coefficient)	Average Annual Rate of Growth in Per Capita Demand (Percent)			
Canada	1.8	3.6	0.2	0.7	2.5	7.9	5.4
United States (50 states)	1.5	3.0	0.2	0.6	2.1	0.5	−1.6
Mexico	3.4	2.8	0.4	1.1	4.5	7.3	2.8
Latin America[2]	2.8	1.2	0.5	0.6	3.4	4.6	1.2
Western Europe	1.0	3.7	0.4	1.5	2.5	3.2	0.7
Eastern Europe & U.S.S.R.	1.2	2.9	0.5	1.4	2.6	2.2	−0.4
Republic of South Africa	2.3	3.9	0.4	1.6	3.9	0.7	−3.2
Africa, excl. South Africa	2.3	1.7	0.3	0.5	2.8	2.2	−0.6
West Asia[3]	2.8	2.5	0.3	0.8	3.6	3.3	−0.3
South & Southeast Asia[4]	2.5	1.1	0.6	0.7	3.2	0.6	−2.6
India	2.4	0.8	0.5	0.4	2.8	0.1	−2.7
Japan	1.0	8.7	0.5	4.4	5.4	−2.1	−7.5
Other East Asia[5]	2.6	1.8	0.5	0.9	3.5	3.5	0.0
Oceania	2.1	2.4	0.2	0.5	2.6	5.7	3.1
The World (less Communist Asia)	2.0	2.4	0.2	1.0	3.1	2.2	−0.9

[1] Includes all cereal grains—wheat, rice, maize, sorghums, millets, barley, oats, and rye.
[2] Excludes Mexico; includes Cuba, Guyana, Jamaica, Trinidad, British Honduras, and Surinam.
[3] Afghanistan, Cyprus, Iran, Iraq, Israel, Jordan, Lebanon, Syria, and Turkey.
[4] India, Pakistan, Ceylon, Burma, Cambodia, Thailand, and South Vietnam.
[5] Korea, Taiwan, Philippines, Malaysia, Singapore, and Indonesia.
[6] Based on estimates made by U.N. or AID and projections 1965–70 made by FAO for the Indicative World Plan.
[7] Based on estimates of GNP at constant market prices published by U.N., AID, Joint Economic Committee of Congress, Far East Economic Review, or FAO.
[8] Indices of Agricultural Production, by Region of the World, Foreign Regional Analysis Division, ERS, USDA, and Quentin M. West, Foreign Supply and Demand Projections; Outlook for U.S. Agricultural Exports, AFEA meeting, College Park, Md., August 23, 1966.
SOURCE: Prepared by the Economic Research Service of the U.S. Department of Agriculture at the request of the author from the data compiled by that agency and regularly used by it.

TABLE 4.3

Average Annual Rate of Growth in Population, Per Capita GNP and Per Capita and Total Demand for Cereals,[1] Compared with Average Annual Rate of Growth in Total Cereal Production, by Regions of the World, for the Period 1965–70

Region	Average Annual Rate of Growth in Population[6] (Percent)	Demand Factors				Average Annual Rate of Growth in Cereal Production[8] (Percent)	Production Surplus over Demand (Percent)
		Average Annual Rate of Growth in Per Capita GNP[7] (Percent)	Income Elasticity for All Cereal (Coefficient)	Average Annual Rate of Growth in Per Capita Demand (Percent)	Average Annual Rate of Growth in Total Demand for Cereal (Percent)		
Canada	1.8	2.5	0.2	0.5	2.3	1.0	−1.3
United States (50 states)	1.3	2.3	0.2	0.5	1.8	4.2	2.4
Mexico	3.5	2.3	0.4	0.9	4.4	2.7	−1.7
Latin America[2]	2.7	1.4	0.5	0.7	3.4	2.7	−0.7
Western Europe	0.6	3.4	0.4	1.4	2.0	1.0	−1.0
Eastern Europe & U.S.S.R.	1.1	3.7	0.5	1.8	2.9	1.9	−1.0
Republic of South Africa	2.8	2.5	0.4	1.0	3.8	7.8	4.0
Africa, excl. South Africa	2.4	1.7	0.3	0.5	2.9	2.3	−0.6
West Asia[3]	2.5	2.8	0.3	0.8	3.3	1.0	−2.3
South & Southeast Asia[4]	2.4	1.7	0.6	1.0	3.4	5.1	1.7
India	2.4	1.9	0.5	1.0	3.4	5.0	1.6
Japan	0.8	7.0	0.5	3.5	4.3	−0.1	−4.4
Other East Asia[5]	2.7	1.8	0.5	0.9	3.6	1.9	−1.7
Oceania	1.7	2.0	0.2	0.4	2.1	3.7	1.6
The World (less Communist Asia)	1.9	2.5		1.1	3.0	2.9	−0.1

[1] Includes all cereal grains—wheat, rice, maize, sorghums, millets, barley, oats, and rye.
[2] Excludes Mexico; includes Cuba, Guyana, Jamaica, Trinidad, British Honduras, and Surinam.
[3] Afghanistan, Cyprus, Iran, Iraq, Israel, Jordan, Lebanon, Syria, and Turkey.
[4] India, Pakistan, Ceylon, Burma, Cambodia, Thailand, and South Vietnam.
[5] Korea, Taiwan, Philippines, Malaysia, Singapore, and Indonesia.
[6] Based on estimates made by U.N. or AID and projections 1965–70 made by FAO for the Indicative World Plan.
[7] Based on estimates of GNP at constant market prices published by U.N., AID, Joint Economic Committee of Congress, Far East Economic Review, or FAO. For 1965–70, largely based on FAO Indicative World Plan data.
[8] Indices of Agricultural Production, by Region of the World, Foreign Regional Analysis Division, ERS, USDA, and Quentin M. West, Foreign Supply and Demand Projections; Outlook for U. S. Agricultural Exports, AFEA, meeting, College Park, Md., August 23, 1966.
SOURCE: Prepared by the Economic Research Service of the U.S. Department of Agriculture at the request of the author from the data compiled by that agency and regularly used by it.

cultural plants, and develop government programs that are designed
to increase production—not hinder it.

All this is not to argue that there is not a world food problem.
But it is to argue that during the period 1950–1970 population
growth, on a world basis and for most developing regions, has actually run behind rates of food production increase. *Hence, the
concept of a runaway population growth is in basic error.* Further,
it is argued here and in the pages to come that the per capita availability of food supplies for the world and for most developing regions is likely to increase, however slowly, over the period 1970–
2000 rather than diminish.

There is a world food problem, however, and we are already
aware of one of its components from Chapter 3. Millions of people
around the world living primarily in the developing countries and
primarily in the tropics suffer from undernourishment, malnutrition, and in some cases actual hunger. We do not know this from
nationwide clinical studies or family consumption surveys; we know
it from spot clinical studies, local family consumption surveys, and
national estimates of food production and food requirements.

We conclude here, as we did in Chapter 3, that there were about
2.0 billion persons in the world living in countries with inadequate
diets on the average in 1959–61; most people in those countries
were undernourished, many were suffering from malnutrition, and
some were experiencing outright hunger. This is a crude measure;
it may be too low or too high by 100 million people, and it tells
very little about the incidence of that undernourishment, malnutrition, and hunger. But it is not a fictitious figure; it succintly
describes the vastness of the world food problem. It should also be
made clear once again that this food problem is not limited to in-
sufficient calories; both the USDA and the FAO studies point out
the desperate shortage of protein in the world in relation to the
need.

Further, as the world population increases, and to the extent that
total food production increases at the same rate, there is no increase
in the world per capita availability of food. Hence the undernourishment and the malnutrition problem will widen directly with the
population increase. Where there were 2.0 billion persons living in
areas and regions with inadequate diets in 1959–61, there will be

2.2 to 2.4 billion people in 1970, depending upon the improvement in diets in the developing world. And there could be 3.0 to 4.0 billion such people in the year 2000. This is one aspect of the world food problem.

But there is a second component to the problem which is rarely considered in popular treatments; it is the economic component. A starving man rarely riots and he rarely shoots anybody; he becomes docile, he gets sick, and finally he lies down and dies. So it is not the starving people of the world who are likely to cause trouble for the Western man, in his warm and comfortable house. The men and women who riot in the streets and overthrow governments may be malnourished, but they are not starving. They are men and women who have money in their pockets, but cannot find food in the marketplace (at least not food at stable prices), and therefore are not able to improve the quantity and quality of their diets when they feel they have earned the right to do so. This is the economic aspect of the world food problem which causes governments in developing countries around the world to tremble and shake and sometimes to fall.

Let us consider this aspect more carefully, for it has serious implications. Although food production has increased at a rate slightly in excess of population growth over the period 1950–1970, rising personal incomes in both the developed and developing regions of the world have caused the average per capita *demand* for food to increase importantly during the 1950's and 1960's. Rising personal incomes may have caused the per capita demand for food around the world to increase by as much as 1.0 percent per year during the 1950's and 1960's. For example, the demand for cereals, on a per capita basis, appears to have grown 1.0 percent or more per year for the world as a whole for the period 1955–70, and at much faster rates for some areas of the developing world (see Tables 4.1, 4.2, and 4.3, columns 4). When we add this increase in the demand for food, on a per capita basis, to the rate of increase in population, we find that the total demand for food in the world probably increased at a rate of about 3.0 percent per year over the 1950–70 period.[12]

[12] For a good discussion of these food demand factors see the report by Thorkil Kristensen, Secretary-General of the Organization for Economic Cooperation and Development, *The Food Problem of the Developing Countries*

Thus, it seems reasonable to conclude that the total demand for food in the world was increasing at an annual rate slightly faster than the increase in food production during the 1950's, and that demand continued to stay modestly ahead of production in the 1960's.

This was and is a world picture. Let us, therefore, look at what was happening by regions, since regional developments in food production and consumption are of critical importance in making food available to local people. Nonetheless, the global picture is important too, for where total world demand outruns total world food production on a continuous basis for 20 years, it cannot help but have a tightening effect on total world food supplies—as indeed it has had.

Referring again to Tables 4.1, 4.2, and 4.3, we see that rates of increase in the total demand for cereals exceed rates of increase in production for many regions during each of the periods under consideration (the discussion is limited to cereals, since data on the total demand for food is not available by regions). It is not unusual for increases in the demand for cereals to outpace increases in production by 1 percent or more per year for many of the developing regions of the world: Latin America, South and Southeast Asia, and Other East Asia, for example. (Rates of increase in total demand in excess of rates of increase in production are denoted by negative numbers in the last column of Tables 4.1, 4.2, and 4.3.) Increases in per capita demand for cereals resulting from increases in personal incomes, when added to population growth, cause the total demand for cereals to march ahead of increases in production in most of the developing regions most of the time. And since cereals constitute the principal component of the food supply in most of the developing regions, whenever the demand for cereals exceeds production, the food supply tightens and a food supply problem results.

(Paris, OECD, December 1967), pp. 21–26. Although it would be improper to apply the coefficients of income elasticity presented in Tables 4.1, 4.2, and 4.3 here to absolute measures of GNP, it does seem logically correct to apply those coefficients to rates of change in GNP, on the assumption that rates of change in personal incomes are equal to the rates of change in GNP given in Tables 4.1, 4.2, and 4.3. This is our procedure, since rough estimates of GNP are available but not estimates of personal incomes.

When the increase in the total demand for food exceeds production for a long period of time, as it has in South and Southeast Asia, what is the direct result? It will take one of two forms depending upon government policies. If the government attempts to hold a ceiling over food prices, or somehow make food supplies available to the poor at "fair" prices, it will discover that its "fair price shops," or distributive outlets, are regularly sold out of supplies. It cannot acquire and dispose of as much food as consumers want to buy at those prices. In this policy situation Mr. Average Consumer in a developing country finds that he cannot, in fact, increase his food consumption because the additional food is simply not available to buy. If, on the other hand, the government has no overt food policy, the competition for scarce supplies will simply push food prices upward, and consumers will find that they have not purchased additional quantities of food with their increased money incomes; they have simply used their increased money incomes to purchase the same quantity of foods at higher prices. In this case, price inflation holds food consumption to levels consistent with the existing supplies.

Why don't the countries short on food supplies increase imports from the surplus-producing countries and thereby ease their deficit problem? The first answer is that they do to the extent possible through both commercial imports and food aid. But commercial imports of food are limited by the scarce supplies of foreign exchange available to those countries with which to pay for commercial imports, and food aid is limited by the generosity of donor countries. Thus, a developing country is often unable to import the quantities of food required to satisfy consumer demands at stable prices.

The indirect consequences of this economic effect are varied and unpredictable, but all involve resentment and anger on the part of consumers in the countries involved. Sometimes this leads to rioting; sometimes to overthrowing the government through the ballot box, or with guns; and sometimes it causes consumers to turn to the Communists with their seductive solutions, or to military dictatorships. But one thing is certain: underprivileged individuals who have worked and struggled to increase their incomes and who have additional food money in their hands, when confronted by empty food markets and/or higher food prices, are not inclined to lie down like starving men and women and die. On the contrary, they tend to react strongly and often violently to redress this kind of economic injustice. This is the core of the world food problem in the late 1960's, *and it could become more acute and more extensive in the 1970's.*

A Restatement of the Problem

The world food problem as it exists in the late 1960's and the foreseeable future thus has three principal components.

1. Some 2 billion people in the world live in countries and regions with inadequate food supplies, where most of the inhabitants suffer from undernourishment and malnutrition. Many experience outright hunger. In the main, these regions are to be found in the tropics and encompass the developing portions of the globe. In terms of population absolutes, this component of the problem is growing.

2. The total demand for food in the world and in several regions in the underdeveloped world has been increasing more rapidly than food supplies. Total demand does not exceed food production by reason of population increases alone. It exceeds food production because money incomes are rising around the world, giving rise to an increase in the per capita demand for food. When this increase in the per capita demand for food is added to the growth in population, we find that the total demand for food has been increasing somewhat more rapidly than food production in the race between the two. This condition leads to a serious economic problem that takes the form of rising food prices, empty food shops, or a combination of both.

3. Food shortages and rising food prices in the developing countries give rise to social and political unrest in the countries involved. Individuals who cannot find food to buy, or see their increased incomes dissipated as a result of higher food prices, are willing to take whatever political action appears to hold promise of correcting this situation. They have turned to violence in the past to achieve "economic justice" and we can expect them to do so in the future.

The present-day world food problem differs to an important degree from the popular version of that problem and from older versions. The popular version foresees millions of people starving to death as the world population explodes beyond the capacity of the globe to produce food. Older versions of the problem saw millions of people starving in far-off China, or India, or even possibly Ireland, as the result of a crop failure.

But the present-day world food problem does not result from crop failures (although it may be complicated by crop failures) and it does not involve world-wide famine or even regional famines. It results from a combination of circumstances where millions of people with inadequate diets experience an increase in money incomes through the development process, but these rising money incomes do not result in rising real incomes (at least not in full) because the foods they expected to buy are not available in sufficient quantity to realize their aspirations. Thus, these people fail to achieve their food consumption expectations; they become frustrated; and they turn to some kind of political or mob action to try to solve their problem. This is indeed a new kind of food problem. It is a problem linked to development and failure in the development process, rather than to crop failures and regional famines.

Some Complicating Factors

But social processes and social problems are rarely neat and clean. They are commonly dirtied up by special circumstances, which we will call complicating factors. The world food problem is overlaid and distorted by two complicating factors that are often interrelated. The first is fluctuations in crop production resulting from variations in the weather. Unusually good weather and good crops do not cause serious problems in countries chronically short of food, but bad weather and a poor crop, where reserve stocks are limited, can lead to widespread hunger and starvation unless food can be imported by some means.

This latter point suggests the second complicating factor. Poor, or limited, transportation facilities can militate against the effective distribution of food in surplus-producing countries, and it can quickly lead to famine conditions in a food deficit country that suffers the misfortune of a local crop failure. Thus, variations in the weather and limited transport facilities can lead to an uneven distribution of food supplies through time and space. The general world food problem described above is often hidden and distorted by the vagaries of weather and poor transportation facilities.

A good example of the first complicating factor, a poor crop year, is that of India in 1965. Food production had been increasing at a pace slightly ahead of population growth during the decade 1955–64, but total food demand was increasing more rapidly than food production, thus tightening the supply situation each year and contributing to an ever more precarious situation. Then food grain production fell from 89 million tons in 1964–65 to 72 million tons in 1965–66 as the result of a failure in the annual monsoon. Domestic food grain production fell by almost 20 percent in one year as the result of a poor crop, and millions were threatened by hunger and starvation. Fortunately, food grain imports into India were greatly stepped up in 1965–66, on both a cash and concessional basis, and widespread famine was averted.

In this case reasonably good transport facilities enabled the government of India, with the assistance of the United States and other friendly nations, to move large grain stocks, first through the Indian ports and second into the large cities, thereby avoiding a heavy incidence of starvation and death in the large cities. Undernourishment and hunger could not be and were not avoided. And it was India's unhappy lot to experience drought conditions in specialized areas, principally in the states of Uttar Pradesh and Bihar, in 1966–67. This second consecutive bad year of course further complicated an already desperate food situation.

It is not correct to conclude from these two poor crop years, however, that population has outrun the food supply in India and that India is to be haunted by the Malthusian specter year after year until 2000 or 2050. In fact, food grain production in 1967–68 shot up to 97 million tons and raised the per capita availability of food grains back to the peak level achieved in 1964–65. Further, as noted in Chapter 2, India has the potential to increase grain yields significantly and thereby expand food production more rapidly than the historical record of the 1950's and 1960's—perhaps even to catch up with demand.

An example of poor and inadequate transport and communications is found in Brazil. Brazil is a rich country in terms of natural resources, and in much of southern Brazil agriculture is highly productive. But for generations the northeastern region has experienced extreme poverty. It is often argued that the heavy reliance there on sugar production is the cause of its chronic poverty; whatever the reason, widespread and chronic poverty is the prevailing situation. Undernourishment, malnutrition, and even hunger are commonplace in the region. Migration to the south has eased the conditions of poverty in northeastern Brazil but it has not eliminated them. Because of lack of transportation, communications, and human mobility, northeastern Brazil exists in the backwash of an otherwise general condition of economic development.

An even more dramatic case occurred in the Indonesian islands in 1964. Partial failure of the dry-season rice crops in parts of Java and Bali in 1963 led to skyrocketing prices and starving times because of inadequate government stocks, a faulty distribution system, and an inadequate transportation system.

The dramatic case of crop failure and famine in an isolated community or region thus continues to be a possibility in this modern world. But the more common case is one of inadequacy of transport, communications, and human mobility, which lead to pockets of poverty and so to inadequate diets and nutrition—a possibility in all modern nations, including the United States.

In summary, then, the world food problem of the 1960's, which is a problem of very great magnitude, is often pulled out of focus and called to the attention of the man in the street by a particular crop failure or isolated case. But two poor crops in a row, even in India, do not mean that the world is now confronted with a Malthusian crisis.

The Modern Solution

The humane, modern solution to the world food problem obviously does not entail striking a balance between food supplies and the demand for food by means of an increased incidence of malnutrition, hunger, misery, and a return to high death rates. It entails the social and economic actions taken in the Western world over the past 200 years—a combination of declining birth rates and increased food production. But the tempo of development and the nature of human expectations in the developing world have changed; we do not in the latter half of the twentieth century have 200 years to achieve the humane solution for the developing world.

The developing world wants that solution *now* in the 1960's and 1970's. The pressure to reduce birth rates and to increase food production has become very great. Governments and national commitments to ideologies are going to rise, fall, or be sustained by the length of time it takes the development process significantly to increase *real* per capita incomes, including food consumption. This, then, is the setting for Part II of this book—a highly charged, volatile social and political setting. The analysis of the world food problem cannot be leisurely or academic. It must lead to solutions that have the capacity to cope with the problem and are manageable in the world in which we now live.

II

Approach and Analysis

5

A Multiple Approach
to the Problem

THE WORLD FOOD PROBLEM is real; it is huge; and it is complex. Because, in the 1960's, at least 2 billion people live in countries with national average diets that are deficient in some way (i.e., in calories or proteins or some other nutrients), there is an immediacy to the problem as well as a vastness. Because the total demand for food has been increasing more rapidly than food production for most of the developing world throughout the 1960's, and the end of this imbalance is not in sight, there is a long-run aspect to the problem in addition to the economic considerations. And because food supplies are distributed unevenly through time and space, there is an emergency aspect to the problem which is both unpredictable and localized. The question is thus posed—How is this huge, immediate, long-run, nutritional, economic problem with its emergency and unpredictable overtones to be dealt with? How are national leaders and men and women with international responsibilities to cope with a problem of so many dimensions?

A multidimensional approach is sketched in this chapter. Its components are developed at length in the chapters comprising Part II of this book. In the main, no new data are presented and no new analyses are developed, although it is hoped that some novelty emerges in connection with the discussion of agricultural development. The purpose of the next seven chapters is to develop piece by piece the component parts of a solution to the world food problem—a solution that can deal effectively with that problem in the real world in which some men take action and others procrastinate, some produce and others don't, and some create and give of themselves and others lie and steal.

It is hoped that the comprehensive view developed here on paper, with its multiple approaches, will help men and women around the world to understand and appreciate what must be done, if we are to resolve the world food problem in a satisfactory way in the critical decades of the 1970's and 1980's.

The Need for a Multiple Approach

A family planning program or a plant-breeding program for rice initiated in 1968 will not help those 2 billion persons, give or take 100 million, already experiencing dietary deficiencies in 1968. But food aid, or commercial food exports, from surplus-producing countries can help a good number of them. An effective family planning program and an effective plant-breeding program, along with the right combination of economic programs and policies and political organization, though, might succeed in bringing the rates of increase in total food demand and total food production into balance for certain developing countries in Asia by 1975 or 1980. But food aid alone is not likely to bring rates of increase in total food demand and total food supply into balance for major regions of the developing world by 1975 or 1980.

Different elements of the world food problem require different approaches. Increased food production *requires* the extension of new and improved technologies and practices to farmers, the availability of new and improved producer goods (e.g., seeds, fertilizer, and water pumps), the price and income incentives to induce farmers to employ technological know-how and nonfarm producer goods, the economic infrastructure to provide necessary services (e.g., credit, transport), and the social and political organization to bring about all these conditions. Starving people *require* food now. The production of a food surplus in rural areas of a developing country *requires* that urban consumers be productively employed and earning incomes with which to purchase that food surplus, if the development process is to be sustained. Sustained economic development, hence increased food consumption, *requires* that savings be made and invested, that labor be transferred from rural areas to urban areas and reemployed, and that producer goods needed by farmers be produced in factories and distributed to farmers.

Thus, we see that different aspects of the world food problem require different approaches. And since there are numerous aspects to the problem, a multiple approach is required within the total solution. But another perhaps more important point is suggested in the paragraph above. Increased food production, improved food distribution, and improved diets do not occur in a vacuum. They take place as integrated parts of the total development process. Farmers do not produce food to meet the dietary needs of consumers in urban areas, or to meet the food consumption goals of a national government or some international agency. They produce food to provide a livelihood for themselves and their families through home consumption and what they can purchase from the sale of their surplus produce. And consumers, likewise, buy what they want or what they can afford, not necessarily what they should buy to satisfy nutritional requirements. Certainly they don't make purchases just to help farmers. Food is produced, distributed, and consumed as a part of the operating economy; it is not produced and moved about in some mechanical fashion to meet dietary or consumption requirements. Food production and consumption expand with an expansion in the economy, because an expansion in the economy means that more productive resources are being devoted to food production, that more food is being produced, and that more purchasing power is being allocated to the purchase of food.

The food problem cannot be abstracted from the operating economy and treated in a mechanistic or isolated fashion. A whole series of events must occur in a developmental process, each in the interest of millions of decision makers, if food production is to increase in relation to food demand and thereby increase the per capita consumption of food: the employment of more and better producer goods in agriculture, the sale of the increased farm output at profitable prices, the release of redundant farm labor, the employment of that released labor in productive and remunerative nonfarm jobs, an increase in the real incomes of the labor released by agriculture, the purchase of increased quantities of food by these new nonfarm workers, the sale of the increased output of the nonfarm enterprises to farmers and urban workers at profitable prices. It is a long and involved process, and food production and consumption will increase on a sustained basis only to the extent that the total development process expands as a harmonious whole.

David Bell, vice president of the Ford Foundation, uses different words to make this point, but arrives at the same conclusion. He argues:[1]

> Another way of emphasizing the same point is to say that if agricultural production is to grow in developing countries, changes must occur far beyond the reaches of the agricultural sector. Internal markets must grow based on rising urban and industrial incomes. Transportation, storage, and marketing must be improved. Fertilizers, insecticides, and machinery must be manufactured or imported and in either case distributed. Financial arrangements must be created. Educational and research systems must be developed. Agricultural development therefore requires progress in the whole economy; it cannot take place in isolation.

Increasing food production and per capita food consumption in a developing country as a means of correcting the food problem of that country thus requires a satisfactory state of development first, for the agricultural sector, and second, for the overall national economy of which the agricultural sector is a part. A solution to the food problem of the developing countries requires a solution to their *total economic development problem.* Food is just one product, albeit a very important product, which consumers want more of, and demand more of, as their incomes rise. How to make their real incomes rise—that is the question.

The Components of the Multiple Approach

There are many ways to slice a melon. Similarly, there are many ways to categorize the components of an effective solution to the food problems of the developing countries. (If the food problems of the developing countries are solved, the world food problem will

[1] *U.S. Domestic and Foreign Policies and World Food Needs,* an address to the Illinois University Central Symposium on the Land-Grant University and World Food Needs, Urbana, Ill., October 17, 1967.

be solved; there may then arise farm problems in the developing countries similar to those found in the now developed countries, but therein lies another tale.) Another analyst would certainly end up with a different list—perhaps in greater detail or with a different emphasis, but the five components listed below are thought by this writer to be absolutely essential to a solution to the world food problem. And they are sufficiently inclusive to bring into the discussion all the specific measures that warrant consideration. It is hoped that the rationale for the categories will emerge in the pages that follow.

1. *Population control by birth control*

The development and execution of vigorous and effective programs of birth control in the developing countries are necessary to slow down rates of population growth and hence moderate the rates of agricultural and general economic development that must be achieved. The task of achieving nutritionally adequate diets for the populations of the developing world will be eased and made more feasible if the rates of population growth can be slowed down to something less than 2 percent per year.

2. *Foreign food aid*

Food aid to the developing countries can be of great assistance during the next 20 years: (a) in helping to feed those persons currently suffering from undernourishment and malnutrition, (b) in helping to feed those additional persons who will become malnourished and hungry before a scientific and more productive agriculture comes into being in each of the developing countries, and (c) in helping to feed those persons living on the brink of starvation when an occasional bad crop year strikes. Food aid from the developed countries to the developing countries can buy time and ward off starvation when there is not time to produce a second crop or to develop the economy of that nation.

3. *Economic and technical assistance*

The ingredients for an effective birth control program, an effective agricultural development process, and an effectively operating general economy do not emerge instantaneously out of the air. In the Western world the technologies and capital items prerequisite to these processes at first came very slowly and now very swiftly from education, research, and personal savings in the milieu of private and public enterprise. The length of time required by the developing countries to mount the programs and to achieve the agricultural and economic development required can perhaps be reduced from 200 years to 25 or 50 years by the transfer of modern basic science and technologies from the Western world to the developing world, by their purposive adaptation to the conditions of the developing countries, and by generous loans and grants of capital to the developing countries.

4. Agricultural development

Present rates of agricultural development—the shift from traditional agricultures to modern, scientific agricultures—must be speeded up. The infusion of new technologies and capital, the actions and ambitions of individual farmers, and the actions of progressively oriented governments must all be integrated into a pattern of food and fiber production that lifts annual rates of increase from 2.0 to 2.5 percent to 4.0 percent per year or more. This must occur if food production increases are to come into balance with food demand increases.

5. A balanced and growing general economy

The nonfarm-produced resources (e.g., fertilizers, improved seeds, pesticides, and water pumps) required to sustain a rate of increase in food production of 4.0 percent or more per year will not be produced, and therefore the food itself will not be produced, unless the total economy is growing at a rate consistent with an agricultural growth of 4.0 percent or more per year. This means that the overall economy must be growing at a rate that will absorb the surplus products and the surplus labor of the agricultural sector and produce the nonfarm goods demanded by that sector. A modern, scientific agriculture can come into being, operate successfully, and be sustained only by an overall national economy that is developing in comparable fashion.

Interrelations and Implications of the Multiple Approach

It can be argued with some justification that there are only two parts, or components, to the solution of the world food problem: the slowing down of population growth in the developing countries and the speeding up of food production in those same countries. All else is peripheral. When these two aspects of the problem are solved in theory and practice, the problem will be solved.

In one sense this is a correct formulation of the approaches to a solution to the problem. Like a pair of scissors cutting through cloth, the world food problem will be solved as the blade of food production rises to meet the falling blade of population growth. Further, the many and varied elements of the problem can be grouped together and analyzed under those two principal headings. But they will not be treated that way in this volume, since by training and experience the author is prepared to deal with the problems of food supply and agricultural development in depth, but not so with population problems.

Reducing the rate of population growth through the practice of birth control involves family relationships and social organization, and programs designed to control the number of births per family must deal with human values, social attitudes, and personal relationships. Birth control programs must relate to fundamental human values and highly intimate human relationships, and such programs will succeed only insofar as they can change those human values and relationships; they will succeed only insofar as they can induce men and women to inform themselves about techniques of contraception and then to act on that information by adopting technologies that affect their personal sex life. But these are problems and issues on which the author lacks both expertise and familiarity.

Thus, the approach here to birth control as a part of the solution to the world food problem will be to report on recent experiences with birth control programs, to describe the current and prospective state of the technology, to advocate strong birth control policies on the part of governments and private organizations, and to suggest the probable impact of prospective birth control programs on population growth. Penetrating analyses of the technology of contraceptive practices and rates of acceptance of those practices will have to be found elsewhere.

The other four components, however, all relate to the world organization of the production and distribution of food. The components

foreign food aid,
economic and technical assistance,
agricultural development, and
a balanced and growing general economy

are linked together in an economic continuum. *Food aid* can deal with immediate and pressing food problems in the developing countries, where reserve food stocks are in existence in the surplus-producing countries. *Economic and technical assistance* becomes a way of speeding up the development process in the developing countries; as we have learned, economic and technical assistance is not a short-run activity, but the effect of successful economic and technical assistance is to reduce the time span of the development process. *Agricultural development* is that critical component "living" in many cases on the borrowed time provided by food aid, making application and use of economic and technical assistance, and absolutely dependent upon national development policies and modernizing actions that result in increased food production and improved distribution. It is the process whereby many national and international policies, hundreds of specific projects and programs, and millions of decisions by farmers mesh and interact to increase farm output. A *balanced and growing general economy* provides the organizing structure for increased food production, improved distribution, and increased food consumption in harmony and congruence with the operation of all other sectors and activities of the national economy.

The emphasis given to each of the four components in solutions to the world food problem is of critical importance. Food aid is needed to meet pressing food shortage problems in the short run, but too great an emphasis on food aid can dampen the will of developing countries to take those modernizing actions required to move their agricultures from a traditional to a scientific state. Economic and technical assistance can speed the development process *if it is effectively done,* but it cannot take place at a more rapid rate than the institutions and the peoples of the developing countries can absorb. Agricultural development must relate to and be consistent with the inflow of economic and technical aid on one hand and relate to and be consistent with growth and development of the overall economy on the other. And attention must be given by those concerned with the welfare of the developing nations to the development of a set of effective economic and political institutions (e.g., a money and banking system, a tax system, a road system, and a marketing system), and to a favorable environment for enterprise (e.g., a minimum of centralized control and regulation) if the general economy is to grow and function smoothly.

In other words, the right admixture of the four components is required to solve the world food problem. Unfortunately, no formula exists for prescribing the financial and resource support that should be given to each of these components. Nor is it likely that a general formula with quantitative specifications will be constructed during the next two decades, when it will be sorely needed. Such specifications would have to vary considerably among countries and regions because of differences in physical environment, the state of economic development, and cultural and ideological structures; a formula worked out for one country or region would have scant applicability for other countries and regions. And, to date, little has been done in working out a systematic formulation of the component elements for a solution to the food and development problem for even one country.[2]

[2] The Food and Agricultural Organization of the United Nations is currently (1966–68) attempting to develop an Indicative World Plan for Agricultural Development. This plan would "indicate" for countries and regions what must be done in the way of farm reorganization and development, institution building, production of producer goods (e.g., fertilizer and insecticides), and the establishment of government policies to increase agricultural production in the developing countries. A beginning is just being made, and it will probably be many years before a truly useful plan emerges. But it is a step in the right direction and we can hope that the FAO will persevere and ultimately bring forth an "indicative plan" that will serve as a useful guide to the developing countries. See the FAO conference document, *Indicative World Plan for Agricultural Development, A Progress Report,* 14th Sess., Rome (November 1967), C67/15.

Typically, governmental agencies, private organizations, and foundations from the developed nations pick a developing country for political or quixotic reasons and undertake to develop some particular piece or aspect of it (e.g., a university, a land-reform program, a milk program for pregnant and nursing mothers). The haphazard aspect of the selection and undertaking of programs to assist in the development of economically backward countries is further accentuated by the fact that many agencies and organizations, national and international, are involved, *but no one is really in charge.* The developing country cannot be, at least not in a technical sense, because it lacks the professional and organizational skills. Agencies from friendly nation states cannot be in charge for political reasons; one sovereign nation cannot allow another nation to "interfere" in its domestic problems. Private organizations and foundations lack the power, and often the resources. Thus, each agency, government or private, tends to pick a piece of the development process in which it is interested and "assist" the developing country. In this context, however, the efforts by the developing country itself, and by agencies from friendly countries, government and private, are not likely to add up to a total effort which has the capacity to achieve rapid economic development in the country and thereby solve its food problems. Success in the "assisted" sectors of the society and economy is restrained by backwardness and underdevelopedness in integrally related sectors. Successful research in new plant varieties, for example, will not lead to increased production unless the fertilizer required by the new varieties is also forthcoming and in the quantities needed.

Let us consider the assistance efforts of the United States to the developing world in this connection. For reasons of historical accident and domestic politics, it is probably true that the United States government (excluding defense and military assistance) has placed greatest emphasis on foreign food aid, somewhat less on economic and technical assistance, still less on agricultural development in the developing countries, and almost none on the need for a balanced and growing general economy in those countries.[3] Of

[3] For the period 1953–66, expenditures of AID and predecessor agencies for development loans and grants and technical assistance amounted to $7.5 billion; the dollar value of PL 480 exports in all categories over the same period was $15.7 billion.

course, it must be recognized that, if wisely used, financial support and resources provided under the category "economic and technical assistance" would contribute to agricultural development and balanced growth of the overall economy.

It is also probably true, from the point of view of solving the long-term food problems of most developing countries, that the pattern of emphasis noted above should have been in just the reverse order. We gave the developing nations food because we saw hungry people and we had surplus food stocks, but their greatest need was to bring into being a set of enterprises that could produce fertilizer and pumps, research organizations that could develop new and higher-yielding plant varieties and control plant and animal diseases, and a set of marketing institutions that could distribute food products efficiently.

We as a government have helped them develop institutions of higher learning here and there (which ultimately may have a great payoff), but we have not, with few exceptions, worked with them to develop research and experiment stations to produce the new plant varieties and the package of practices surrounding each variety that can greatly increase output per acre. We gave some economic assistance, but not nearly enough. Only in one component, foreign food aid, has United States assistance been generous in relation to the need, and here in some cases it has been too generous. The mixed assistance provided to developing countries by the United States has been governed more by the needs of the domestic United States economy than by the needs of the developing countries.

Since the typical developing country lacks the technical competence to identify and specify its requirements for development, and therefore the requirements for resolving its food problems, and since the haphazard approach of different agencies from different foreign countries working in the developing country is not likely to result in a rational approach to development, and therefore to a solution of the food problem, let us consider the following approach. Would it not be wise for a rich and powerful private organization like the Ford Foundation, or the relevant agency in the United Nations, to work with each developing country in order to develop *a total and systematic approach,* a national development strategy, for dramatically increasing the rate of economic growth for the country, and thereby making it possible for that country to solve its food problem by internal production and commercial trade?

In terms of our categories, this systematic approach, or national strategy, would specify first, what kinds of food aid and quantities it would need over some reasonable planning period, say five years; second, the total amount of financial aid and its uses, and the specific kinds of technical assistance, that it would need over the planning period; third, the research, farm investment, and incentive programs, the nonfarm producer goods, and the kind of new educational, credit, and marketing institutions that would be required to increase the annual rate of food production to the probable level of food demand; and fourth, the organizational, institutional, and investment developments called for in the overall economy to permit it to grow at a rate that would increase real personal incomes to the level where enforced malnutrition, undernourishment, and hunger were eradicated.

To a limited degree, this systematic approach is beginning to take shape in the economic and technical assistance area. The great need for coordination among assistance efforts in a given developing country was not discovered by the author of this volume; it has been recognized by those engaged in economic and technical assistance work for a long time. In this context, the World Bank, one of the strongest and best-staffed international agencies, has taken the lead. David L. Gordon describes its coordinating efforts as follows:[4]

The first major initiative toward attaining coordination was taken in India, in 1958. In that year India, midway through its Second Five-Year Plan, confronted a serious balance of payments crisis. The World Bank convened a meeting of the principal creditor countries (United States, United Kingdom, Federal Republic of Germany, Canada, and Japan), with the IMF participating as observer. The ad hoc nature and purpose of the group were reflected in its original title, Meeting on India's Foreign Exchange Situation. But the participants soon recognized the value of continued consultation on development assistance to so important an aid recipient. Meetings

[4] "Coordinating Aid to Developing Countries," *Finance and Development, Fund and Bank Review*, Vol. III, No. 2 (June 1966), pp. 132–133.

of the Consortium, as it came to be called, were scheduled on a
regular basis; . . .

A Consortium for Pakistan was organized in October 1960, two
years after the initial Indian meeting, also under World Bank spon-
sorship. Its purpose from the start was to mobilize resources for
Pakistan's economic development, on a long-term, continuing basis;
and its membership and mode of operation are virtually identical
with those of the Indian group. Frequently, the meetings of the two
consortia follow one another immediately.

In subsequent years, there have been discussions of possible coordination machinery for several other countries. Those on Nigeria
were the first to bear fruit, in the shape of something called a consultative group (CG), in April 1962. Other CG's have been organized for Colombia, the Sudan, and Tunisia—all, like that for Nigeria, sponsored by the World Bank—and for Ecuador under the
auspices of the Inter-American Development Bank. . . .

Staff resources, indeed, constitute the crucial limitation, because
the leadership of a CG requires elaborate preparation and sustained
effort. The magnitude of the work load is suggested by the following summary of the responsibilities which the Bank considers it
should be prepared to undertake in relation to a typical CG:

(a) making periodic comprehensive reports on the country's development possibilities, problems, and performances as a
basis for the group's deliberations;

(b) commenting on the country's estimate of its aid requirements, making recommendations as to the types and terms
of aid appropriate for it, and highlighting any problems arising from unduly burdensome debt accumulation;

(c) helping the recipient government to prepare or revise a development program, or advising on problems of execution,
where such assistance is desired;

(d) assisting the government, as may be necessary and desired,
in identifying projects, in their preliminary screening, in ar-
ranging for feasibility studies, etc., and in relating other technical assistance to the needs and priorities of the investment
program;

(e) advising the government and group members as to the sectors and, where adequate feasibility studies exist, the projects that deserve priority for external financing.

The Bank proposed, therefore, to sponsor not more than five or
six new CG's, at a maximum, during the fiscal year 1965–66. So

far, it has committed itself in fact to undertaking these responsibilities for East Africa (comprising Kenya, Tanzania, and Uganda), Korea, Malaysia, Morocco, and Thailand, in addition to the groups established earlier. . . .

But these efforts at coordination fall short of the systematic planning outlined above and of what is needed country by country. It is an expensive and time-consuming process, as David Gordon makes clear, but it is essential to achieving rapid economic and agricultural development in the less developed countries. Given the total, systematic approach to development sketched above for a particular country, individual agencies and governments around the world could be encouraged to assist with pieces of the development process that would fit together and add up to increased national productivity, including increased agricultural productivity. Anything less than this is not likely to lead to rapid economic growth, hence to rising real per capita incomes, hence to a solution to the food problems of the developing countries in the 1970's. And to talk of solving the food problem in a vacuum is nonsense.

Increasing food production by movement to a modern, scientific agricultural plant does not mean planting gardens in backyards or cultivating new lands. Those backyards and new lands no longer exist, at least not in the sense that they can be readily exploited by individual families. The exploitation of new land in the future will certainly involve lands under the oceans and in tropical rain forests, which will, in turn, involve new forms of research, heavy investments, and new ways of farming. For these reasons, then, we now talk about solving the food problems of developing countries through the modernization of agriculture, the transition to a scientific agriculture. But a modern, scientific agriculture involves an interdependent agriculture—an agriculture that depends upon (1) the constant inflow of new production techniques and new and additional producer goods, and (2) the movement of surplus farm products to distant deficit areas through complex marketing agencies at remunerative prices to farmers and marketers. All this means that the overall economy must be functioning smoothly and efficiently; where it is not, a modern, scientific agriculture cannot be established and supported.

This is the crux of the matter; food production can be greatly increased in the developing countries, but not by a simple tinkering with some element of the food and agricultural sector; it can be increased greatly only by moving to a modern, scientific agriculture which is part and parcel of the total development process.

This total, systematic approach to the development problem, and so to the food problem, of a developing country is not beyond the realm of possibility. At least some people in the Ford Foundation are thinking about it, and so is the Food and Agricultural Organization, as it struggles with its Indicative World Plan for Agricultural Development. The technical agencies of the Pan-American Union are trying to get this concept of a total national plan of development established in Latin America. In most cases, these various efforts have not yet met with success. Lack of vision, lack of trained personnel, and lack of resources explain the lack of success with this total approach so far. But there is intellectual activity, and there is now some experience with the coordination of assistance efforts. Thus, there is reason to hope that a total systems approach to the development problems of the developing countries will become a reality in the 1970's and 1980's.

The Basic Requirement: General Economic Development

A multiple approach to the world food problem has been sketched in this chapter. But all the components except one—population control by birth control—lead to increased food production and improved food distribution as an integral part of a general economy that is growing in a balanced manner. The multiple approach developed here thus seeks to achieve a rate of growth in the general economy that can sustain a rate of increase in food production equal to or modestly greater than the rate of growth in food demand. We say a rate of growth in the general economy that can *sustain* the required rate of food production, because increases in food production are dependent on the operation of the general economy in five specific ways:

1. The general economy must produce, or pay for the importation of, the producer goods required by a modern, scientific

agriculture (e.g., improved seeds, fertilizer, insecticides, machines);
2. The general economy must absorb in remunerative jobs the surplus labor released by agriculture;
3. The general economy must generate the personal incomes among nonfarm people to purchase the surplus products of agriculture at prices that provide an incentive for farmers to increase production further;
4. The general economy must generate the savings to support the rates of investment required by farm and nonfarm productive enterprises; and
5. The total economy, farm and nonfarm, must provide the tax revenues to support the infrastructure, the research organizations, and the educational system required by a modern, scientifically based farm and nonfarm economy.

Whenever and wherever one of these linking relationships breaks down or fails to develop, the development of the whole economy falters and food production will fail to achieve the rates of increase required of it. Increases in food production cannot take place independent of the development of the general economy and the above five relationships. Food production in a modern economy is simply one important sector of a productive operating economy.

The old, conventional approaches to the world food problem are turned upside down by the conceptual view given above. Food planners and politicians cannot simply say, "Grow more food and maintain contact with reality." A farmer will grow more food on his fixed land base as (1) a package of new practices and producer goods are developed and made available to him; (2) he is convinced that the package of practices and producer goods will increase his production; (3) credit is available to him at a price and in time for him to make economic use of it; (4) he sells his surplus product at prices that will induce him to continue to make the extra effort; and (5) he is able to increase his real income position through the purchase of additional producer and consumer goods. And food planners and politicians cannot create these five conditions in a world unto themselves.

These conditions will become a reality to the farmer when, and only when, the general economy produces them. So once again we return to that critical point: the food problem of the developing nations must be approached and solved by the effective development of their economies. The multiple approach sketched here represents a series of policy steps consistent with that view, which culminates in the final basic requirement—a balanced and growing general economy.

Summary

We have argued here that the food problems of the developing world cannot be solved by tinkering a bit with the food supply. We have argued that placing a brake on population growth through effective birth control methods and programs is critically important in increasing per capita food supplies over the next 20 years. We have further argued that per capita food consumption can be increased by a multiple approach to the food production problem. This multiple approach includes the four principal components: foreign food aid, economic and technical assistance, agricultural development, and a balanced and growing general economy.

In developing the concepts of, and the interrelations among, these components, it was argued that they constitute progressive steps in a continuum of actions required to establish a world organization of the production and distribution of food with the capacity to deal with the world food problem. In other words, the world food problem will be solved only to the extent that a proper mix of actions is taken within these four components. But since the final component involves the achievement of a balanced and growing general economy, it turns out that the production and distribution of the kinds and quantities of food required to solve the food problems of a country will be achieved only when its general economy is growing satisfactorily. The solution to the food problems of the developing world, it is argued, is absolutely dependent upon the achievement of satisfactory rates of economic development in the developing countries.

6

Population Control
by Birth Control

THE MODERN WORLD population explosion is a very recent occurrence—an occurrence of the post-World War II years. It has
come about not through a sharp increase in birth rates around the
world, but rather through a sharp reduction in death rates. And
what makes the problem particularly difficult is the fact that the
most rapid increases in population are occurring in the underdeveloped regions of the world. Asia with a population base of 1.8
billion in 1965, or just about half of the world's population, has
rates of increase running up to 2.7 percent per year in some areas.
If these rates were to continue unabated until the year 2000, Asia
alone would have over 4.4 billion people, or more than a billion
more persons than all the people living in the world in 1965.

Latin America, whose total population was close to 250 million
in 1965, and Africa with some 310 million, under recent growth
trends would each have another half billion or more persons by
the year 2000. In the world as a whole, a continuation of recent
trends would result in a total population of about 7.4 billion by the
magic year 2000. And nothing short of major world disaster is
likely to prevent the world population from increasing to some 6.0
billion people by 2000.

Obviously this dramatic increase in human population, in which
the doubling of numbers is now occurring every 18 years in parts of
Latin America and every 33 years for the world as a whole, cannot
go on indefinitely. Such rates of population growth make the
achievement of levels of living in line with the expectations of the

100

average man in the developing world impossible, and, of course, ultimately raise the question of the availability of sufficient living space. The crucial question, however, is not whether this very great expansion in human numbers will be slowed down and brought under control. The crucial question is: *How will the reduction be achieved and how soon will it come about?*

Many of the economically less developed countries where the problem chiefly occurs are unprepared to deal with it in knowledge, in attitudes, in public policy and public institutions, and in means and facilities. In many of these countries, where the rate of infant mortality used to raise the basic question of survival, children under fifteen years of age already represent 40 to 50 percent of the total population and continue to be further augmented by still rising rates of growth.

What is required in each of the countries now characterized by rapid rates of population growth is a "demographic transition"— the reestablishment of a balance between rates of mortality and rates of birth. In the past, population stability, or balance, was maintained by high rates of mortality and high rates of fertility. Now that death rates have been dramatically reduced (and further reductions are apt to occur in the developing countries), it is necessary to restore a balance by achieving a corresponding reduction in birth rates.

Perhaps without exception, today's economically developed countries have gone through a period in their history characterized by high rates of mortality and high rates of birth. The process of change from high rates to relatively low rates of both mortality and birth in these countries has typically come about over a long period of time, with death rates falling first and birth rates declining later. This demographic transition was accompanied in most, but not all, cases by corresponding improvements in economic and social conditions—in employment and income, nutrition, housing, health, sanitation, education, and leisure.

This demographic transition may be viewed graphically for Denmark in Fig. 6.1. Prior to 1800, population growth in Denmark was held in check by death rates that were almost as high on the average as birth rates—about 30 per 1,000. During the nineteenth century, death rates in Denmark declined persistently, although un-

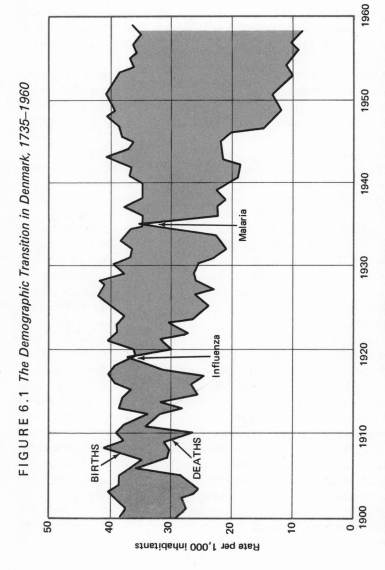

FIGURE 6.1 *The Demographic Transition in Denmark, 1735–1960*

SOURCE: *Population and Food Supply*, FFHC Basic Study No. 7 (New York: United Nations, Office of Public Information).

102

evenly; birth rates, on the other hand, remained constant at slightly over 30 per 1,000. After 1900, birth rates too began to decline in Denmark. Thus, by 1960 the demographic transition from a state of high birth and death rates and a stable population to a state of low birth and death rates and a relatively stable population was complete.

Ceylon in the twentieth century is in the same demographic stage as was Denmark in the nineteenth century (Fig. 6.2). Death rates are falling as a result of disease control, but birth rates are holding almost constant at a high level. The great requirement of

tes
'op-
tries
mily

Willard W. Cochrane,

ERR.

Transpose the illustrations(but no

on pages 102 (Fig. 6.1) and 104 (F. ed

of

ed

s

s

mum population which the earth can support is open to debate and the length of time in which present growth trends could continue is also subject to judgment. *But the inherent instability of the present relation between declining death rates and relatively fixed birth rates is not debatable.* Something must give.

This logic, together with a vast fund of knowledge on population, economic, and social interrelations, permits Dr. Taeuber to develop the following hypotheses with respect to population developments.[2]

[1] Hearings before the Committee on Agriculture, House of Representatives, 89th Cong., 2nd Sess., February 14, 15, 16, 17, and 18, 1966. *World War on Hunger*, pp. 6, 7.
[2] *Ibid.*, pp. 6, 7.

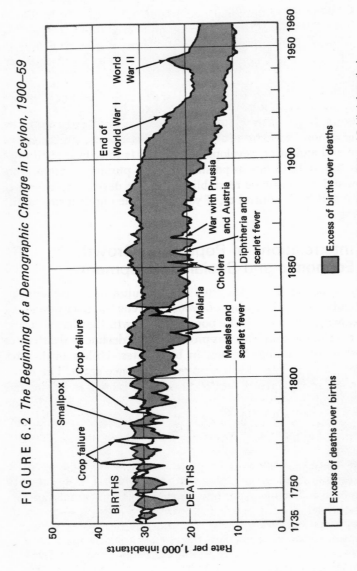

FIGURE 6.2 *The Beginning of a Demographic Change in Ceylon, 1900–59*

SOURCE: *Population and Food Supply*, FFHC Basic Study No. 7 (New York: United Nations, Office of Public Information).

1. Population growth as it is now occurring will not continue indefinitely, nor even for any substantial period of time in the future. The question is the time and the process of the movement to lesser rates of growth, not the fact of eventual occurrence.
2. The forces of modernization, reinforced increasingly by the plans and programs of governments, are conducive to later ages at marriage, smaller families among those who marry, and greater opportunities for those children who are born.
3. The sciences and technologies concerned with human life are not limited to those relevant to the prevention of disease and the postponement of death, nor can they be so contained. Advances in the bio-medical sciences and technologies relevant to human reproduction and in the behavioral sciences associated with communication and motivation have already made the extension of family planning a feasible component in development plans and programs. Stated concisely and without equivocation, a government which wishes to develop an operating program to reduce birth rates has available to it knowledge of and means for limitation that are both acceptable and effective.

    As to point 2, many countries have plans and programs to reduce population growth. Point 3 is that the government which has such a program has available to it the feasible technology.
4. A slowing growth of population in the future that is consistent with economic and social development must involve continuing declines in death rates along with declining birth rates. The control of birth is not a panacea, nor does it proceed in isolation from the other aspects of a moving society and economy. Those aspirations for the future which involve family planning are products of economic and social development, advancing health and nutritional status, and expanding education.
5. It is probable that retrogression in health and nutrition would alter the structures of aspirations and slow the developmental processes that are associated with declining birth rates. Translated into direct terms it is probable that widespread famine in India would slow the development and the success of the birth control program. It is fortunate indeed that this statement has had to be made in conjectural form, that the demographic processes of economic failure are not available for field

analysis. However, the evidence in development is so incisive and so pervasive that the hypothesis may be formulated as follows: The rising death rates of economic failure would delay the development of small families as ideals, goals, and achievements in peasant societies.

6. There are no immediate demographic solutions to problems of hunger and malnutrition; there are no long-run solutions to problems of food and nutrition that do not involve demographic components. Solutions to the problems of population and food are interrelated; unless the resolution of problems of population growth is pushed immediately and assiduously through the control of the quantity of new life, long-run solutions to the problems of food will be delayed if not thwarted. The basic reasons for the interconnections of problems lie in man's span of life. The children who will enter school 6 years from now, in 1972, are already born. All who will reach labor force ages prior to 1980 are now living. So also are all those who will be aged 34 and over at the end of the century. The problems of an existing population may be alleviated but they cannot be solved by reducing the annual increments to the population through births.

7. Unless priorities are accorded programs for voluntary, effective, and major extensions in family planning, the problems of the future are likely to be intensifications of those of the present. The possibilities for the resolution of tomorrow's economic and social problems are related directly to those actions that are taken now for the solution of the problems of high birth rates, even though these present actions may not be sufficient as solutions to or even major alleviations of today's problems.

8. Economic and social advance; health, nutrition, and vitality; education and aspirations; employment opportunities *and smaller families*[3]—these are inseparable aspects of the development process.

This set of hypotheses, or statements, is well summarized in Dr. Taeuber's final statement. "Economic and social advance; health, nutrition, and vitality; education and aspirations; employment opportunities *and smaller families*—these are inseparable aspects of the development process." Rising real incomes, modernization of social organization, technological advance, education, and rising per-

[3] The italics are mine.

sonal aspirations provide both the means and the incentive for smaller families; and smaller families are both the means to and the end result of economic development. The question is not whether family planning, or birth control, should be advocated; they are a part of the development process, which is upon us. The relevant question is: How is the practice of family planning, or birth control, to be assisted and pressed so as to avoid the incongruous buildup of population in the early stages of the development process?

Contraceptive Techniques and Motivations

For individual families wishing to control their size, for organizations interested in birth control programs, and whole nations seeking to control rates of population growth, a wide range of contraceptive methods is available. There are the older nonmechanical methods, which include *coitus interruptus* and rhythm techniques. There are the modern mechanical devices, which include the diaphragm, the cervical cap, condoms, jels and creams, sponges and tampons and suppositories. There are permanent methods involving either male or female sterilization. And finally, there are the recent methods which include intra-uterine devices and oral contraceptives.[4]

Some of these methods are more effective than others; permanent sterilization is obviously completely effective, but many people are repelled by the idea. The diaphragm if properly used, with strong motivation, is highly effective; but improperly used, with weak motivation, it is an ineffective device. Oral contraceptives, which are popular and effective among high income, highly motivated American women, are at present an impractical device for village women in South Asia because of the high costs involved. The intra-uterine loop, which in the early 1960's aroused the hope that it would be the salvation of the less developed world because of its relative cheapness and permanence, turns out to have certain undesirable side effects unless fitted properly by a trained techni-

[4] For a technical discussion of contraceptive methods see Mary Steichen Calderone (ed.), *Manual of Contraceptive Practice* (Baltimore, Md.: The Williams & Wilkins Company, 1964).

cian. Further, the device is not 100 percent effective even when in place, and losses are not uncommon—sometimes without the knowledge of the wearer. And since the developing countries find it difficult to produce the trained technicians to insert and check on the women using the device, programs for reaching the village women with intra-uterine loops have developed slowly.

There are many methods, but no perfect method. Some are too costly, some unacceptable to the persons involved, some require too much medical skill, and all require a high degree of motivation.

The government of India, which has openly espoused family planning for many years, has until recently relied upon such permanent techniques as sterilization and intra-uterine devices. But it is discovering that it simply does not have the medical capacity to reach the masses with these sophisticated techniques. It is not that these methods have been rejected by Indians generally; it is that the masses cannot be reached with these methods by the existing medical capability. Thus, the government of India in 1967 is turning to a do-it-yourself program involving a simple device, the condom. Condoms are being mass produced and mass distributed at a very low price—at less than one cent a piece. It is hoped and expected that, with the new motivation for smaller families, condoms will become widely used as a contraceptive device. In other words, India is diversifying its birth control program. It will move ahead as rapidly as it is able with such sophisticated devices as sterilization and intra-uterine loops. But it is hoping and expecting personal motivation to speed up the drive to smaller families through the widespread use of the cheap, simple device, the condom.

What is suggested above, and what becomes exceedingly clear from discussions with family planning technicians in the field, is that there is no "best" contraceptive method for every society. Each society must develop a program involving methods which are consistent with its resources, needs, and social values. In some societies, this may mean heavy reliance on practices that are repugnant to Western men and women—for example, induced abortion and *coitus interruptus*. Finally, the real problem is not technique; it is motivation. The best devices become ineffective where the motivation for small families is lacking, and family size can be and has been severely restricted without any modern gadgets (by abortion, for example) where the motivation is strong.

Controlling the size of families, hence the rate of population growth, by family planning thus really goes back to personal and social motivation. If the leaders of the less developed countries can convince their people that smaller families will lead to improved material well-being as well as family survival, then family planning will take hold. And it will take hold much faster in 1970 than it did in 1870 because the techniques of contraception are greatly improved. Improved techniques plus high motivation can lead to dramatic results in population control. But improved techniques without high motivation mean very slow progress.

Population Policies in Developing Countries[5]

India, Nepal, and Pakistan

The first country to adopt a national policy to control population growth was *India*. The beginnings, in the mid-1950's, were modest. Major bottlenecks were lack of an administrative structure to reach India's enormous rural population, and acute shortages of medical personnel, especially of women doctors. Except for financial subsidies, authority rests with the individual states. Organization in the Ministry of Health has moved slowly, and the government has been slow to adopt the newer methods of contraception. Nevertheless, the program has gained momentum, as indicated by the data on expenditures in the following table.

India's Family Planning Expenditures, 1951–71

Five-Year Plan		Expenditures (Millions of Rupees)
First	(1951–1956)	1.5
Second	(1956–1961)	21.6
Third	(1961–1966)	261.0
Fourth	(1966–1971)—Allocation	950.0

[5] This section (pp. 109–18) is reprinted with permission from the excellent article by Dudley Kirk, "Prospects for Reducing Natality in the Underdeveloped World," *The Annals of the American Academy of Political and Social Science, World Population* (January 1967), pp. 51–60.

Annual expenditures have risen from 13.8 million rupees in
1961–62 to 60.5 in 1964–65 and to an estimated 120 in 1965–66.[6]
The last two represent per capita expenditures of about two and
four cents. The Fourth Plan allocation implies an annual expendi-
ture of $25.4 million or about five cents per person. Food shortages
have made India's efforts more urgent. Symbolic of this is the
change in name from Ministry of Health to Ministry of Health and
Family Planning.

The Indian program has relied chiefly on clinics, which num-
bered 15,808 in July 1965. Although rhythm and conventional
mechanical and chemical methods were first offered, IUD's were
introduced in 1965, with one million inserted by mid-1966. Since
1963 over 100,000 male and female sterilizations have been per-
formed per year in "sterilization camps" temporarily set up for this
purpose. The cumulative total of sterilizations is soon expected to
exceed one million. Oral contraceptives have not yet been approved
for general use in India.

Impressive as these recent achievements are, they have not had
any measurable influence on the Indian birth rate, except perhaps
in the largest Indian cities, where family planning seems to be
spreading in the population (but probably as much through private
as through government services). The object of the program is to
reduce the annual birth rate from over 40 to 25 per thousand population "as soon as possible." Targets rise annually to 1971 when
it is hoped to have 19.7 million IUD users, 4.5 million sterilizations,
and 4.7 million condom users.[7] Success in this magnitude is indeed
necessary for a major impact on the Indian birth rate. India is a
country of almost 500 million people, with some 100 million
women in the reproductive ages and some 20 million births annually.

Interested in these developments in India, *Nepal* incorporated a
family planning program in its Third Plan, 1965–1970, but it has
yet to be implemented.

Pakistan formulated a population control program in the late
1950's which was allocated 30.5 million rupees in the Second Five-

[6] B. L. Raina, "India," in Bernard Berelson, *et al.* (eds.), *Family Planning
and Population Programs: A Review of World Developments* (Chicago: The
University of Chicago Press, 1966).
[7] *Ibid.*, p. 119.

Year Plan (1960–1965). The objective is to supply family planning services through the existing health services in hospitals, dispensaries, and rural clinics for voluntary participation of couples in limiting family size and spacing of children.

These efforts encountered many of the problems noted in India. In the first four years only 9.4 million rupees[8] of the budgeted expenditures of 24.7 million were actually used.[9] The problems related more to administration and organization than lack of funds. The plan for reaching 1.2 million women as contraceptive users and the targets for distribution of contraceptives, specifically condoms and foam tablets, were met only at the level of 17 percent and 15 percent, respectively.[10]

In July 1965 the Family Planning Directorate was upgraded to one of the most ambitious in the world today. Its five-year budget of 300 million rupees represents an average annual budget of about 12 cents per person. A major innovation is to be the insertion of IUD's by midwives, under medical supervision. These midwives will receive incentive payments for referrals and insertions. By 1970 no less than 50,000 village midwives are to be recruited and given a five-week training course.[11]

Korea and Taiwan

More immediate success has been achieved in two smaller Asian countries, South Korea and Taiwan. *South Korea*'s Supreme Council for National Reconstruction adopted a national family planning policy in 1961 as an integral part of the development plan. The targets were more specific than in most countries as regards training, use of contraceptives, and effects on the rate of growth. By April 1965 some 2,200 full-time field workers had been recruited and trained, one for each 2,500 women in the childbearing ages.[12] Main reliance of the program is now on the IUD. Insertions were 112,000 in 1964, and 233,000 in 1965,[13] against targets of 100,000

[8] One Pakistan rupee equals 21 cents.

[9] E. Adil, "Pakistan," in Berelson, *et al., op. cit.,* p. 127.

[10] *Ibid.,* p. 128.

[11] Government of Pakistan, *Family Planning Scheme for Pakistan During the Third Five Year Plan Period, 1965–1970,* pp. 3, 10.

[12] Government of Korea, *Korea, Summary of First Five-Year Economic Plan, 1962–1966.*

[13] Ministry of Health and Social Welfare, Government of Korea, *Monthly Report on IUD Insertions* (mimeographed).

and 200,000, respectively. The latter is estimated to be about 15 percent of the target women, that is, those exposed to the risk of unwanted pregnancy. IUD's and conventional contraceptives are being manufactured in Korea.

The official objective is to reduce the rate of population growth from a current estimate of 2.9 percent per year to 1.8 percent in 1971. The Economic Planning Board estimates that by 1980 full implementation of the family planning program will bring down the rate of growth to 1.16 percent compared to 3.15 without a reduction in the birth rates. The difference in growth rates will mean a per capita income 36 percent higher in 1980 than would be the case in the absence of a fertility decline.

These ambitious objectives would sound unrealistic were it not for the fact that the government program is clearly "swimming with the tide" of social change. Attitude surveys show an overwhelming approval of family planning in the Korean population and a rapid increase in contraception and abortion,[14] the latter perhaps because of Japanese influence. Though not yet approved by the government, a bill is currently before the Korean Assembly to legalize induced abortion.

In the absence of accurate vital statistics, it is difficult to measure year-to-year changes in the birth rate. An indirect measure, ratios of children under five to women in the childbearing ages, does strongly suggest a recent rapid decline in the birth rate, especially in 1965. Although this decline was already in process, the greater rate of decline in 1965 might reflect the effects of the government program in 1964, when it first reached mass proportions.

Taiwan does not have an official population policy, but family planning services are now provided throughout the island by the Provincial Department of Health. Impetus for the island-wide program stemmed from the mass action research program in the city of Taichung[15] (in which it was first established that the IUD would

[14] According to a survey made in 1964, one out of three pregnancies among married women in Seoul is terminated by induced abortion.. See S. B. Hong, *Induced Abortion in Seoul, Korea* (Seoul: Dong-A Publishing Company, 1966), p. 78.

[15] This is fully described in Bernard Berelson and Ronald Freedman, "A Study in Fertility Control," *Scientific American*, Vol. 210, No. 5 (May 1964), pp. 3–11.

be widely accepted in a mass campaign) and from experimental projects begun in 1959 under the euphemistically called "Prepregnancy Health Program." This term paid tribute to the sensitivities of the United States Agency for International Development (AID), which was providing indirect assistance to the health services. The expanded action program for the island as a whole was initiated in 1964, and in 1965 the program effectively achieved the target of inserting 100,000 IUD's.[16]

The principal feature of the Taiwan plan is insertion of 600,000 IUD's within five years.[17] Were there no removals or expulsions this would mean a loop for one-third of the married women of childbearing age, including those marrying in the interim. Since a substantial percentage of the IUD's are not retained, the net effect will probably be less. Oral contraceptives are being introduced on an experimental basis to provide an alternative method for women who cannot or do not wish to use the IUD.

Mainland China

Government interest in family planning in *Mainland China* goes back to 1956 and 1957 when a birth control campaign was initiated by the government and services were provided in government health clinics. In 1958 a change of policy slowed the campaign to very low gear, but by 1962 renewed governmental interest became evident. In January of that year import regulations were revised to admit contraceptives duty-free. The government advocated later age at marriage. Japanese doctors visiting China in 1964 and 1965 reported that family planning was being advocated as part of maternal and child health programs and that all methods of contraception, including sterilization and abortion, were available. Oral contraceptives and IUD's manufactured in China were apparently becoming increasingly popular.

According to Premier Chou:

Our present target is to reduce population growth to below 2 percent; for the future we aim at an even lower rate. . . . However, I do not believe it will be possible to equal the Japanese rate (of about

[16] Government of Taiwan, *Family Planning in Taiwan, Republic of China, 1965–1966* (1966), p. iii.
[17] Government of Taiwan, *Taiwan, Ten Year Health Program, 1966–1975*.

one percent) as early as 1970. . . . We do believe in planned parenthood, but it is not easy to introduce all at once in China. . . . The first thing is to encourage late marriages.[18]

Many of the 17 million Communist party members and 25 million Young Communists have received birth control instruction, and they, in turn, are expected to become models and teachers. One son and one daughter are now considered an ideal family size.[19]

Far too little is known about the Chinese program, but it may well be the most important national program in the world, if for no other reason than the tremendous numbers involved. The Chinese population may now be as high as 800 million, equal to about one-fourth of the human race.

Middle East and Africa

Four countries in the Middle East and North Africa have adopted national family planning programs. In the *United Arab Republic* (UAR) the government's interest goes back to 1953, when a National Population Commission was established and a few clinics were opened. Government policy dates from the May 1962 draft of the National Charter, in which President Nasser declared:

> Population increase constitutes the most dangerous obstacle that faces the Egyptian people in their drive towards raising the standard of production. . . . Attempts at family planning deserve the most sincere efforts supported by modern scientific methods.[20]

However, a substantial program was not initiated until February 1966, when the government launched a widespread campaign using oral contraceptives.

In *Tunisia* an experimental program to develop a practical family planning service with IUD's was started in 1964. The success of this experiment led to a national campaign with a goal of 120,000 IUD's.[21] An unusually interesting feature of the Tunisian program

---

[18] As reported by Edgar Snow in *The New York Times*, February 3, 1964.
[19] *The Sunday Times* (London), January 23, 1966.
[20] UAR, Information Department, *The Charter* (draft presented by President Nasser on May 21, 1962), p. 53.
[21] A. Daly, "Tunisia," in Berelson, *et al., op. cit.*, p. 160.

has been the use of Destour party members as a major source of information and publicity. The program may have been set back by President Bourguiba's speech on Woman's Day, August 12, 1966, against celibacy and in favor of a young vigorous population.

In April 1965 *Turkey* repealed an old law against contraception and provided the legal framework and financial basis for a nation-wide family planning program.[22] Full-time family planning personnel are to be trained and added to the Health Ministry, and supplies are to be offered free or at cost. Interesting features of the Turkish program are plans for an informational campaign on birth control in the armed forces (to provide a "ripple" effect when the conscripts return to civilian life) and incorporation of demographic and biological aspects of population into the school curriculum.

Morocco decided in 1966 to adopt a national family planning program to be introduced by stages through the public health clinics in the various parts of the country. A national sample survey of attitudes on family planning has been started by the government.

Although *Algeria* has no population policy or program, Dr. Ahmed Taleb, Minister of National Education, stated on the opening of the school year (fall 1966):

> . . . we have to fight an extremely high birth rate. If nothing is done to stop this growth rate through birth control, the problem of educating all the Algerian children will remain unsolved.[23]

Latin America

Latin America has the most rapid rate of population growth of any major region of the world. This has not generally been a matter of much public concern, partly because of the traditional position of the Catholic Church and partly because Latin-American countries have a historical image of themselves as underpopulated.

Two forces are rapidly changing this disinterest. One is the growing recognition that high growth rates are obstacles to achieving planning goals. In many countries population is growing faster than food supply; the difficulties in providing public education, health services, and other facilities are formidable; and the intrusive prob-

---

[22] T. Metiner, "Turkey," in Berelson, *et al., op. cit.,* p. 136.
[23] Translation from *La Presse,* Tunis, Tunisia, September 30, 1966.

lem of unemployment and underemployment has serious political as well as economic implications as people flock into the cities. A second element is the growing concern, especially in the medical profession, over the problem of induced abortion. The possibility of family planning appears to be gaining favorable attention both among responsible leaders, and among large segments of the population, according to sample attitude surveys in eight Latin-American capitals (coordinated by the United Nations Latin-American Demographic Center in Santiago, Chile).[24]

Latin-American countries may be less likely to adopt formal population policies than other parts of the underdeveloped world owing to the influence of the Church. However, natality regulation has been approved for the public health service in *Chile,* and several major birth control projects using public health facilities exist in Santiago. In *Honduras* the Minister of Health recently announced that family planning is to be an integral part of preventive medical services. In *Jamaica* a Family Planning Unit has been established within the Ministry of Health with administrative costs provided by AID. In *Colombia* the private Association of Medical Faculties has established a Population Division, which has organized a nationwide program for training health officers in family planning. In October 1966 AID authorized the use of counterpart funds to finance this program. In *Peru* a government-sponsored population studies center was established to "formulate programs of action with which to face the problems of population and socio-economic development." *Barbados* has had an official policy favoring family planning since 1954, expressed chiefly by subsidy of the private Family Planning Association.

Evaluation of Family Planning Programs

Most government family planning programs are very new, and it would be unfair to expect major results so soon. Their very existence in so short a time is in itself remarkable. Operating through the existing health network, generally under the Health Ministry,

[24] C. A. Miro and F. Rath, "Preliminary Findings of Comparative Fertility Surveys in Three Latin-American Cities," *Milbank Memorial Fund Quarterly,* Vol. XLIII, No. 4 (October 1965), Part 2, pp. 36–68.

most programs are still largely clinic-oriented despite the common experience that other means may be more effective. Problems of organization; administration; production, distribution, and supply of contraceptives; and shortage of skilled personnel are more serious than the question of finance.

Partly because of their newness, the programs have tended to place great emphasis on the magic of the new contraceptive methods. They all have shied away from abortion, which has been a major factor in reducing birth rates in large populations as in Japan, the Soviet Union, and eastern Europe. The present female-oriented programs minimize the role of male participation, which, if not for presently recommended methods, is nevertheless important for information and motivation. Few of the programs have thus far made use of mass communication, and Ministries of Information and Education have yet to be effectively involved.

Since very few of the countries of the underdeveloped world have sufficiently accurate vital statistics to measure year-to-year changes in the birth rate, other means must be sought. Censuses can be used to measure natality changes, but these occur too infrequently for the purpose at hand. In the absence of official data, sample registration and periodic sample population surveys are conducted to provide data for measuring year-to-year changes. These have come to be known as Population Growth Estimate (PGE) Studies. Experimental projects of this type are going forward in Pakistan, Turkey, and Thailand.

As programs accelerate, the deficiency in accurate vital data will become increasingly important. In-service data can give good measures of the scope of the programs and their success in achieving targets. However, the number of contraceptive "users," as measured by accepters, can be very deceptive, since failure of the method and, even more important, failure of couples to use methods as required, can significantly reduce "use-effectiveness." This is true of IUD's as well as other effective methods such as oral contraceptives and condoms. Many women do not retain the IUD's or have them removed. In the national program in Taiwan 62 percent of the women still had the IUD in place at the end of twelve months, 52 percent at the end of eighteen months. Experience elsewhere has been better, up to 80 percent retention at the end of a year. In all methods there is substantial shrinkage between ideal use and actual effectiveness in preventing pregnancy.

It should also be noted that family planning programs are most likely to succeed rapidly in countries of greatest socioeconomic advance, where realization of the smaller family ideal has already made some progress. The success of a program in countries like Korea and Taiwan chiefly reflects rapid progress in other ways. In such countries mass acceptance of government services is not an equivalent gain in family planning practices, since many of the couples concerned were already practicing family planning (perhaps by less effective methods or abortion) or would have done so regardless of a government program. In these countries the government program may accelerate a trend already in existence. Indeed, in some countries, the influence of the program on couples to use private sources of supply, methods not requiring supplies, and abortion may well surpass the effect of the direct services offered. Yet this indirect effect is least susceptible to measurement.

Summary and Conclusions

The picture that emerges is a range in birth rates of 20 to 25 per 1,000 population within a decade in the most progressive parts of East and Southeast Asia, and possibly within two decades in India and Mainland China if those countries avoid war, disaster, and social chaos. By that time, one can expect important reductions in the birth rate in all of the larger developing countries in Asia, in the Middle East and North Africa, and in Latin America. Taking the underdeveloped world as a whole, within two decades I expect to see the solution well in sight, though not yet fully achieved.

These conclusions imply great efforts and accomplishments in the face of cultural resistance and inertia. The achievements will not be easily won, nor will they forestall the massive population growth that, in the absence of catastrophe, will be with us at least through the 1970's. The critical problem of world population growth will remain, though in the longer run there is now real hope for its solution.

Implications for the Food Problem

Birth control, or family planning, programs are just getting under way in Asia and are just being talked about in Latin America. Thus it is too early to predict how soon, or to what degree, these programs will have a significant dampening effect on population growth. But as the summary statement of the previously quoted section indicates, there are now reasons to believe that rates of population growth will be slowed down by birth control programs in some of the densely populated countries of the developing world in the decade of the 1980's. We now have reason to hope that the population explosion can eventually be brought under control.

A realistic solution to the world food problem does not, however, require a reduction in the rate of population growth to zero. If the rates of population growth in the more densely populated developing countries can be reduced from a range of 2.5–3.0 percent (the current range) to a range of something like 1.5–2.0 percent, the food problem in those countries can be managed without too great difficulty. Crop production in many of the densely populated developing countries is increasing at between 2.0 and 2.5 percent per year. With the improvements in technology and economic organization that seem possible for most of those countries within the next decade, rates of increase in crop production could increase to between 3 and 4 percent per year.

Now, if rates of population growth can be held to 2 percent in these countries, and increases in the per capita demand for food resulting from increased personal incomes run around 1.0 percent per year, then we have an increase in the total demand for food of about 3.0 percent per year. This compares favorably with a possible increase in crop production of between 3.0 and 4.0 percent per year. Given these ranges of magnitude for increasing food demands and food supplies, the food problem for the developing countries becomes a manageable one.

It could be, for reasons of limited educational resources and limited housing, that a 2.0 percent rate of population growth per year is too high for the densely populated developing countries. And, certainly a 1.5 percent rate of population growth per year would enable the average consumer in such countries to enrich his diet somewhat, where a rate of 2.0 percent might not. It should be recognized that a rate of increase in *crop* production of, say, 3.5 percent per year converts into a lower rate of increase in *food* production, where an increasing proportion of that food supply takes the form of animal products. This results from the fact that the production of a pound of animal product requires several pounds of grain. If, then, the composition of a nation's food supply is changing so that it involves a higher proportion of animal products, increasing amounts of its crop production must be used to feed the increased livestock population; hence these crops are not available for human consumption. Thus, if the quality, as well as the quantity, of a nation's food supply is increasing, the increase in the overall rate of food production (measured in pounds or calories) will be lower than the rate of increase in crop production.

It seems clear from this that if developing countries are enjoying reasonably rapid economic progress, so that the per capita demand for food is increasing in the neighborhood of 1.0 percent per year, then in the usual case, crop production must increase to 4 percent per year or the rate of population growth must fall to at least 1.5 percent per year. Unless one or the other of these two things occurs, the average consumer is not going to improve the quality of his diet—increase his consumption of animal products —in accordance with his expectations as based on his increases in money income. And it is exactly this kind of *economic* food problem that leads to social unrest, demonstrations, and the overthrow of governments either through the ballot box or by force.

As we play with the percentages in this section, it would be easy to say that "in all probability a rate of population growth of 1.5 percent per year will be reached in the densely populated developing countries by the middle 1970's and the most serious food problems will be averted." But it is probably nearer to reality to say that "those same countries will be exceedingly fortunate to have their rates of population growth reduced to 2.0 percent per year by the end of the 1970's." If the latter turns out to be the case, it seems likely that serious undernourishment and widespread hunger will be averted in those countries in the 1970's, but that they still may experience serious food problems arising out of the economics of the situation; the increased demand for high-resource-using foods (e.g., animal products) resulting from rising money incomes will not be fully satisfied.

But serious problems or not, population control by birth control is one component, and a vitally necessary component, of a total solution to the world food problem. Without effective birth control programs in the developing world, the world food problem will be solved only through prodigious efforts, if at all. With effective birth control programs, the world food problem is reduced to manageable proportions. In the latter context, potential developments in agriculture can save the day.

7

Foreign Food Aid

FOOD AID is a specialized form of foreign economic aid. It may be described as the provision of food supplies by one country or international organization to a food deficit country or group of countries on some kind of concessional basis—perhaps as a gift or grant, perhaps as a sale for a nonconvertible currency, or perhaps as a long-term loan at a favorable rate of interest. This type of economic aid has played an increasingly important role in the total aid program of the United States to developing countries since the mid-1950's.

As we shall see, food aid has certain strengths and certain weaknesses; which predominates depends on how food aid is employed and on the conditions of the situation. There is really no substitute for food aid when a very poor area or country suffers a crop failure. Assistance in the form of food must be provided, or people will starve. But the continued shipment of food stocks overseas to a developing country on a concessional basis may dampen the incentive to increase the agricultural productivity of the recipient country or countries. Thus, it is not helpful to say categorically that food aid is a good form of economic assistance or a bad form of assistance. It depends. And since food aid has become an important form of economic assistance, we need to analyze its potentials and limitations for dealing with the world food problem.

The Historical Record

The United States

Foreign food aid has a long history in the United States. During World War I and in the years immediately following, the United States operated large programs of famine relief. These programs were first designed to provide food to our allies, but in 1919 and 1920 large famine relief programs were placed in operation to help both the victors and the vanquished. In 1940, the United States had on hand large stocks of wheat, cotton, and corn—stocks accumulated under the agricultural price and income support programs of the depressed 1930's. These stocks were shipped to Britain, the Soviet Union, and other allies under the Lend-Lease Act of 1941. Without doubt the food supplies shipped to Britain in 1941, when that country stood alone against the forces of Hitler, contributed significantly to her survival. Food aid was also of great assistance to the Soviets throughout World War II.

Following World War II, the United States became engaged in the largest food relief operation in history. Food production in Europe did not recover immediately after the war and widespread undernourishment and hunger among millions of European urban dwellers resulted. In this setting, political unrest was on the rise in Western Europe. To combat widespread food shortages and political unrest in Western Europe, the United States made large-scale donations of food in 1945, 1946, and 1947.[1] Then, on November 17, 1947, President Truman recommended to Congress the Marshall Plan or the European Recovery Program. Under this foreign aid program, food aid again played an important role, but fortunately for the success of the program, it took place between 1948 and 1949, a period of emerging American farm surpluses.

But food shortages, hunger, and famine were not peculiar to Europe; food problems were endemic in Asia during this period. In 1943, crops had failed in India and thousands starved to death. Famine threatened India and Pakistan again in 1952. Civil war in China disrupted production and there was famine among the refugees. The Arab countries of the Near East were swamped with refugees from Israel. And all of these countries lacked the foreign exchange to buy food.

In the late 1940's, the food and hunger problem had become a world problem. The need for food around the world was both real and compelling, but there was no effective machinery for transfer-

---

[1] The generosity and niggardliness of the United States in dealing with the post-World War II food problems of Western Europe are explored in depth by Allen J. Matusow in *Farm Policies and Politics in the Truman Years* (Cambridge, Mass.: Harvard University Press, 1967), Chapter 7.

ring food from surplus-producing areas to deficit areas. At the same time, surpluses of food were beginning to accumulate in the United States; this was the case in the late 1940's before the Korean war and again in the early 1950's after the war.

How could we in the United States use the food we were producing beyond our commercial requirements at home and abroad to meet the needs of hungry people around the world without adversely affecting food production and commercial trade of other countries? The answer was found in the concept of "additionality." The United States developed and pursued the policy of shipping surplus foods to needy nations, provided those shipments did not displace normal commercial sales. The United States would give, or sell on easy terms, surplus foods to needy countries if they could show that this food was *in addition* to the food they regularly bought through commercial channels. The idea was embodied in Public Law 480, signed in 1954, which authorized the donation of food to international relief organizations and the sale of food to needy countries for the nonconvertible currency of those countries. In the operation of Public Law 480 programs, the United States has thus been "paid" for the food received in the nonconvertible currencies of the recipient countries. Some of this "soft currency" has been spent in the country of origin; for example, some of this money has been used by the United States in the recipient countries to cover the costs of maintenance of our embassies and military installations. But the bulk of it has either been loaned or given to the countries receiving food aid to carry out development projects, or held idle in those countries. A side effect of American food aid, as operated under Public Law 480, has been the buildup of large blocks of nonconvertible currencies, owned by the United States, in the recipient countries.

The volume of food shipped under Public Law 480 increased steadily from 1954 to 1961. During this period, the primary emphasis of the United States program was on getting rid of surplus stocks of food rather than on economic development. This is not to say that the United States program did not have a humanitarian motivation in making food available to millions of people around the world. However, the law clearly required that only commodities then in surplus supply could be shipped. As a result, when United States stocks were reduced to reasonable levels, offers to give, or sell, such products under Public Law 480 were withdrawn. This was the case periodically with such items as butter, dry-skim milk, cheese, and vegetable oils. Wheat continued in surplus throughout the period 1954–61 and generous quantities were made available around the world. Thus, Public Law 480 contained a legal framework for the international transfer of food supplies to food deficit countries, but the primary emphasis in the 1950's was on the elimination of domestic surpluses.

The basic attitude toward foreign food aid began to change in 1961. Both President Kennedy and Secretary of Agriculture Freeman believed strongly that food aid could be used to support economic development—whether specific projects or general economic development. This philosophy of using food aid to induce, or support, development gained strength in the Johnson Administration. And, as of 1968, the view was widely shared that food aid has a legitimate role to play in support of project development or general economic development.

Thus we see that the concept of foreign food aid has changed to an important degree over 50 years. Food aid was first conceived as a weapon of war; next it was viewed as a humanitarian gesture to starving people caught in the aftermath of war; next as a political weapon to minimize political unrest; then as a means of disposing of unwanted food surpluses; and now as a resource to be used in the support of economic development. The concept, food aid, too has *developed* since World War I.

As discussed above, the food aid program of the United States has since 1954 been carried out primarily under Public Law 480 (the Agricultural Trade Development and Assistance Act of 1954). During the period 1955–66, the original act was amended extensively to meet changing conditions. But in 1966 the food aid program was operated under four titles:

Title I, the heart of the original enactment, provides for the sale of U. S. agricultural commodities to friendly countries with payment in the currency of the recipient country.

Title II authorizes donations of farm products held in stock by the Commodity Credit Corporation (CCC) for famine and disaster relief, community development, school feeding, and other economic development purposes overseas.

Title III provides for the disposition of CCC-owned surplus

commodities to carry out two separate programs. They may be used (1) for domestic donation programs administered by appropriate federal, state, and local government agencies or by recognized voluntary, nonprofit, charitable and relief organizations, and (2) for foreign donations to needy peoples through American voluntary agencies and international organizations. The use of such commodities is also authorized for barter to obtain certain strategic materials, and for the procurement of off-shore goods and services.

Title IV provides for sales of commodities on credit for dollars. The dollar credit is repayable over an extended period at relatively modest interest rates. The purpose of this title is to assist developing countries which have reached an appropriate stage in the evolution of their economies to become dollar customers of the United States, while at the same time conserving their financial resources for use in the development process.

In 1966 the Congress extended the basic food aid legislation, Public Law 480 (PL 480), for another two years—or through 1968. The new program is built upon the old program, but it also has some new and distinct features.

There are six main elements to the new United States food aid strategy:[2]

Emphasis on self-help. The War on Hunger must be fought and won within the countries where hunger exists. Our food aid and other forms of assistance must go primarily to those who do the most to help themselves. The key to victory over hunger is self-help.

Policy for a non-surplus era. In the past, our food aid programs have been based on the existence of food surpluses in the United States. These surpluses are gone. Until the less-developed countries are able to provide for themselves, our domestic farm programs must be geared to ensure that we produce enough to meet pressing foreign needs as well as the demand here at home.

Population programs. Rapid population growth can make the dream of plenty a nightmare of famine. This is an enormous problem. It is clearly a matter for the conscience of each family and each nation.

[2] *Annual Report on Activities Carried Out Under Public Law 480, 83rd Congress, as Amended, During the Period January 1 through December 31, 1966,* The White House, Washington, D.C., November 6, 1967, p. 2.

We will never dictate an answer, nor intrude on the decision others must make for themselves. But many countries have voluntarily decided that the time has come to confront the population challenge. We stand ready to respond to the requests for help from these nations in formulating and carrying out effective programs.

Integration of all U.S. assistance programs. Relief from immediate suffering is only part of the War on Hunger. It gives precious time and strength for a larger task. The developing countries must use this time to gather the resources and skills to improve their agricultural production so that they can ultimately stand on their own feet. This is the goal of our technical and economic assistance. Clearly, our food aid must be closely related to these other forms of help in a single, carefully integrated approach to the entire food problem.

Increased private investment. There is no easy or simple answer to the scourge of poverty and hunger. No single program, no single plan, and no single government holds the key. We must marshal the sum of our experience. We must bring to bear more and more the capital and know-how of private enterprise—both in the United States and in the developing nations themselves.

A multi-national effort. The food deficit is a world problem. Developed nations must join in an international undertaking to combat hunger and modernize agriculture. The United States cannot shoulder this responsibility alone. In meeting the world's food needs, the common interest lies in common effort. In sum, we propose to enlist the very best talent—private and public, of all nations, rich and poor.

Whether these new features of the food aid programs of the United States will be emphasized and implemented remains to be seen. But if they are, those programs will have turned a sharp corner and started moving in a new direction. The disposal of agricultural surpluses held by the United States government, which dominated the food aid programs in the 1950's and early 1960's, is over. In its place has come the concept of using food aid to induce the developing countries to take actions required for their development—actions to increase their own food production and to support family planning efforts.

Further, food aid shipments under the 1966 law are no longer limited to "surplus products." The United States has pledged itself to provide food and fiber products needed by the developing countries which can be produced on surplus acres in the United States; it is also seeking to get other developed countries to increase their food aid efforts through both bilateral and multilateral efforts.[3] The food aid program of the United States shifted 180 degrees between 1960 and 1967; by 1967 it was no longer oriented toward surplus disposal but was moving instead in the direction of serving as a catalytic agent to induce development efforts on the part of the developing nations. Whether this is a short-term response to the elimination of heavy surpluses in the United States in the period 1965–67, or a long-term trend, remains to be seen. A return of food and fiber surpluses in the United States could bring to the fore once again the old surplus disposal philosophy.

But there are new and dramatic forces at work in food production in the developing world in 1968. The new, high-yielding varieties of rice, IR–8 and IR–5—developed at the International Rice Research Institute at Los Banos in the Philippines—are sweeping westward across South Asia, increasing yields by 50 to 100 percent. And the new, high-yielding varieties of wheat—first developed in Mexico and later adapted to Asian conditions—are sweeping eastward across West and South Asia, and again increasing yields by 50 to 100 percent. Similar developments are beginning to take place in the production of maize, sorghums, and millets. The impact of these developments, which in 1968 are at most only two years old, is causing observers of the Asian scene to speak of the food grain production revolution and the possibility of a worldwide grain surplus within five years.

Whether a world grain surplus materializes by 1973 remains to be seen, but certainly a revolution in food grain *production* is under way in Asia. And this production revolution has important implications for the food aid programs of the United States, which have had a product composition heavily weighted by wheat and other grains. The potential new role of PL 480 food shipments to an important recipient country like India is already being discussed.

---

[3] This, for example, was an important feature of the grains agreement negotiated in the Kennedy Round negotiations under the GATT at Geneva, Switzerland, in May 1967. See *International Grains Arrangement 1967*, FAS, USDA, FAS-M-195 (November 1967), pp. 41–45.

The government of India can now look forward with some degree of realism to the time when it will no longer be dependent on the United States for 6 to 8 million tons of grain annually under PL 480. It can foresee the possibility of limiting imports of grain to two kinds of uses: (1) the avoidance of famine in a really bad crop year, and (2) the rebuilding of stabilization stocks following a bad crop year.

Whether the United States can or will hold the reserve grain stocks for the developing world, releasing them only to meet unforeseen contingencies and shortages arising out of adverse weather and crop disease epidemics, is open to conjecture. But this, indeed, would be another new role for the United States and a costly one. In this role the United States would produce a grain surplus *purposely*, and carry the surplus as insurance against crop failure in some part of the developing world.

The World Food Program

The World Food Program was established by the United Nations and the Food and Agricultural Organization during the winter of 1961–62; it is difficult to say which of the numerous resolutions of these two bodies made the program a reality.[4] The World Food Program is thus a joint organ of the United Nations and of the Food and Agriculture Organization and reports to both of them. This unusual administrative relationship reflects the strong interest of both of these organizations in the major aim of the program, which is to stimulate economic and social development through economic aid in the form of food. The resources of the program are derived from voluntary contributions in commodities, services, and cash, pledged by members of the United Nations and members and associated members of FAO. The program was authorized in 1962 to aim at securing contributions of $100 million from these sources, with a cash component equal to one-third of the total. This budget carried the World Food Program through 1965,

---

[4] A fuller discussion of the World Food Program may be found in the *Report on the World Food Program by the Executive Director*, United Nations and Food and Agricultural Organization of the U.N. (Rome, 1965); and in *World Food Program*, Report of the Thirteenth Session of the United Nations, FAO Intergovernmental Committee, WFP/IGC: 13/21 (May 1968).

at which time the program was renewed for three years covering 1966, 1967, and 1968.

A goal of $275 million was established for the new program for the three-year period, made up of contributions of commodities, cash, or services. The United States agreed to match with commodities the equivalent value of contributions by all other countries. But by May 1968 pledges to the program had reached a total of only $186.8 million, of which food commodity contributions amounted to $126.2 million, services to $24.4 million, and cash to $36.2 million. The program has again been extended; this time through 1970. The budgetary target for this two-year period has been set at $200 million and in May 1968 pledges had reached a total of $129.1 million. Thus we see that the World Food Program is a going concern, but obtaining adequate financial support is extremely difficult.

With these kinds of resources, the program has sought a constructive approach to the world food problem, although certainly not a total solution to it, because of the program's limited size. Taking the view that the basic cause of undernourishment and hunger around the world is poverty, for which long-term economic development is the ultimate solution, and bearing in mind the need to develop a constructive approach to the problem, the primary purpose of the program has been to use food stocks in ways that promote the economic and social development of the recipient countries. The program is also expected to deal with food needs arising out of emergencies, and to assist social groups requiring extra care for reasons of particular vulnerability (for example, nursing mothers and infants). Its central objective, however, is that of eliminating the conditions which make food aid necessary; *its central purpose is thus to encourage development rather than to provide charitable relief.*

The World Food Program is essentially multilateral. Its resources are provided by many countries, and the pledged commodities can be supplied to any country which is a member of the U.N. or a member or associate member of FAO. Food supplies, as well as cash and services, which are contributed to the program are pooled: a donor country cannot require that its contribution be earmarked for a specific country. The program is also multilateral in that there is no direct contact between a donor and recipient country: the execution of the program is entrusted to an international secretariat.

Projects involving the use of food to induce and support economic development are extremely diverse, but program officials classify such projects under four broad headings: settlement projects, livestock projects, labor-intensive projects, and school-feeding projects. A brief description of a project or two under each of these categories is given below to illustrate the use of food aid in a development context.[5]

The earliest of World Food Program-aided projects is that for the resettlement of the people of Wadi-Halfa in Sudan, who have been displaced by the rising waters of the High Dam at Aswan. The 50,000 persons involved are being moved 1,300 kilometers upstream to Khashm-el-Girba where land is being brought under cultivation with irrigation from a local dam constructed for this settlement. Between January and mid-September 1964, 32,000 people moved with their 15,000 head of livestock and arrived at Khashm-el-Girba. The World Food Program contribution is about $1.6 million, as compared to $71.8 million invested by the Sudanese Government. New villages have been laid out, and government services in the fields of health and education, including agricultural extension, have been made available. Arrangements have been made for mixed farming and for the cultivation of both food and commercial crops. The World Food Program supplies, as in the case of all settlement projects, are expected to tide over the period of transition until the settlers can become self-supporting. Current progress suggests that this huge operation will run according to schedule.

• • •

Increase of milk production is to be doubly desired in most developing countries: it contributes to a much needed improvement in the people's nutritional status and, by encouraging mixed farming, improves land management and increases farm incomes. Among the soundest of the World Food Program projects aimed to achieve these advantages is the one at Anand in India, where coarse grains are being supplied for the preparation of a compounded feed con-

[5] Reprinted from the *Report on the World Food Program by the Executive Director*, pp. 32, 35, 36, and 38–39.

taining a mixture of local ingredients. The mixing plant where the feed is to be made represents an investment of $2.5 million; the value of World Food Program aid is $1.2 million. The machinery and the technical supervision it calls for have been made available by the generosity of the Oxford Committee for Famine Relief under the auspices of the Freedom from Hunger Campaign. The project is thus one of many examples of the way in which multilateral aid in food may be combined with other forms of foreign assistance to make a viable undertaking. The assurance of success in this case lies in the fact the enterprise is run by one of the best organized milk co-operatives, which is promoting an extension program among its members as well as selling the feed mixture to them, so that locally-produced feed grains may take the place of World Food Program supplies by the time World Food Program aid comes to an end.

• • •

Labor-intensive projects offer classic conditions under which food can be made available for mobilizing unutilized labor in undertaking environmental improvements of long-term productive significance. Of the many projects in this category now under way, mention may first be made of those for afforestation and watershed protection in Turkey. In one case, the planting of quick-growing species of trees (a task calling for 1.4 million man-days of labor) will promote the conservation of soil and water, and will augment the natural resources of the country in the long run. The World Food Program contribution of less than $1 million is accompanied by about $7.5 million of Government investment. The second project in this category is primarily designed to protect the Kizilcahamam watershed in Turkey by control of water in the tributaries of the Kirmir river. The activities to be aided in this project are all part of the rehabilitation operation in which afforestation and road construction play the most notable part. One hundred kilometers of new hillside roads are to be built, and although afforestation is long-term investment, the returns of the project in terms of the other collateral activities to the 19,000 villagers, of whom many work on it in the off-season, seem almost immediate.

• • •

Of the four principal categories of World Food Program-aided projects, that for the feeding of school students and other trainees presents the least number of apparent complexities. The food supplied is generally served by an institution in cooked form for immediate consumption, an arrangement which admits the least possibility of its misapplication or misuse. Controlled conditions also make it possible to assess with considerable accuracy the impact of the food on the direct beneficiaries, if not upon a wider circle. At the same time, food aid in this field can be recognized as providing support to a basic ingredient of social advance, no less than of material improvement. Poor diets are supplemented and nutritional habits reformed in age groups where these advantages have a powerful effect. School attendance is improved, while support to middle-grade education and technical training schemes assists in the formation of a body of supervisory and skilled personnel whose availability is crucial to the process of development as it is presently shaping in many countries.

A project of this type in Mauritania exemplifies the emphasis given to secondary education: World Food Program aid of $380,000 will permit a significant increase of enrollment at this level with an additional cost to the authorities of only $65,000. One good result of this project, which is receiving useful support from the FAO expert in the country, is to introduce the desirable habit of fish-eating to a people previously unaccustomed to it, although there are potential sources of local supplies, and fisheries and fish-processing industries have been recently established.

The World Food Program also has at its disposal a pool of food-stuffs from which aid can be given promptly in cases of natural disasters and special emergencies. Emergencies for which such aid has been given include shortages of food supplies arising from unforeseen or uncontrollable causes, such as earthquakes, floods, and droughts, as well as refugee migration. The World Food Program cannot, on the other hand, be regarded as a means of relieving conditions of scarcity which are not the result of unforeseen disasters. The policy position of the program is that chronic undernourishment and malnutrition can be overcome only by economic development in general and by agricultural development in particular.

Experience with the World Food Program in its first years of operation have been good. It has demonstrated that food aid can be used to support certain kinds of developmental projects, if those projects are well conceived. It has demonstrated also that a multilateral approach is acceptable in many situations where a bilateral approach is not. But for reasons of national and international political aspirations, there has not been a willingness to expand the

World Food Program beyond an essentially pilot project level. The funding of a multilateral food aid program commensurate with the size of the world food problem is not easily achieved.

Food Aid Programs: The Magnitudes

Food aid by the United States has been and continues to be big business.[6] Agricultural exports under Public Law 480 for the period 1954–67 amounted to $17.2 billion, and throughout the mid-1960's agricultural exports under PL 480 averaged about $1.5 billion per year (see Table 7.1). The largest share of these exports was shipped under Title I, sales for foreign currency; nearly $11.0 billion worth of agricultural products was shipped under this title during the period 1954–67.

The principal recipient countries have been: India, Pakistan, UAR, Yugoslavia, and Brazil. All of these countries had received under Title I agricultural products valued at more than $500 million by December 31, 1967, and India had received products in excess of $3.3 billion. Most of these countries received food assistance from the United States under the other three titles of PL 480 as well.

In summary, Public Law 480 has supplied food aid to 116 countries, containing about one-half of the world's population. It has prevented mass starvation in India. It has improved the diets of more than 40 million of the world's schoolchildren. It has helped some countries to achieve truly outstanding records of development —Taiwan, Israel, and South Korea, for example. And the United States has "earned" billions of dollars of foreign nonconvertible currencies from Title I sales of farm products, which have been used: (1) to pay for the expenses of the United States government in those countries (e.g., embassy costs, military costs), (2) to lend to the countries involved to support development projects, (3) to support market development projects in those countries (i.e., to promote the sale of U.S. farm products in those countries), and (4) to support many other activities, including research and education.

---

[6] For a detailed description of the food aid program of the United States see the annual publication, *Annual Report on Activities Carried Out Under Public Law 480, 83rd Congress* . . . , currently issued by The White House, Washington, D.C.

TABLE 7.1

Value of U. S. Farm Products Shipped Under Public Law 480, Compared with Total Exports of U. S. Farm Products, July 1, 1954, through December 31, 1967[1]

(In millions of dollars)

| Calendar Year | PUBLIC LAW 480 | | | | | | Commercial Sales[2] | Total Agricultural Exports | PL 480 as Percent of Total |
	Sales for Foreign Currency	Long-term Dollar Credit Sales	Government Donations for Disaster Relief and Economic Development	Donations through Voluntary Relief Agencies	Barter	Total PL 480			
July–December 1954	—	—	28	20	22	70	1,304	1,585	5
1955	263	—	56	186	262	767	2,081	3,199	24
1956	638	—	65	187	372	1,262	2,459	4,170	30
1957	760	—	39	175	244	1,218	2,970	4,506	27
1958	752	—	43	159	65	1,019	2,622	3,855	26
1959	731	—	32	111	175	1,049	2,748	3,955	27
1960	1,014	—	49	124	117	1,304	3,371	4,832	27
1961	878	1	93	151	181	1,304	3,541	5,024	26
1962	1,007	42	81	178	137	1,445	3,554	5,034	29
1963	1,162	52	99	160	74	1,547	4,026	5,584	28
1964	1,239	97	62	186	123	1,707	4,618	6,348	27
1965	926	143	73	180	188	1,510	4,693	6,229	25
1966	820	226	79	132	260	1,517	5,317	6,881	22
1967	716	187	108	179	314	1,504	4,849	6,386	24
July 1, 1954, through December 31, 1967	10,906	748	907	2,128	2,534	17,223	48,153	67,588[3]	25

[1] Export market value.
[2] Commercial sales for dollars include, in addition to unassisted commercial transactions, shipments of some commodities with governmental assistance in the form of short- and medium-term credit, export payments, and sales of government-owned commodities at less than domestic market prices.
[3] Columns 6 and 7 do not add up to the total, since food aid provided under mutual security programs is not included in this table, but in the 1960's this has been a minor amount.

SOURCE: *Annual Report on Activities Carried Out Under Public Law 480, 83rd Congress, as Amended, During the Period January 1 through December 31, 1967*, The White House, Washington, D.C., April 3, 1968, Appendix, Table 1.

135

But all has not been success either. The United States holds in the recipient countries millions and millions of dollars' worth of nonconvertible currencies which it cannot use and which, if it did, would lead to serious inflationary pressures in the countries involved. Food aid has not always been used in ways that contribute to development; the pressure of surplus disposal has caused food aid to be substituted for development in some cases. And in some cases food assistance from the United States may have delayed, or slowed down, national programs of agricultural development.

Food aid has indeed been big business for the United States. Where wisely used, it has made a significant contribution to the solution of the world food problem. But it has too often been pushed as a means of surplus disposal rather than a resource for development.

Impact of Public Law 480 Shipments on Selected Recipient Countries[7]

Israel

Israel was the largest recipient of PL 480 commodities on a per capita basis in the early years of the program; the average value of product per person was $81 over the period 1954–61. These relatively large imports of PL 480 commodities did not, however, discourage domestic production; in fact, domestic agricultural production increased under their impact. This was the case for at least two reasons. First, the Israeli government used these PL 480 imports to moderate a price inflation as it decontrolled food prices and rationing; in this context legal prices rose, black market prices fell, and since nearly all production at the farm was paid for at legal prices, the net result was an increase in real prices to farmers. Second, imports of feed grains provided the base for an expansion in livestock production, particularly poultry. Thus, it is generally concluded that food aid under PL 480 made a significant contribution to expanded food production and economic development in Israel

[7] For a good discussion of PL 480 in operation see the article, "Development through Food Grants and Concessional Sales," by Lawrence W. Witt, in Carl Eicher and Lawrence Witt (eds.), *Agriculture in Economic Development* (New York: McGraw-Hill Book Co., Inc., 1964).

in the late 1950's and early 1960's. As one observer has said, for Israel, food aid under Title I "has been almost as good as free dollars."[8]

In sum, Israel used food products received under PL 480 as a productive resource in development. With this food aid Israel was able to take economic policy actions which contributed to overall economic development, including the expansion of agricultural production, particularly livestock.

India

While Israel has had the largest PL 480 program on a per capita basis to date, India has received the largest total volume of PL 480 shipments—about 30 percent of all Title I shipments. But it is much more difficult to evaluate the impact of this volume of food aid on the development of the Indian economy than in the case of Israel; the assessments vary widely, in fact. But our evaluation is as follows.

First, PL 480 shipments have been integrated into the national development plans of India; they have been used as a resource in the implementation of successive Five-Year Plans. It may be argued that these plans were overoptimistic or wrongly formulated, but it cannot be argued that food aid has not been made an operational part of each plan. Second, total food consumption in the short run has increased as a result of PL 480 imports, because farm prices have never declined sufficiently either absolutely or relatively, as the direct result of these imports to induce a reduction in production equal to, or anywhere near, the volume of PL 480 imports.[9] Although it is true that the government of India has for political reasons pursued food requisitioning and pricing policies that have had a negative effect on agricultural production, it is not true that PL 480 shipments have sufficiently depressed farm prices, hence production, to bring about a reduction in the total supply of food available to consumers. Third, PL 480 shipments to India have for

---

[8] A. E. Kahn, "Agricultural Aid and Economic Development," *Quarterly Journal of Economics*, Vol. LXXVI (November 1962), p. 591.

[9] See the analysis and estimates of Jitendar S. Mann in his article, "The Impact of Public Law 480 Imports on Prices and Domestic Supply of Cereals in India," *Journal of Farm Economics*, Vol. 49, No. 1 (February 1967).

extended periods of time saved millions of persons from serious undernourishment, starvation, and death. Fourth, it is probably true that the assurance of continued food assistance from the United States has permitted Indian planners and political leaders to postpone needed investments and to pursue pricing policies that have in turn slowed down the process of agricultural development in India. In other words, India has in the past pursued a development policy that could not be sustained without a continuous and large-scale inflow of food aid for many years to come. But, fifth, it is possible that, with wise investment, marketing, and pricing policies in agriculture over the decade 1965–75, overall economic development in India will be much more advanced as the result of the food aid received than it would be without that aid.

There are political considerations too. In the view of this writer, India would not have survived until 1968 as an open society with viable democratic institutions without the great transfer of food to India that has taken place on a concessional basis. Food riots, political unrest, and communistic activity were likely to have toppled the government of India long before this. And if India does survive as an open society with strong democratic institutions to the year 2000, with all the stresses and strains that threaten to tear it apart, one important reason for that survival will be the large food aid program from the United States, which lessened the great and continuous threat of too little food.

Tunisia

In the late 1950's Tunisia became a model for using food products, received as food aid, as wage payments in work relief projects. Wheat received by Tunisia under Title II was used to pay workers employed on agriculturally related projects concerned with water conservation, tree planting, road repairs, and forest management. As many as 200,000 workers were employed on such projects in 1961. Workers were paid a wage that amounted to about 70 cents per day, of which one-third was paid in cash and two-thirds in wheat.

From the Tunisian viewpoint, this work-project type of program was considered highly successful. Americans involved in the program were also pleased with results at the time, although there is some question now whether all of the projects were as well planned as they should have been. But on balance, the Tunisian experience suggests that well-designed projects with good administration can use food effectively, as part of the wage payment, in work projects.

Latin American Countries

Generally speaking, food aid programs in Latin America have not made a contribution to the development of the countries involved. Food shipments under various titles of PL 480 have typically been used to cope with emergencies (e.g., earthquakes) or to substitute for an inadequate agricultural development. In other words, food aid from the United States has most often been used to feed hungry people—hungry as the result of natural catastrophe, or because agricultural production failed to keep pace with expanding populations and expanding demand. This is not to argue that it is wrong to feed hungry people, but to point out that food aid in Latin America has not made a significant contribution to the increased productivity of the countries involved. In Latin America there has been a strong tendency to substitute food aid for development.

Potentialities and Limitations

Food aid can be used in four principal ways with beneficial results —that is, where the advantages clearly outweigh the disadvantages.

First, to feed the hungry in areas of extreme food shortage resulting from crop failure, war and its aftermath, and catastrophes such as earthquakes and fires. In situations such as these where people would starve unless they received food, it is obviously advantageous to provide that assistance.

Second, to provide lunches to schoolchildren and pre-schoolchildren in poverty areas where undernourishment and malnutrition among children is commonplace. If children are to grow into productive and creative adults, they must have nutritious diets. Thus, a feeding program that can give nutritious lunches to children, who would otherwise experience undernourishment, malnutrition, and even hunger, must be good.

Third, to serve as payment in kind to workers employed on

specific development projects, for example, road building, land clearing, ditch digging and repairing, and the building of simple structures. Roads and water management are essential elements of agricultural development, and programs which can produce these elements without curtailing the production of other needed goods and services are desirable. Thus, where food can be used as a wage-good to pay workers to produce roads and ditches, the development process has been abetted, and the program must be viewed as desirable.

Fourth, to substitute for commercial imports of food called for in a national development plan, thus releasing scarce foreign exchange for the importation of other producer, or incentive, goods called for in the plan. In this case food aid constitutes an additional resource, which is made an integral part of the total development plan, and serves to move the development of the economy forward at a more rapid rate than otherwise would be the case.

In each of these four uses of food aid someone or something is saved that would otherwise be lost, or something is produced or constructed that otherwise would not have come into being. And since a third party has not been hurt as the result of these programs, nor the supply of some other good reduced by an equal amount, these uses of food aid must be judged as advantageous.

All developing countries cannot, of course, make equally effective use of these four forms of food aid. A country that is not experiencing a disaster, or an emergency, has no need for the first type. A country with a reasonably adequate food supply can provide its own school lunch program. A country lacking in the skills of economic planning and the execution of development projects cannot make effective use of the third type. And a country that does not rely on a national development plan cannot use the fourth.

But a country that is suffering from a crop failure, or is desperately short of food, will probably require food aid of the first two forms to avoid suffering among its peoples. And a country that can plan effectively and execute its plans with verve will speed up its development process through the third and fourth forms of food aid. So food aid, appropriately used, does have an important role to play in the development process and in coping with food problems.

Food aid can have detrimental effects to a recipient country in at least three situations.

First, food aid imports that act to depress farm prices in the recipient country, and thereby reduce farmers' incentives to expand production, can hardly be judged to be desirable. Obviously, where food aid imports induce, first, a price decline and, second, a negative production response to that decline which then reduces the total available food supply, the food aid program must be judged injurious to the country. The issue is less clear, however, where food aid imports are employed to moderate a price inflation. This may or may not have harmful consequences, depending on a number of considerations: the original terms of trade between agriculture and nonagriculture, the magnitude of the inflation, the consequences of the inflation in terms of political stability, balance of payments, and so on.

Second, food aid imports that substitute for commercial food imports—thereby releasing foreign exchange for the importation of consumer goods that do not contribute to development—are difficult to justify. Released foreign exchange which is used to purchase and import such items as big black Cadillacs for the use of high government officials is not likely to contribute to the development process.

Third, food aid imports which permit responsible officials to put off decisions to modernize and thereby increase the productivity of their domestic agriculture can lead to a false sense of security and possibly to economic disaster. A development process underpinned by food aid, rather than by commercial trade or a developing agriculture, will certainly encounter trouble and possibly disaster with a termination of that food aid. The increased food production required by the developing economy will not have come into being; hence the food requirements cannot be met by an increased food production capacity developed within the country. In this case, food aid will have permitted the country to live in a fool's paradise.

The discussion above does not suggest that foreign food aid must lead to an unbalanced development or inhibit development. It does suggest, however, that food aid can tempt decision makers to take the easy route to alleviating immediate food problems. Thus, both the recipient country and the donor country must be on their guard against this aspect of food aid; food aid properly used can save lives and governments, but there is always the danger that, like a drug, it will become habit-forming and ultimately debilitating.

Some Administrative Questions

Certain questions about the effective or wise administration of foreign food aid continue to arise and be debated. Four such questions are:

1. What time span is desirable for a food aid commitment: three months or three years?
2. How should food aid programs be conducted—on a bilateral basis between national governments, or by an international agency, or a private charitable agency?
3. Should food aid be provided free within the recipient country, or should it be sold?
4. How can the principle of additionality in food aid shipments be realized in practice?

These questions continue to be debated because each has more than one side to it. No single administrative rule provides a satisfactory solution to each question in every situation. Good administration with respect to each question varies with the situation.

What time span is desirable for a food aid commitment? A food aid program capable of meeting an emergency must obviously be geared to the length of run of that emergency. A food aid program to deal with an earthquake might have a legitimate duration of one to three months. But a program designed to cope with a crop failure would probably have to run one year, possibly a year and a half.

On the other hand, food aid programs designed to mesh with development projects or development plans might properly run two to five years. A country that is really trying to integrate food aid, as a productive resource, into a five-year development plan needs a five-year food aid commitment. But even here there can be no hard and fast rule. It may be wise administrative policy to limit food aid commitments to, say, six months, if the donor country has reason to believe that the recipient country is importing nonproductive goods with the foreign exchange released by its receipt of food aid.

Further, putting the negotiation of a food aid contract on an annual basis may contribute to the achievement of certain development objectives within the recipient country (e.g., the creation of reserve stocks or the establishment of fertilizer factories). Or it could mean irresponsibility on the part of the donor country in limiting its food aid commitment to its available disposable surplus.

In a rational world, food aid in support of a long-term development plan should be long term in duration; effective planning dictates such a conclusion. But in the emotional, often irrational world in which we live, prudent administration may dictate short-term food aid commitments.

How should food aid programs be conducted? Without question, most private charitable agencies have done an excellent job in child-feeding and school lunch programs. They have the interest and the know-how to conduct these kinds of food aid programs. But they lack the interest, the know-how, and the financial resources to engage in food aid programs designed to fit into, and hence contribute to, the national development plan of a country. An international agency is better equipped to cope with the economic considerations of such a task. And international agencies have the advantage of being able to move into politically sensitive situations where individual national governments are not welcome. Thus, international agencies are playing an increasingly effective role in providing food aid.

But even international agencies find it difficult to raise the financial resources to support really large-scale food aid programs. National governments rarely give economic assistance, including food assistance, to an ally, former enemy, or developing nation without expecting something in return—perhaps air bases, perhaps a partially convertible currency, perhaps at least a neutral position in world politics. Thus, large-scale foreign assistance, including food assistance, usually entails some *quid pro quo* on the part of the recipient country; if the *quid pro quo* is not forthcoming, the assistance is not forthcoming. In other words, donor countries are willing to make food assistance available on a large scale only when they maintain control over the granting process, hence over what they hope to receive in return. In this last instance, administrative policy generally becomes subservient to the national aims and objectives of individual countries.

Should food aid be provided free within the recipient country?
Food that is given free of charge to a charitable agency is usually
distributed free of charge, or at an extremely low price that covers
only the distribution costs, under school lunch and child welfare
programs in developing countries. And most would agree that this
is as it should be.

But a country that is integrating a food aid program into its development plan—and is using the food so received as an additional
resource—cannot conveniently give that food away. First, the developing country typically "pays" the donor country in its own currency, which is a cost to the government in terms of its budget even
though its currency is nonconvertible, or only partially convertible.
Second, the food resource is commingled with all other foods
and deployed through the regular distribution system; hence it is
impractical to consider giving it away while similar foods alongside
it are being sold. In this situation, the food resource is "purchased"
by the government and sold to consumers like other units of food;
it simply constitutes an additional resource to be used and consumed in the regular operation of the economy. But as an additional resource it may serve to moderate an inflationary spiral or
enlarge the food supply available to workers and thereby contribute
to an increase in their real income.

Thus, whether the food received by a recipient country under a
food aid program should be given away free or is sold depends upon
the conditions under which it is received and under which it is used.
Food that is received and handled outside the regular channels of
commercial trade, as in the case of child-feeding programs, should
be, and typically is, distributed free of charge. But food that is received and handled within the regular commercial channels of
trade, although purchased perhaps on long-term credit or nonconvertible currency, typically is, and should be, sold to consumers. It
is important to recognize that most food received by countries
through aid programs does not come to them free of charge; typically it comes under some form of concessional sale, and therefore
at some cost to the recipient country.

*How can the principle of additionality in food aid shipments be
realized?* This question has given rise to much sharp debate in international trade circles. In fact, an international consultative com-

mittee with a membership drawn primarily from the leading agricultural export nations was established in Washington to consult on these matters, following the adoption of the PL 480 export program.

As a matter of practice, each PL 480 agreement worked out and signed with a recipient country has defined, on the basis of historical experience, the volume of commercial imports that is *normal* for the commodities affected by the agreement, with the understanding that the recipient country would not reduce its commercial imports below the defined normal levels. But such agreements, of course, were worked out between an importer and exporter, each of which had a strong interest in, first, reaching an agreement and, second, making the commodity amounts as large as possible. Further, it should be recognized that after an agreement is a year or two old and the recipient country has undergone some development, it becomes increasingly difficult to say what were normal commercial imports and what constitutes an addition to normal commercial imports. These points were argued over long and hard in the Washington consultative committee, with some give and take on both sides.

Operational experience with these food aid programs suggests that PL 480 shipments substituted for commercial imports by 25 to 30 percent in the typical situation, but in a few unhappy cases the substitution rate reached 50 percent. Stated differently, PL 480 shipments generally have been in addition to normal commercial imports by some 70 to 75 percent. But these are "iffy" estimates based on operational experience rather than rigorous studies in which the influence of important variables is held constant.

In retrospect, it can be said that an effort was made to see that PL 480 shipments were in addition to normal commercial imports. But the negotiators were biased in favor of the agreements, and historical trends were quickly outmoded as useful guides to what constituted normal commercial trade. Thus, it seems likely that PL 480 shipments substituted to an important degree for commercial imports; but solid estimates of the degree of substitution involved do not exist. Future agreements must therefore be based upon current analysis, negotiation, and consultation. There does not seem to be a more exact process.

Implications for the World Food Problem

It was fashionable in the 1950's among professional internationalists, economists, and diplomats to look upon food aid as a dirty practice engaged in by the United States to unload its burdensome farm surpluses. In the early 1960's food aid gained a high degree of respectability, due largely to (1) the establishment of the World Food Program under the auspices of the U.N. and FAO, (2) tightening food supplies around the world after a series of poor-to-bad crops in China, the Soviet Union, and India, and (3) the increasing difficulty of obtaining general economic assistance funds from the Congress of the United States. But in the late 1960's it has again become fashionable to deprecate food aid by arguing that food aid programs *alone* cannot solve the world food problem and that the real solutions must take the form of population control through family planning *and* more rapid agricultural development.

It certainly is true that food aid alone cannot cope with the world food problem. But very few thoughtful observers of the world scene have ever suggested that it could; a few overoptimistic American farm politicians may have suggested it as the sole solution, but not many others. What proponents of food aid have argued is as follows. First, food can and should be used in emergencies to alleviate starvation and save lives. In emergency situations of critically short food supply there is no substitute for food aid. Second, food can be used as a resource in economic development to achieve a more rapid rate of development than would otherwise occur. The provision of free dollars might be a more efficient form of economic assistance, and food supplies received as economic assistance may not always have been used wisely in the development process. (But then, for that matter, free dollars received as assistance have not always been used wisely by developing countries.) But food is a resource, and it can be used effectively in certain situations to speed development.

Third, when a nation such as the United States has surplus food stocks on hand, it should use those food stocks in food aid programs to alleviate undernourishment, hunger, and starvation and to facilitate economic development. Fourth, the United States as the leader of the free world should maintain a generous strategic reserve of food and fiber, and undertake the production necessary to maintain that reserve from which it would operate bilateral food aid programs and contribute to the World Food Program of the U.N. and FAO.

In other words, most proponents of food aid are not suggesting that it is the sole solution to the world food problem. But they do argue that it has an important role to play in the total solution. It can save lives in starving times, when the peoples involved cannot survive until the economy has developed further, or even until the next crop is harvested. And it can be used as a resource to support workers as they shift from low-productivity jobs in farming to higher-productivity jobs in the construction of irrigation works, or in bicycle shops, or as brick producers and layers. The expanded and more productive economy can then either produce more food domestically or purchase it from abroad. A "food surplus" in existence somewhere, which can be used to support workers as they leave farming and take up more productive nonfarm jobs, is a prerequisite of the development process. Sometimes that "food surplus" can be purchased commercially from abroad to keep the development process moving; England and Western Europe did this during the nineteenth century. Food aid can play a comparable role for the densely populated developing countries in the twentieth century, and it can support a more rapid rate of development than would otherwise be possible.

The question might be asked: How does the support of a development process involving the transfer of workers from low-productivity jobs in farming to higher-productivity nonfarm jobs contribute to the solution of the food problem of such countries? It might be suggested that such a process actually intensifies the problem by drawing workers out of agriculture. The answer to this question runs somewhat as follows. First, by definition and in fact, the workers transferring out of agriculture were producing very little in agriculture, and have shifted into jobs that are more productive than their old jobs. Although those workers are no longer producing food, they are producing something that is worth more to society than the farm product they had been producing. Thus, they are in the position of having something more valuable to exchange for food produced elsewhere than the value of their old product from farming. So they can acquire more consumer goods, including more food, than they could in their old jobs. Since they now produce more, they can now consume more. This is the argument for the individual worker.

Second, we will recall that transforming a traditional agriculture into a modern, scientific agriculture requires the production of increased amounts of producer goods, such as machinery, fertilizer, insecticides, and improved seeds, as well as transportation, storage, and processing services in the nonfarm sector for use in, and distribution to, the farm sector. The farming operation cannot become more productive unless these producer goods and services are made available to it. And they cannot be made available to the farm sector unless the nonfarm sector is undergoing the development which enables it to produce such goods and services. Thus, agricultural development and increased food production are dependent upon general economic development. A food aid program that contributes to and supports general economic development and the production of the producer goods required by a modernized agriculture thus contributes to increased agricultural productivity and to the increased availability of food.

It should be recognized, however, that food aid is often a less efficient means of supporting economic development than general economic aid (i.e., free dollars), for a number of reasons. The developing country may not be short on the resource of food; hence this form of specialized assistance is not useful. Food aid is a specialized resource, which can be used only in specific ways at specified times; hence it may force the economy into a form of development that is not of the highest priority. Finally, there is always the danger that food aid will in one way or another dampen the motivation to modernize the agricultural plant.

So we conclude that food aid can be used to buy time in the development process, but it is not always the most efficient means of doing so. Wisely used in certain situations, food aid can hasten development, but it is easy to use it unwisely and in the wrong kinds of situations. Food aid should thus be given generously to assist populations through critical periods of short supply, be used judiciously in support of development projects and plans, and be withheld or withdrawn where it is used to substitute for rather than promote economic development.

8

Economic and Technical Assistance

FOREIGN ECONOMIC ASSISTANCE is concerned with the provision of additional productive resources, or the financial means to obtain those resources, by the developed countries to the less developed countries on some kind of concessional basis—perhaps outright grants, perhaps on a long-term basis at favorable rates of interest, perhaps programs of technical assistance free of charge. Whether the additional resources supplied to a developing country are profitably employed depends upon a host of things: whether the resources are really needed; whether they are integrated into a rational development plan or productive project; whether the skilled manpower is available in the country to assure their effective use; and so on. In short, foreign economic assistance can greatly speed the development process, *if* the resources transferred to the developing country are effectively employed. But it is a fact that such resources often are not employed effectively, or as effectively as they could be.

Thus, the answer to the question: "How much economic assistance should be provided to the developing countries in the future?" is not to cut it off completely, or to provide it lavishly. Foreign economic assistance to a particular developing country must be tailored to the absorptive capacity of that country in terms of total assistance and the forms of that assistance.

But it must be remembered that a given country's capacity to absorb foreign aid is not an absolute; it varies with the skill and wisdom with which the assistance is provided and the sector of the

149

economy receiving the aid. It is relatively easy, for example, to transplant a steel mill down to the last bolt and have it in production soon after the last bolt is put in place (the wisdom of erecting a steel mill may, however, be highly questionable). But expanding the use of a technology, such as fertilizer, in the agriculture of an economically underdeveloped country is another matter. First, the use and benefits of fertilizer must be demonstrated to hundreds or thousands of peasants. Second, an organization must be developed to distribute that fertilizer. Third, new plant varieties will probably have to be made available to make efficient and economical use of the fertilizer; and so on. The capacity of traditional agricultural societies to absorb new technologies quickly is deceptively limited. Great wisdom and staying power must be the prerequisites of the nations, and their agencies, that take on the job of assisting developing countries to modernize their agricultural plants.

Size and Distribution of the Total Assistance Effort[1]

The total flow of government grants, loans, and private capital from the 15 member countries of the Development Assistance Committee (DAC) to the less developed countries and multilateral agencies in 1967 exceeded $11.3 billion.[2] The total net flow of loans, grants, and private capital to the less developed countries and to the multilateral agencies from the 15 DAC countries for the period 1960–67 amounted to some $76 billion.

Government bilateral programs of the DAC member countries have constituted the largest share of the flow of financial assistance to the less developed countries in the mid-1960's, ranging from $5.5 billion in 1964 to $6.2 billion in 1967 (see Table 8.1). However, governmental bilateral flows increased in a steady progression over

[1] Most of the data presented in this section are taken from three publications of the Organization for Economic Co-operation and Development (OECD): *Development Assistance Efforts and Policies, 1967 Review* (September 1967), pp. 13–15 and 33–70; *The OECD Observer* (February 1967), pp. 27–29; and *OECD Press Release*, Press/A(68) 34, Paris, July 4, 1968.

[2] The 15 member countries are Australia, Austria, Belgium, Canada, Denmark, France, Germany, Italy, Japan, the Netherlands, Norway, Portugal, Sweden, the United Kingdom, and the United States.

TABLE 8.1

The Total Flow of Financial Resources from DAC Members to the Less Developed Countries, 1964–67

(In millions of U. S. dollars)

	1964	1965	1966	1967
Total Government, Net[1]	5,855	6,202	6,506	6,970[2]
Bilateral	5,476	5,753	5,970	6,200[2]
To multilateral agencies	379	449	536	770[2]
Total Private, Net[1]	3,285	4,227	4,056	4,390[2]
Bilateral	3,147	3,980	4,028	4,110[2]
To multilateral agencies	138	248	28	280[2]
Total Government and Private	9,140	10,429	10,562	11,360[2]

[1]Gross disbursements minus repayments on earlier lending.
[2]Preliminary
SOURCE: *OECD Press Release,* Press/A(68) 34, Paris, July 4, 1968, p. 3.

the period 1964–67; the largest variations in the flow of economic aid occurred in the private sector. Total private capital flows increased from $3.3 billion in 1964 to $4.2 billion in 1965 and then dropped off modestly in 1966. Within this total private flow, the largest share has been provided by the United States, and the fluctuations in the total private flow have been brought about by fluctuations in the amount supplied by the United States.

Looking at a slightly different span of years, 1960–65, for which a country breakdown is available, the 15 DAC countries provided a bilateral flow of financial resources to the less developed countries of $50 billion. Of this total, the United States provided $25.9 billion, or 52 percent; France provided $7.8 billion, or 16 percent; the United Kingdom provided $4.6 billion, or 9 percent; Germany provided $3.4 billion, or 7 percent; Japan provided $1.9 billion, or 4 percent; and all other DAC countries provided a total of $6.3 billion, or 12 percent.

These flows of financial assistance were directed to more than 150 less developed countries on five continents. The largest share, 43 percent, of official bilateral flows went to Asia. Africa received 28 percent, Latin America 15 percent, Europe 9 percent, and Oceania 5 percent. Because of the dense population in Asia, however, the per capita flow of financial resources there was only $20, as compared with $46 to $49 per head for Africa, Europe, and Latin America.

The data presented above for the donor countries are in absolute terms. To compare the efforts of different-sized countries in a meaningful way, the data should be related to the productive capacity, or national income, of the donor countries. When the assistance efforts of the 15 DAC countries are put on a relative basis, the differences are no longer great. Taking the 15 DAC members as a group, the total flow of financial resources to the developing world, as a percentage of national income, remained close to 1.0 percent in each of the years during the period 1963–65, and then dropped rather sharply in 1966 (see Table 8.2). Four countries—Belgium, France, the Netherlands, and the United Kingdom—were at or above 1.0 percent every year of the period 1963–66; the United States was close to providing 1.0 percent of its national income as foreign assistance in the period 1963–65, but slipped rather badly in 1966.

TABLE 8.2

The Net Flow of Financial Resources as a Percentage of National Income, 1963–66

(In percent)

Country	Total Official and Private Flow			
	1963	*1964*	*1965*	*1966*
Australia	0.68	0.73	0.80	0.71
Austria	0.10	0.33	0.68	0.66
Belgium	1.67	1.42	1.73	1.31
Canada	0.43	0.43	0.47	0.66
Denmark	0.17	0.44	0.19	0.28
France	2.06	2.07	1.87	1.70
Germany	0.83	0.89	0.85	0.81
Italy	0.84	0.57	0.59	1.28
Japan	0.51	0.48	0.73	0.69
Netherlands	1.12	1.18	1.53	1.49
Norway	0.50	0.48	0.71	0.29
Portugal	—	—	0.94	1.14
Sweden	0.42	0.48	0.47	0.64
United Kingdom	1.04	1.23	1.26	(1.16)
United States	0.94	0.92	0.98	(0.76)
Total DAC countries	0.96	0.95	1.00	0.88

SOURCE: OECD, *Development Assistance Efforts and Policies, 1967 Review*, p. 105.

In the past, planning for development in many less developed countries has been weak, or poorly done; hence the basis for establishing priorities among projects has approached guesswork rather than rigorous analysis. Further, there were many things that needed to be done urgently in each developing country. In this context, donor countries have tended to select for foreign assistance those projects that interested them, or in which they had some economic or political interest. Typically, economic assistance efforts by the donor countries have not been integrated into national development plans; donor countries have simply "picked off" for support those projects in which they had some interest.

Given this kind of selection process, there has been a strong tendency in the past for the assistance agencies of the donor countries to support the development of infrastructure and industrialization. Their efforts have focused on specific, construction-type projects, such as power plants, harbor facilities, hospitals, roads, and plants for making steel, aluminum, and cement. Such projects have had the advantage of great attractiveness to the less developed country, as well as administrative simplicity for the assistance providers. This was the period of edifice building—power plants and steel mills—for national aggrandizement.

But a new trend in foreign economic assistance began to take shape in the middle and late 1960's as the consequence of several factors. These factors include: (1) improved national planning for economic development and the establishment of rational developmental priorities; (2) the failure of agricultural production in many less developed countries to increase as rapidly as the demand for food; (3) the now recognized need for skilled manpower; and (4) the population explosion.

The new trend in foreign economic assistance involves providing support for broad areas of human and developmental activity. Perhaps the greatest shift in the mid-1960's has been the rapidly increasing recognition of the need to speed development in the food and agriculture sector; another area where new emphasis is being placed is in family planning; and a third area of growing importance is that of technical assistance. The broad problem of building a body of highly trained professionals and administrators, both in the developing countries and in the developed countries, to work on the problems of the developing world on a long-term basis is receiving increasing attention. Thus, the focus in foreign economic assistance is shifting from specific projects and construction to planning, administration, agricultural education, and relevant research activities.

In terms of this newer concept of economic and technical assistance, the president of the International Bank for Reconstruction and Development, George G. Woods, stated in 1965, "A preliminary Bank inquiry, carried out country by country and based on the judgment and experience of the Bank's country specialists and area economists, suggests that the developing countries could effectively use, on the average over the next four years, some $3 billion to $4 billion more external capital per year than has been provided in the recent past."[3] This leading expert on the external capital requirements of the less developed world thus suggests that there is need for a flow of financial resources from the developed to the less developed world of about 30 to 40 percent more than now takes place. This is one estimate, and perhaps the best estimate, of the total world requirement for foreign economic assistance that we have in the late 1960's and early 1970's.

Events during the period 1965–67, including the escalation of the Vietnam war, have however caused a number of observers, including Mr. Woods, to take a less sanguine view of future foreign economic assistance. Mr. Woods is reported (on the editorial page of *The New York Times* of November 15, 1967) to have warned that "the hopeful Decade of Development once promised for the nineteen-sixties has degenerated into a Decade of Disappointment pointing to disaster." As of 1967, the foreign assistance effort of the United States government reached a new low of some six-tenths of 1 percent of national income, and continues to fall, despite an increased effort by the private sector.

John Pincus, a Rand Corporation economist, recently gave the answer to how much aid is needed—"All they can get." He argues as follows:[4]

[3] OECD, *Development Assistance Efforts and Policies, 1966 Review* (September 1966), p. 63.

[4] "External Aid: Some Considerations," *Development Digest*, Vol. V, No. 3, Agency for International Development, Washington, D.C. (October 1967), pp. 3–4.

Realistically speaking, there isn't enough money to fill the economic gap in any reasonable time period. Even to fill it halfway within a generation is impossible in practice.

For those who remain unconvinced, let us look at the "success" stories of economic development—thirteen countries whose output has grown at more than 6 percent annually since 1950. They are Greece, Yugoslavia, El Salvador, Jamaica, Mexico, Nicaragua, Trinidad, Iraq, Israel, Jordan, South Korea, Thailand, and Taiwan. Most of these countries are small, with a population of less than 20 million. Most have either received massive U.S. aid—four to fifteen times the worldwide average per capita—or else struck it rich through minerals, tourism, or staple exports. Finally, measured by comparative export growth rates, they have been much more competitive in world markets than less developed countries as a whole. These success stories (with all the problems they still face barely hidden behind the facade of aggregate growth rates) account for only about 6 percent of the people who live in developing countries. To have covered the remaining 94 percent with the same amounts of aid per capita, aid appropriations from the U.S. and other donor countries would have had to be about three and one half times higher than they actually were over the past 16 years. But aid outlays, after rising sharply from the early 'fifties through the early 'sixties, seem to have stabilized. The inference is that, in view of other claims on rich nations' resources, present aid levels reflect aid's value to society as perceived by the donors.

As far as the economic gap is concerned, then, there seems no practical way to fill it with the amount of aid that would be needed from the recipients' viewpoint; from the donors' standpoint, there seems no strong urge to raise the ante. How much aid do the developing countries need? The answer seems simple. All they can get.

The United States Experience

During the long period 1953–67, the Agency for International Development (AID) and predecessor agencies spent a total of $27.6 billion on economic assistance to foreign countries, and for the most part to developing countries.[5] Of this total, a little over 30 percent went to the Far East, a little less than 30 percent to the

[5] See AID, *Operations Report*, W-129, Washington, D.C., December 12, 1968, p. 68.

Near East and South Asia, almost 14 percent to Europe, about 10 percent to nonregional activities including the international organizations, about 10 percent to Latin America, and about 5 percent to Africa.

In terms of dollars spent by the United States for economic assistance over the period 1953–66, by far the largest share ($15.9 billion) went for defense support, or assistance related to political and security objectives. Thus, it is clear that the total foreign economic assistance effort of the United States has been weighted heavily in the direction of defense and security. Development loans have accounted for $5.9 billion; this category covers loans designed to stimulate economic development through the support of internal projects and the purchase and importation of needed products (e.g., fertilizer). Technical cooperation and development grants have accounted for $3.0 billion; this category provides for technical assistance and related support to develop the social, political, and economic resources of the aided countries. Finally, other expenditures, including contributions to international organizations, accounted for $3.8 billion.

The foreign economic assistance commitments of the United States for the fiscal year ending June 30, 1967, were somewhat larger than for the average year of the 14-year period 1953–67. AID's commitments by budget category for fiscal 1967 were as follows:

	(millions of dollars)
Development and Alliance for Progress loans	1,109
Political and security objectives	718
Technical cooperation and development grants	315
Contributions to international organizations	144
Contingency fund	50
Administrative and other expenses	79
Total	2,415

But the foreign economic assistance effort of the United States has encountered increased resistance in the Congress, and has been significantly reduced as a result. The Congressional appropriations for fiscal 1968 for the same categories were as follows:

	(*millions of dollars*)
Development and Alliance for Progress loans	904.3
Political and security objectives	600.0
Technical cooperation and development grants	180.0
Contributions to international organizations	130.0
Contingency fund	10.0
Administrative and other expenses	71.3
Total	1,895.6

Thus, at a time when the economic and technical assistance needs of the developing countries are increasing and the national income of the United States is increasing, the funding support of economic and technical assistance from the United States is decreasing absolutely. And after the promise of economic assistance equal to 1.0 percent of their national incomes, which the DAC countries have talked about if not actually pledged, the effort of the United States government in 1968, has fallen close to one-half of 1.0 percent of its national income. Under budgetary pressures from the Vietnam war, the United States in the latter part of the 1960's is ignoring its moral commitments and political interests in other parts of the developing world. As a result, we may anticipate an increased number of casualties among the struggling developing nations, as their production performances fail to match their consumer expectations.

The statistical evidence of the impact of foreign economic assistance on the less developed countries is scanty, but it is encouraging. In a study made by the Council of Economic Advisers of a selected group of less developed countries (26 in all)—each of which received economic assistance from the United States during the period 1946–62 in excess of $300 million, or more than $30 per capita—it was discovered that 17 of the 26 countries had an annual rate of growth of 1.5 percent or more in real per capita GNP for the years 1957–62; and 13 of those countries had an annual rate of growth of 2.0 percent or more in real per capita GNP (see Table 8.3).[6]

[6] See *Economic Report of the President,* transmitted to the Congress (January 1964), together with the *Annual Report of the Council of Economic Advisers,* The White House, Washington, D.C., January 20, 1964, pp. 160–164.

TABLE 8.3

Selected Characteristics of Less Developed Countries Receiving U. S. Economic Assistance of More Than $300 Million, or More Than $30 Per Capita, 1946–62[1]

Country	Population, 1962 (Millions)	Growth Rate of Real GNP 1950–62[2] (Percent Per Year)	Per Capita Real GNP		U. S. Economic Assistance Obligated Fiscal Years 1946–62	
			Amount 1961 (U. S. dollars)[3]	Growth rate, 1957–62[4] (percent per year)	Total (millions of dollars)	Per capita (dollars)
Israel	2.3	10.4	814	6.0	879	382
Greece	8.5	6.3	431	4.7	1,785	210
Jordan	1.7	7.0	184	4.3	325	191
Taiwan	11.9	7.7	145	4.2	2,045	172
Liberia	1.0	5.3	159	3.8	125	125
Brazil	75.0	5.6	186	3.3	1,737	23
Panama	1.1	5.8	416	3.0	100	91
Iran	21.6	5.2	211	2.8	732	34
India	452.0	3.8	80	2.5	3,867	9
Thailand	28.7	5.4	97	2.3	338	12
UAR (Egypt)	27.3	(5)	120	2.1	608	22
Bolivia	4.0	4.2	113	2.0	258	65
Philippines	29.6	5.8	117	2.0	1,334	45
Colombia	15.6	4.6	283	1.8	360	24
Mexico	37.1	5.8	313	1.7	761	21

Pakistan	96.6	2.3	79	1.6	1,854	19
Tunisia	4.3	2.9	161	1.5	293	68
Guatemala	4.0	4.7	175	1.4	158	40
Chile	7.9	4.1	453	.8	675	85
Peru	11.6	3.4	181	.3	388	33
Turkey	29.2	4.5	193	.0	1,580	54
Indonesia	98.6	(5)	83	−.1	682	7
Costa Rica	1.3	5.6	344	−.3	89	68
Nicaragua	1.6	5.8	213	−.8	66	41
Argentina	20.6	1.5	379	−.9	572	28
Paraguay	1.9	(5)	130	−4.0	58	31

[1] Excludes countries in which economic development has not been a prime objective of U.S. economic assistance and countries where aid programs have been terminated: South Korea, South Vietnam, Laos, Cambodia, Yugoslavia, Libya, Morocco, Poland, Lebanon, Spain.

[2] Based on GNP in 1961 prices; since 1950 data were not available for all countries, the following substitutions were made: 1951 for Philippines; 1954 for Jordan; 1957 for Bolivia, Iran, Liberia, and Tunisia; 1956 for Thailand. Growth based on average of 2 years at beginning and end of period.

[3] GNP unadjusted for inequalities of purchasing power among countries.

[4] Data for 1956–62 for Thailand; 1959–62 for UAR; 1954–62 for Jordan. Growth based on average of 2 years at beginning and end of period.

NOTE: See footnotes above for necessary substitutions where data are not available for specified dates. Per capita data may not check exactly with data shown in this table because of use of unrounded data.

SOURCE: Economic Report of the President, transmitted to the Congress (January 1964), together with the Annual Report of the Council of Economic Advisers, The White House, Washington, D.C., January 20, 1964, p. 160.

159

It would be a mistake to attribute the rapid gains in real per capita incomes in 17 countries to economic assistance from the United States alone and to ignore, first, the fact that 9 countries did not experience such spectacular successes and, second, that many elements go into the economic development of a country besides U. S. economic aid. *But one very important relationship does emerge from Table 8.3.* The five countries—Israel, Greece, Jordan, Taiwan, and Liberia—which achieved the highest rates of growth in real per capita income (all above 3.5 percent per year) also received the greatest amounts of economic assistance on a per capita basis. This could be a coincidence, but the relationship between per capita income growth and per capita aid received for the 26 countries is really too strong to conclude that it happened by pure chance. The countries that received economic aid on a really large scale during the period 1946–62 (i.e., more than $100 per person) are the countries that achieved really rapid rates of growth in gross national product, both on a total and a per capita basis.

Among the countries receiving lesser amounts of economic assistance (i.e., less than $100 per person) some did well and some not so well in growth of real per capita GNP. But even among these countries there is some tendency for the amount of aid to be associated with growth in GNP. The relationship between economic aid and economic development appears to be the following: where economic aid is massive on a per capita basis, the effect on the rate of growth of per capita real income is positive and overwhelming; but where aid on a per capita basis is modest, other factors may override the influence of that aid and cause the rate of growth of per capita real income to be large or small, or positive or negative.

It is important to stress also that three countries—Israel, Taiwan, and Greece—which in the Council study had high rates of growth in GNP in conjunction with large amounts of economic aid, also achieved rates of increase in crop output of 9.7, 4.5, and 3.7 percent per year respectively over the period 1948–63.[7] Such rates of increase in crop output range from exceptional to very good. Thus, we observe that Israel, Taiwan, and Greece, which were among the top 5 countries for growth in per capita GNP in the Council study,

[7] See *Changes in Agriculture in 26 Developing Nations, 1948–63,* Foreign Agric. Econ. Report No. 27 (November 1965).

were also in the top 12 countries for rate of increase in crop production in the USDA study. Liberia was not included in the USDA study and so cannot be compared; and Jordan, which was in the top 5 countries in the Council study, falls to the bottom of the 26-country list in the USDA study of agricultural output. But 3 countries, Israel, Taiwan, and Greece (out of a total of 4 for which a direct comparison can be made), were the recipients of very large amounts of aid, experienced very rapid rates of growth in real per capita income, and also achieved high rates of increase in crop output. Thus the statistical evidence suggests that the flow of economic assistance, general economic development, and agricultural development are all related—not perfectly, but certainly significantly.

Problems of Achieving an Effective Use of Economic Assistance

It is not easy to achieve an effective use of foreign economic assistance in a developing country. This is true for a number of reasons. As was mentioned earlier, recipient and donor countries tend to be edifice-minded; both have a propensity to build steel mills, dams, and harbor facilities, since both can point to such structures with pride. Donor nations and their agencies have special interests in developing countries, ranging from development theories that they wish to verify to military objectives; these special interests may or may not fit the vital needs of the countries involved. To date, most developing countries have not been able to formulate and carry out a national strategy of development which allocates all resources, including foreign economic assistance, along lines that speed the development process. This systematic national strategy might take the form of a free market model, a mixed-capitalistic model, or a rigorous planning model. But whatever its form, the strategy must have the capacity to allocate resources and integrate productive activities in such a way as to produce and distribute goods and services efficiently and in accordance with requirements (by whatever criteria), and so enable the total national product, GNP, to grow. But such systematic strategies have typically been lacking in the developing countries.

As has been demonstrated on numerous occasions,[8] a perfectly free market (in which market prices direct the allocation of resources, and personal gain, or profit, provides the incentive to undertake productive activities) is a highly efficient form of economic organization. It can, for a given state of consumer tastes and preferences and productive technology, produce and distribute the goods that consumers want in the most efficient manner, that is, at least cost. Thus, the free market provides one model that developing countries might use to allocate resources and integrate productive activities, including foreign assistance, systematically and efficiently.

But, for a number of reasons, very few developing societies have adopted the free market as their model of economic organization. First, complete reliance on a free market does not permit, or enable, a society to undertake social objectives that require the use of productive resources for which the income payoff is distantly removed or not directly accountable to those providing the resources—for example, military defense, basic research, or the education of the masses. No person or private party in a free market situation can provide the kinds of services described above; the relationship between provision of service and receipt of remuneration is too distant and too tenuous.

Second, a free market is likely to starve, or restrict, the development of an adequate infrastructure (i.e., road system, water system, electric power system, etc.); the cost of providing adequate infrastructure facilities is so great that private entrepreneurs find it difficult to amass the requisite capital at one time; and again there is some difficulty in relating provision of service to payment for these kinds of service. Hence, there is a tendency for the development of infrastructure to lag under a free market.

Third, the free market model does not provide a convenient means for a society to change, or restructure, itself—effect a land reform, rehabilitate a slum area and the people in it. A free market economy allocates resources and integrates productive activities efficiently in a static situation; it does not lend itself to the purposeful change of society itself. Consequently, few societies have felt that

[8] See Tibor Scitovsky, *Welfare and Competition* (Homewood, Ill.: Richard D. Irwin, Inc., 1951), Chapter 8, The Efficiency of Production.

they could rely exclusively on a free market to organize and direct their economic activities.

A good number of developing nations have pursued a mixed-capitalistic system in which government has (1) provided certain social services deemed important to those nations (e.g., elementary and secondary education, medical services, and the conservation of natural resources) and (2) underwritten the financing of, or actually constructed, much of the economic infrastructure (e.g., roads, canals, power lines, sewer systems, etc.). But the production of most producer and consumer goods and services has been reserved to private business operating in an essentially free market. In other words, governments have made the critical investment decisions in the areas of social services, education, research, and economic infrastructure, but decisions on the production, distribution, and consumption of conventional goods and services have been left to private individuals and groups in an essentially free market. This was the path that the United States and the British dominions followed with considerable success in the nineteenth and the first half of the twentieth centuries. More recently, Israel, Thailand, Taiwan, Hong Kong, and Japan have followed this general economic model with good-to-excellent results in the development of their economies.

This mixed approach to resource allocation and production integration is not a tidy one; but if followed with a pragmatic realism, in which results are continually reviewed and evaluated, it offers several important advantages. First, detailed planning of the private sector, by which most producer and consumer goods and services are produced, is obviated. A high degree of freedom in the production and distribution of these goods is provided, in which individual creativeness and enterprise is fostered, with the likely result that productivity per unit of resource employed is increased; and market prices provide a relatively simple and effective means for directing and redirecting resources into new and necessary activities as consumer wants and productive methods change. Second, an institution—government—is identified and made responsible for making those great decisions that affect many or all members of society, such as free educational services for every child, or the water management of an entire river valley. In other words, the great decisions

on the use of resources that affect all citizens are made by an organization that is responsible in some way to all citizens. Third, the
important consideration in a mixed model is not doctrine or form,
but whether the approach works—does it increase resource productivity, integrate production processes (i.e., not produce all bolts and
no nuts), and accelerate development?

In other words, the responsibility for providing those services
that are not easily and readily provided by private individuals or
groups and typically are not paid for by the consumer at the time
of their use (e.g., education, transportation facilities, and water systems) is given over to the government; and the responsibility for
producing and distributing discrete units of producer and consumer
goods and services that private parties can readily purchase and
finance is given to the private sector. But the line between is not
fixed immutably by doctrine or convention.

We know how the free market directs the allocation of resources.
Individuals and groups in the quest of profits, guided by prices,
employ resources in those activities which hold the promise of the
greatest returns and to the point where their marginal cost is equal
to their marginal revenue. But what guides the use of resources in
the public sector? Certainly it is not the profit motive, nor the
marginal calculus. In the larger and basic sense, however, the guide
is the same: it is to use resources in the most productive and efficient manner, as judged by society.

How, then, is this judgment to be made, where prices and profits
have been shunted aside as a guide? There is no unique answer to
the question, but there are pieces of an answer to be kept in mind.
First, in a democracy, the legislature becomes the political market
for making value judgments as to the desirability of undertaking
one activity relative to another. Second, the planning agency in a
democracy or in an authoritarian government can and does make
technical judgments on the costs and returns of one productive activity compared to another. And these technical judgments by the
planning agency become a means by which "the government,"
democratic or authoritarian, can make rational judgments about
alternative production processes or activities (i.e., the government
decision unit is supplied with the information to enable it to select
process A over B, because process A will produce the same amount

of product in value terms as B, but at less cost). Or stated differently, cost-benefit analyses on the part of the planning agency can assist a society to make rational decisions about undertaking different enterprises, even though the planning agency may lack the basis for saying which product or service consumers should have at the expense of others. Third, staff work which *identifies all* the urgent needs of society, describes their costs and benefits, and ranks these needs by an objective set of criteria, can go a long way toward assisting a national society to make decisions in the public sector that contribute to an efficient use of resources.

But many developing countries since World War II have rejected all aspects of the free market model, and have moved toward a rigorous planning model for allocating resources and integrating productive activities. They have done this in some cases because they distrust the free market model as the result of their experience with it under colonial governments; they had seen it rigged against them and operated to their disadvantage. But more often they have turned to a rigorous planning model because they want rapid development and have sought a model which facilitates direct intervention in the economy by government. This rigorous planning does; planning is the means by which government directs the allocation and integration of productive resources. So, the rigorous planning model is often adopted by governments which want to take purposive and direct action to speed the development process.

This is a seductive, and seemingly obvious, policy position. If the economy requires more investment in agriculture to increase cereal production, then why should not government take direct action to achieve this increased investment? But this position overlooks the fact that the operating economy of any society is highly complicated, and the development process even more complex. Direct action to increase cereal production through increased investment, if it is based upon incomplete or incorrect information, may result in more tractors when the situation calls for more fertilizer and improved water management, and it may pull resources out of cereal processing and distribution at the very times when more are required there. Directing resources into their most needed and productive uses in a modern economy is not obvious at all. Thus, a plan which allocates and integrates *all* the resources of an economy to achieve, first, an efficient operation and, second, an increasingly productive operation must be highly detailed, sophisticated in concept, and correct with respect to the technical coefficients of production.

The argument taking shape here is not that the resources of a nation cannot be organized in accordance with a plan to produce efficiently a specified set of goods and services. It can be done, although the effective distribution of those goods and services, where some degree of free consumer choice is present, may be another matter. But such a plan must be detailed, fully complete, and technically correct. And this is an exercise that is probably beyond the technical capacity of most developing nations.[9]

The problem is the following. How is a country which is in great haste to develop economically and therefore seeks to organize its resources according to a detailed plan to *formulate* and *execute* such a rational, detailed plan, when it lacks the exacting technical and administrative skills required by the planning process? There is, of course, no logical solution to this problem. In order to speed the organization and reorganization of productive resources along lines that have the capacity to increase rapidly the national income through the intervention of *planning*, the typical developing country is making demands upon itself which it cannot satisfy. It typically lacks the technical skills to formulate an efficient, rationally integrated plan and the managerial skills to execute the provisions of the plan. Hence, the planning model often stifles development by the promulgation of arbitrary and incongruous regulations, rather than enhancing it. Because of incomplete and incorrect technical information and poor-to-bad administration, the planning model often leads to wrong allocative decisions and bad rules of operation, all of which retard economic development rather than stimulate it.

What, then, is the practical solution for developing countries strongly wedded to the planning model for organizing their productive resources, including additional resources provided through foreign assistance? One approach might be to make greater use of the skilled personnel of international organizations and private founda-

[9] Those interested in the process and problems of planning in less developed countries would benefit from the section "On Planning and Planners," *Development Digest*, Vol. VI, No. 1 (January 1968).

tions in the formulation of workable development plans.[10] In this connection, a workable plan must include not only an input-output tableau consistent with a realistic set of production coefficients, but also the establishment of organizations with the capacity and the mission to allocate and reallocate resources among productive enterprise in order to achieve the production goals of the plan.

A second approach might involve a retreat from rigorous, total planning to the mixed system discussed earlier. Some of the advantages of planning are saved under the mixed system, and the exacting demands for technical information and rational decisions are considerably reduced. Under the mixed system, the government might intervene in the economy in accordance with a strategy of development to achieve certain social objectives: a comprehensive road system; a power grid; an educational and research system; water control for an entire river valley. With proper technical assistance, these kinds of intervention are manageable for a developing country; further, they undergird economic development, but are slow to develop in a free market situation. But the production of most of the goods and services consumed by family units would take place in the free market sector. Individual private operators would provide the technical information required by their respective enterprises, and market prices generated in the competitive system would allocate resources among these same private operators. Thus, the need to plan production and distribution in this broad sector would be obviated, as would the exacting technical information requirements.

Taking the production and distribution of all those goods and services regularly consumed by family units out of the plan lifts an intolerable burden off the few skilled technicians and managers of a developing country, and provides them with the opportunity to concentrate on the building of infrastructure and social services in the government sector. It is a way of gaining freedom for the private sector and at the same time achieving an efficient use of limited planning personnel—with productive results in a number of countries.

[10] For a good discussion of the role of a private foundation and a private university in assisting a country to strengthen its planning process and formulate a series of national development plans, see *Design for Pakistan; A Report on Assistance to the Pakistan Planning Commission by the Ford Foundation and Harvard University*, The Ford Foundation, New York (February 1965).

Special Problems of Technical Assistance in Agriculture

There are some special problems of technical assistance as it affects food and agriculture—at least as far as the United States assistance effort is concerned. These problems are the product of two fundamental misunderstandings on the part of most Americans about agricultural development. The first is that we can simply give, or extend, our *existing technology* to a developing country, expect the farmers of that country to apply it directly, and then stand back and watch food production shoot skyward. The second misunderstanding is that agricultural development is a simple process, which can be reorganized and modernized in a short time. In this view, we should provide a three-to-five-year crash program of economic and technical assistance to a developing country and again stand back and watch its agriculture take off.

It is true that American agriculture is blessed with a highly advanced technology, but it is not true that much of that technology is directly applicable to agricultural conditions in the developing countries. Typically, our machinery does not fit their land holdings and cropping patterns, to say nothing of the power availabilities. Our plant varieties, bred for temperate conditions, do not thrive or perhaps even grow in tropical conditions. Our fertilizer recommendations are not suited to their soil types. And our animal diseases are often completely different from their animal diseases. In fact, very little of our farm technology can be put directly to use in most developing countries.

With a few notable exceptions,[11] because of the first misunderstanding, we have not attacked the problems surrounding the transfer and application of technology to developing countries with our customary national vigor. We have tried in some cases to transplant

[11] The Rockefeller Foundation has established first-rate agricultural research and experimental stations in Latin America with the capacity to develop and adapt modern technologies to the conditions of those countries. It is now engaged in similar activities in the Philippines and India and is becoming active in Africa. See *Progress Report: Toward the Conquest of Hunger, 1965–1966, Program in the Agricultural Sciences*, The Rockefeller Foundation, New York (December 1966).

and develop the Land Grant College idea abroad, together with the Agricultural Experiment Station, but we have discovered that this is a slow process indeed. But with the exceptions noted, we have not developed research centers at home and in the developing countries with the specific mission of adapting Western agricultural technologies to the requirements of specific developing areas. The technical assistance effort of the United States government over almost two decades has studiously avoided any direct work on the adaptation of Western agricultural technology to the specific and peculiar requirements of developing areas. We have spent a great deal of money and effort in extending existing technologies to backward areas, and we have tried to assist developing countries to create their own research centers to do applied research work on local production problems. But we have not manned and supported research centers ourselves either in the United States or in the developing countries to work on the critical problems of adapting modern knowledge and technologies to local situations in developing areas, as we continuously do in the United States for local production problems.

If agricultural production in the densely populated developing countries is to increase significantly, new, higher-yielding plant varieties must be adapted for specific local conditions, fertilizer recommendations must be developed for the local soil types, modern machines and tools must be adapted to local cropping patterns, and power availabilities and the plant and animal diseases of the local areas must be controlled. In time, the developing countries will do all of these things, as we did. But, as we discovered between 1870 and 1920, these developments take time. Meanwhile, if the United States is serious about helping the developing countries to speed the development of their agricultures, it must do very much more in the way of adapting Western farm technologies to the needs of these countries than it has in the past.

Agricultural development is a complex, hence typically slow, process. Agricultural production, for any state of the arts, is a systems problem in which many productive acts must be combined in just the right time sequence to obtain a product. Alter the state of the arts in a significant way and the many sequential acts in the productive system must be combined in a new, perhaps significantly

different, way. And alter the state of the arts in farming continuously and the production system must be altered continuously. But
for an illiterate peasant unused to considering cause-and-effect relationships, this is a tremendously difficult situation. In this new, non-
traditional state of the production arts in which the peasant finds
himself, if he puts together a series of productive acts (which he
really doesn't understand) in the wrong sequence, his output goes
down, not up. Given this state of affairs, the poorly educated peasant is inclined to move slowly and avoid mistakes. This means
either that the agricultural development process moves slowly, or
that a great amount of first-rate production guidance and education
must be poured into the agricultures of developing countries.

The technical assistance effort of the United States has recognized these obstacles to agricultural development only superficially,
and has certainly not been organized to cope with the complexities
of modernizing peasant agricultures. In deference to the general
misunderstanding of Americans inside of Congress and out regarding the potentialities of agricultural development, one aid agency
after another has undertaken foreign technical assistance in spirit,
word, and organization on a short-run, emergency basis. Instead of
building research, developmental, and educational institutions in
the developing countries to work on agricultural production and
distribution problems over several decades, the United States has
concentrated on emergency-type programs and specific development projects, with the result that it has little more technical assistance capacity overseas in 1968 than it had in 1958 (in fact, it may
have less, because of a conscious policy of decreasing the number of
its direct-hire personnel overseas). In sum, the preoccupation of
the United States with the short-term aspects of foreign technical
assistance has led it away from institution building and from creating a technical assistance organization overseas with the capacity
to contribute significantly to agricultural development.

Because of the second basic misunderstanding, we have failed
to build the institutions at home and abroad with the capacity to
work effectively on the varied problems of agricultural development. We have failed to build institutions with the primary mission of doing research and developmental work on the problems of
the developing countries, to staff them with permanent, high-quality personnel, and to fund them on a sustained basis. Rather, we

have elected to make short-term contracts, typically of two to three years' duration, with American universities and other research institutions to undertake a specific project abroad (e.g., work with a government ministry, provide support to a local university) with whatever personnel the contracting agency could find. Sometimes the personnel for these projects has been the best tenured staff of the university, but more often they have been manned by retired staff, or staff hired specially for the duration of the project from wherever they could be found.

These kinds of short-term contracts with American universities and private research and service groups, staffed by short-term nontenured personnel, have not made the contribution to basic and adaptive research, either physical or social, on development problems that is required. They could not. Funds have not been provided the contracting institutions to undertake the research required on a continuing basis. Personnel could not be hired on a permanent basis to undertake fundamental research, because the contract might be terminated in three years, and was expected to be terminated in five or six years. Usually the feedback to the contracting institution of lessons learned on the overseas project has been minimal, since the temporary personnel did not return to the institution or the tenured personnel had no development research project in which to work on their return home. Thus for many reasons the technical assistance system, based upon short-term contracts, which in turn has been based upon our misunderstanding of the development process, has worked against the building up of a systematic body of knowledge on agricultural development that could be applied in developing countries.

The United States system for undertaking technical assistance abroad, based on short-term contractual arrangements, has implicitly assumed that we know all we need to know about development —about plant varieties, about fertilizer requirements, about credit arrangements, about pricing policies, about local customs and mores, and so on—and that all we had to do was to take the institutional arrangements and technologies developed in the United States to the developing country and apply them directly.

But we now know better. We now know that the institutional arrangements and organizations must be compatible with a host of social variables indigenous to the particular country. And we know that the agricultural practices and technologies must be adapted to the physical conditions and production organization of the particular developing country. Nonetheless, we still do not have the institutional organization in the United States to accomplish these things. We are beginning to take steps toward building research and development institutions within American universities with the mission orientation, the staff capacity, and the sustained funding arrangements to work creatively and productively on the physical and social problems of development. But those steps are still feeble and halting.

This is not due to a lack of intellectual leadership. Two Presidential commissions—the Science Advisory Committee and the National Advisory Commission on Food and Fiber—have made strong recommendations on the need for building at home and abroad research institutions that are concerned with basic research and with adaptive research on the development problems of agriculture.[12] The problem has been, and continues to be, one of combating the popular notion that the advanced agricultural technologies of the United States can be transferred directly to the developing countries on a short-term, crash basis with productive results. Once this popular notion is destroyed, it should be possible to obtain funding on a *sustained basis* to build research institutions at home and abroad to concentrate on agricultural development problems on a long-term basis. The key to the problem is *sustained funding*; without such funding, efforts to mount effective research programs at home and abroad sputter and fall by the wayside.

If the technical assistance efforts of the United States government abroad, particularly in the area of food and agriculture, are to be successful, institutions must be developed, with physical plants both in the United States and throughout the developing world (perhaps by individual countries, perhaps on a regional basis, perhaps both) with the primary mission of undertaking research on the problems of agricultural development and extending the findings of such research to the local people. Such institutions might

[12] *The World Food Problem*, A Report of the President's Science Advisory Committee, Vol. 1, The White House, Washington, D.C. (May 1967), pp. 20, 21, 34–36; *Food and Fiber for the Future*, Report of the National Advisory Commission on Food and Fiber, Washington, D.C. (July 1967), pp. 36–37, 134–137.

be attached to existing universities or be independent agencies. But they must be funded adequately and on a sustained basis so that they can

1. assemble a critical mass of high-quality personnel with the capability of dealing with complex development problems;
2. find answers to the production and distribution problems of this generation; and
3. train the personnel and build the institutions in the developing countries that will be capable of dealing effectively with the continuing problems of the next generation.

The time is overdue in the United States to stop talking about solving the food and agricultural problems of the large, densely populated developing countries in the "next five years" and start building the institutions needed to do effective technical assistance work over the next 25 to 50 years. Modernizing agriculture in densely populated areas where new, virgin land is nonexistent is a tricky, complex process which is absolutely dependent, first, on the development of new knowledge through research; second, the adaptation of that new knowledge to local conditions; and third, the systematic application of properly adapted technologies to farming operations. Thus, increasing agricultural production through modernization (that is, changing the technological base of a whole agriculture from a traditional to a modern, scientific form) is absolutely dependent upon the quality and quantity of the research and education effort. Americans must come to understand this and to act accordingly, if they are serious about foreign technical assistance in the field of food and agriculture.

One final important point must be made about technical assistance work in agriculture in the less developed world. The United States and other developed countries are not starting out from zero in this field. The Rockefeller Foundation, working on a long-term basis first in Mexico and later in the Philippines, has learned many lessons and experienced spectacular successes in at least two different directions.[13] First, the Rockefeller people have succeeded in

[13] The story of the development of the new wheat and rice varieties, as well as training programs in the Rockefeller Foundation regional research stations, is well told in *Progress Report: Toward the Conquest of Hunger, 1965–1966*, pp. 38–99.

establishing cooperative research ventures in agriculture in which local people were included from the beginning. These people were trained in research techniques and administration, and the management of the research operation was gradually turned over to them. Second, new, high-yielding varieties of wheat and rice have been developed in these regional research stations, a feat which in the late 1960's is revolutionizing the *production* of these grains in the developing world.

So we are not starting out from zero with regard to foreign technical assistance work. We have the successful experience of the Rockefeller Foundation to guide future American efforts—an experience which has met with success both in training and developing people and in researching and developing important new production technologies. What is needed now on the part of the United States is an emulation of the limited Rockefeller experience many times over around the developing world. The technical assistance efforts of the United States government need the staying power and the cooperative institutional approach that have characterized the Rockefeller efforts. And the developing world needs these strengthened technical assistance efforts duplicated many times over to support and sustain the developments in food and agriculture that are now under way.

Implications for the World Food Problem

The prescription of economic and technical assistance for solving the world food problem cannot be written in this book or anywhere else at the present time.[14] There are too many gaps in our knowledge:[15] lack of information concerning technical production coefficients and resource input requirements, lack of understanding and research findings with regard to development problems, and lack of systematic strategies of development, country by country,

[14] Probably the World Bank group could come closest to writing the prescription of any agency or person, from their systematic appraisals of the development process in each country; but even that group lacks the information inputs to do so.

[15] This the FAO is learning as it struggles to formulate an Indicative World Plan. See conference document C 67/15, *Indicative World Plan for Agricultural Development—A Progress Report*, Rome, October 10, 1967.

which can effectively allocate resources among productive uses. In time we may be able to write a prescription for optimum economic and technical assistance, country by country, as these gaps narrow for each country. But it will be a long time before an exact prescription will be written with a high degree of confidence.

Given the enormity of the world food problem, what then should be our course of action with regard to economic and technical assistance? Should the additional resources provided to developing countries through assistance programs be withheld because we lack the knowledge to employ those additional resources optimally? Our answer is neither an unqualified Yes or No. Rather, it is that economic and technical assistance should be continued, but with an important change in emphasis: *away* from the financial support for the construction of huge edifices (e.g., steel mills and national capital cities) in situations where the national development strategy is either nonexistent or ineffectual, *to* the provision of technical assistance in developing an effective national development strategy, *to* the provision of technical assistance in building institutions to undertake research and service activities on development problems (e.g., plant breeding, labor transfers, credit requirements), and *to* the construction of the infrastructure documented in the national development plan or strategy (e.g., a road system, a primary school system, a major irrigation system).

The world food problem is, as we already know, real and huge. Thus, it would be nonsensical to recommend against the provision through foreign economic aid of additional resources whose productive use can speed the resolution of this problem. But it is also nonsensical to build a huge steel plant out of position with respect to raw materials and/or markets, or a large irrigation works which may lead to a salinization of the land within two decades; such efforts constitute a gross waste of resources, regardless of the magnificence of the structures.

Thus, the following course of action is suggested. First, a great deal more emphasis should be placed on research and educational activities aimed at the problems of development, both in the less and the more developed countries, and dealing with both physical and social problems. This work would provide the basis for making rational investment decisions and undertaking action programs designed to increase production and speed development. Second, much more attention should be directed to, and technical assistance provided for, the formulation of a systematic national development plan or strategy. This work would provide the basis for productive use of the additional resources obtained through economic assistance, as well as of the nation's own resources. Third, given the improved technical knowledge and organizational skill that would result, foreign economic assistance should be employed to provide those goods and services which are indispensable to orderly and sustained economic growth, but which the private sector is unlikely to provide: research stations, school systems, road systems, power systems, credit systems. These are the broad infrastructural elements upon which development flows, agricultural as well as general, and where foreign economic assistance, if wisely used, can make an important contribution.

In sum, foreign economic assistance, wisely used, can help undergird and speed the general process of economic development, which is basic to agricultural development. Foreign technical assistance, properly organized, can make an indispensable contribution to agricultural development by producing specialized knowledge and adapting general knowledge and technology to meet the needs of local developing areas.[16]

[16] The OECD report *Aid to Agriculture in Developing Countries* (Paris, 1968) came to the attention of the author as this book was going to press. The data and ideas of that report are not incorporated into this study, but the reader seeking detailed information on the agricultural aid programs of individual developed countries and multilateral agencies will find the report to be a rich and overflowing source.

9

Agricultural Development: Resource and Production Requirements

OUR ANALYSIS now turns to the specific question of increasing the production of food and fiber products in the developing countries. How is food production to be increased from a rate of growth of, say, 2 percent per year to 4 percent or more in those countries where food production is falling behind the growth in demand? There are some areas in Africa and Latin America where agricultural production may be increased through the settlement and exploitation of new lands on an individual family basis. But this is now the exceptional case; there is little virgin land in the world which can be brought under cultivation except through large-scale collective actions aimed at drainage, irrigation, or the clearing of jungles.

Agricultural development in the 1960's thus means either the modernization of traditional agricultures or large-scale development schemes involving drainage, irrigation, or land clearing. In either case, the individual cannot settle on a piece of new land at the edge of civilization and bring it into production through hard work, brute strength, and a few simple tools. Hence, our concern in this and the following two chapters will not be with the relatively simple, often romantic, and always rugged form of agricultural development that dominated the nineteenth century—the exploitation of new lands by individual settlers; our concern will be with that complex, poorly understood form of agricultural development that

involves a complete change in the technological base of agriculture
—from a traditional to a modern, scientific pattern—often in the
setting of dense populations. This is something which is difficult for
the citizens of developed countries to understand, something which
urban-based planners in the developing countries find even more
difficult to appreciate, and something that is exceedingly difficult
for the peasants, or cultivators, involved to execute.

Traditional Agriculture: The Point of Departure

By definition, the methods of production and patterns of resource
use in a traditional agriculture were established by custom. A man
farms today the way his father and grandfather did before him,
and none can remember how or when their particular productive
methods came into being. This means that the kinds of resources
employed today, the way they are employed, and the combinations
in which they are employed were determined by the availability of
resources and the level of technology in the distant past—perhaps
50 years ago, perhaps 100 years ago, perhaps 1,000 years ago. And,
with the exception of some plantation developments, this is typically the kind of agriculture that we find in economically backward
areas.

Land is the dominant productive resource in traditional agricultures. It was available long ago; it was incorporated into farming
systems long ago when it was relatively abundant and capital was
relatively scarce; and those farming systems, developed in the distant past, which rely heavily on the resource of land, have become
the traditional agricultures of today. The quality of the soil, the
topography of the land, and the climatic conditions associated with
the land control, to an important degree, the kinds of crops grown
and their yield. Land is the dominant resource in traditional production systems in terms of its monetary value and as a determinant
of output.

To this land resource, labor is added—intensively where the population is dense and lightly where the population is sparse. But in
both instances, the productivity of labor is low. It is low because the
capital available to labor for working the land is limited, inade-

quate, and antiquated. The tools, the machines, the water management devices, the improved plant varieties, the fertilizers, and the disease control materials are nonexistent, inadequate, or antiquated. The farm worker's arm is thus not long and strong as it is in modern, scientific agricultures—it is weak and unproductive as in the distant past. And the farmer's arm is often further restrained and rendered unproductive by custom, social mores, and the pattern of social institutions in traditional agricultures.[1] Economists argue long and hard about how low worker productivity is in traditional agricultural situations.[2] Some say that it typically reaches zero at the margin; in other words, labor productivity is so low that some or many workers can be transferred out of agriculture without reducing the total output. Others claim that the product of the marginal worker is positive, but generally lower than the value of his subsistence. Still others argue that although farm workers may be unemployed most of the year, their contribution to production is important because of their work at planting and harvest times. But no one does, or can, argue that worker productivity in traditional agricultures is high, on the average or at the margin. The existing productivity data, unreliable as it is, makes this point clear.[3] In the view of this writer, worker productivity in traditional agricultures is typically very low at the margin—probably approaching zero in some cases and falling below the level of subsistence in many cases. This, of course, means that most agricultural labor in traditional

[1] Gunnar Myrdal makes much of this latter point in his great recent work, *Asian Drama: An Inquiry into the Poverty of Nations,* Vol. II (New York: Pantheon Books, Twentieth Century Fund Study, 1968), Chapters 21 and 22.

[2] For those who would like to explore, or become involved in, this argument, I suggest the following readings as a point of departure: W. Arthur Lewis, "Economic Development with Unlimited Supplies of Labour," reprinted in A. N. Agarwala and S. P. Singh (eds.), *The Economics of Development* (New York: Oxford University Press, 1963); John C. H. Fei and Gustav Ranis, *Development of the Labor Surplus Economy* (Homewood, Ill.: Richard D. Irwin, 1964), particularly Chapters 2 and 5; N. Georgescu-Roegen, "Economic Theory and Agrarian Economics," *Oxford Economic Papers,* new series, Vol. 12, No. 1 (February 1960); T. W. Schultz, *Transforming Traditional Agriculture* (New Haven, Conn.: Yale University Press, 1964), particularly Chapter 4; and Dale W. Jorgenson, *Subsistence, Agriculture and Economic Growth,* Working Paper No. 66, Berkeley, Calif.: Institute of Business and Economics, University of California (April 1965).

[3] *Changes in Agriculture in 26 Developing Nations, 1948–63,* Foreign Agric. Econ. Report No. 27 (November 1965), p. 13.

situations is heavily underemployed and that much of it could be transferred out of agriculture into nonfarm jobs (if and when they are available) without significantly reducing the total output of the agricultural sector.

We have said that the capital employed on farms in traditional settings is limited, inadequate, and antiquated. It is so, first, because farm tools and technologies were primitive and limited when these farming systems evolved and became traditional in the distant past. But the employment of capital is restricted in traditional situations in modern times for economic reasons, too. Rates of interest on borrowed capital tend to be exorbitant, running as high as 30, 40, or 50 percent per year in traditional agriculture; the incentive to employ more capital is thus blocked and destroyed. And the risks of crop failure, market gluts, and sickness and death militate against the use of long-term credit on the part of either borrower or lender. Thus, the physical and economic environment, as well as tradition, operate to block the introduction and employment of new and additional capital. Except for draft animals and a few primitive tools, capital is unimportant or nonexistent in traditional agricultures.

Since the amount of capital available to individual farm families to work the land is extremely limited, and the population is dense and increasing in relation to available arable land, farm holdings *tend* to be small. For example, 84 percent of the farm holdings in India are less than 5 hectares,[4] 66 percent are less than 5 hectares in Iran, 92 percent are less than 5 hectares in the United Arab Republic, 55 percent are less than 5 hectares in Colombia, and 84 percent are less than 5 hectares in the Philippines. It should be noted, however, that although most farm holdings are small in densely populated, traditional agricultures, it is generally true that a relatively few large landowners—some absentee, others active farmers—own a large share of the more productive arable land. For example, in the mid-1950's some 43 percent of the total cultivated land in India was operated in units of 20 acres or more in size.

Thus, because of low labor productivity, limited capital resources, and small land holdings, the typical farm in traditional agricultures tends also to be a subsistence unit. By this we mean

4 One hectare is equal to 2.471 acres.

that most of the product produced on the farm is consumed on the farm. We do not say, however, that everything produced on the farm is consumed on the farm. In the typical case, most of what is produced—say, 70 to 90 percent—is consumed by the human beings and the draft animals on the farm, but some proportion— perhaps 10 to 30 percent—is sold and enters into commercial channels. But just because only 10 to 30 percent of the product of these subsistence units is sold, it does not follow that the families involved are well fed. Very often the surplus for sale is created by skimping on family food consumption, with the result that much undernourishment and malnutrition is found among persons living on farms that market only a small part of their total product.

In the typical case, then, the traditional farmer and his family are dependent upon the production of their farm for sustenance throughout the year, but they are also interested in the market. The level of farm prices will influence importantly whether they can provide a daughter with a dowry, purchase some needed cotton goods, and repay the moneylender.

Finally, the typical farmer in a traditional situation is an illiterate person who cannot read a newspaper, has never heard of a farm journal, and has almost no appreciation of the man-made laws under which he lives or the fundamental cause-and-effect relationships in the physical world which control his production possibilities. Today he probably has some access to radio communication, but information from that source comes from the outside world which he does not know or trust. He is one of the "simple folk" who lives in a village and fears everything outside his intimate family circle—the police, the tax collector, the moneylender, the headman of the village, the town merchants, the army, the weather, the faraway government, and an unknown collection of gods. He lives in a world of fear and ignorance with a farm production system and a level of technology handed down to him from time immemorial.

It is into such a world that modernization must come if food production is to be increased significantly. There is no other way for the densely populated regions of Asia, the arid Middle East, and the uplands of South America. But modernization will not come easily in those regions. There are formidable barriers blocking the way—ignorance, fear, poverty, and tradition.

The Elements of Farm Modernization

Land the farmer must have, whether he be in a traditional or a modern setting. Land is an indispensable resource in the production of food and fiber for any practical level of technology in the foreseeable future. But in modern systems of agricultural production, its importance continues to decline relatively. Farmers do not take what the raw soil and the luck of the climate will yield; they expect to influence the yield, and influence it importantly, by applying new and improved capital inputs and production practices. Farmers in a modern, scientific agriculture expect to and do increase their yield of crops year after year by adding capital inputs to their production organization—more units of existing capital items and new and improved capital items and technologies. The symbol of modern farming is capital. And increasingly capital inputs are produced off the farm; hence they must be purchased.

But scientists, technologists, and farmers have, of course, learned that indiscriminate applications of capital do not yield productive results. Continuous application of one form of capital—say, nitrogen fertilizer—where other units in the productive organization are held constant, quickly runs into diminishing returns. And the interjection of an advanced technology where other elements of the production organization are unchanged can lead to economic or technological disaster. The increased application of capital to land in order to increase production in the quest for higher profits requires the application of capital across a broad technological front: in soil fertility, water management, machinery and equipment, plant varieties, disease control, product storage and handling, and so on. And this, of course, is the way the increased use of capital in farming came about in the Western world; it came in a broad front as it was learned through trial and error that increasing production significantly depended upon many technological elements. But sometimes we seem to forget this when we turn to the modernization of agriculture in a developing country.

Let us, for example, consider the application of a new variety of rice in South Asia. This rice variety may be high-yielding under controlled conditions so far as soil preparation, fertilizer application, water supply, disease and pest control, and harvesting methods are concerned. But leave one or two of these conditions to chance (e.g., too little water or too much water), and the variety may produce a very low yield. Fail to spray at the right time to control a plant disease, or to handle the new variety in a specific way at harvest time, and much of the new crop may be lost. The recipe for obtaining high yields is highly demanding in an advanced technological setting: combine the new resources in the right proportions and the proper sequence and the yield is very good; combine them in the wrong proportions and in the wrong sequence and the yield is worse than with traditional methods.

The above discussion suggests a point about increasing agricultural production which is now generally accepted. To increase crop production rapidly in a traditional situation, farmers must adopt a whole package of resource inputs and practices.[5] As a minimum, this production package must include: (1) new and improved plant varieties, (2) recommended fertilizer applications, (3) disease and pest control, and (4) proper water management. To achieve significant yield increases, the production package will in all likelihood also need to include certain specific land preparation, or tillage practices, and new, improved, and more timely harvesting practices. The adoption of these practices will, in turn, require the availability of (1) new and improved seeds, (2) supplies of fertilizer, (3) supplies of disease and pest control materials, (4) irrigation equipment and supplies of water, (5) new and greater sources of power and tillage equipment, and (6) new and improved harvesting equipment.

It does little good, for example, to apply more fertilizer to old, native varieties of rice; the increased application of fertilizer in such a case simply produces heavier and longer stalks and stems and very little additional grain. It does little good, and it may do harm, to apply fertilizer heavily when the water supply is inadequate; the fertilizer either fails to go into solution and hence does not become

---

[5] Dr. Sherman E. Johnson first popularized this idea (I am not sure where it originated), and it was given prominence in the now famous *Report on India's Food Crisis and Steps to Meet It* by the Agricultural Production Team, sponsored by the Ford Foundation, issued by the government of India (April 1959). Dr. Johnson was the leader of that team.

available to the plants, or it may actually burn the plants and reduce the yield. These things farmers learn in time by trial and error.
But time is short for increasing food supplies in the developing
countries. To increase food production significantly and in a hurry,
there is a need to bring to farmers, and help them adopt, packages
of improved practices and capital inputs that have the capacity to
increase production in particular local situations.

Sherman Johnson and his production team to India summarized
this package argument as follows:[6]

> A few improved practices can be effective if adopted singly, but
> the full benefit from most improvements can be obtained *only* if
> they are adopted in combinations suitable for specific soil and cli-
> matic conditions. Sufficient fertilizers, improved seed, pesticides,
> proper soil and water management practices—all of these, while
> important in themselves, can be *fully effective only if adopted in*
> *combination with each other.* For this reason, improvement pro-
> grammes should be designed to concentrate on the adoption of those
> *combinations of practices* that are most likely to increase food pro-
> duction quickly.

And then they related the package argument to the ever-present
problem of the variability of conditions among local areas:

> Equally important, improvement programmes should be tailored
> to fit the conditions faced by individual cultivators, village by vil-
> lage, block by block, and area by area. It is obviously impossible for
> agricultural workers to give individual assistance to all the cultivators
> in India, but a uniform, blanket approach should be avoided. A
> nation-wide improvement programme should be developed which
> will concentrate on the combination of practices that are most likely
> to increase food production quickly in the different areas.

But, if a package of production practices and resource inputs
is to be made available to farmers, and those farmers are to be
assisted with the adoption of that package, there must be a second
package—a package of services—to convert the first into reality.
What this package of services should include is perhaps debatable,
and it will vary somewhat according to one's definition of service in

[6] *Ibid.*, p. 18.

relation to such things as resources and organization. For example, A. T. Mosher in his stimulating book *Getting Agriculture Moving*[7] lists "The Essentials for Agricultural Development" to be:

Markets for Farm Products
Constantly Changing Technology
Local Availability of Supplies and Equipment
Production Incentives for Farmers
Transportation

and then he lists "The Accelerators of Agricultural Development" as follows:

Education for Development
Production Credit
Group Action by Farmers
Improving and Expanding Agricultural Land
National Planning for Agricultural Development.

But in terms of the conceptual framework under development here, four services seem absolutely essential to the implementation of the production package on farms. Those services are: (1) production education in some one of many forms (i.e., the dissemination of information to farmers about new production methods, practices, and technologies), (2) roads and transport facilities on those roads, (3) production credit, and (4) a market for the surplus production.

The successful adoption within a few years of a whole package of production practices and resources by illiterate cultivators in a traditional setting is completely dependent upon an intensive program of production education—perhaps by extension agents, perhaps by demonstration methods, perhaps through local folk schools, *but certainly by some effective method*. Traditional practices will be replaced by modern practices only as the peasant, or cultivator, learns what the set of new technologies can do and how to use them; education is thus the first required service.

But if new ideas, new resources, and improved equipment are to flow in, and surplus production is to flow out, there must be

[7] Published for the Agricultural Development Council by Frederick A. Praeger, Inc. (New York, 1966).

roads and a means of transport on those roads. An effective transportation system is absolutely essential to the modernization of traditional agricultures. This is the second required service.

The production package described above is a costly one. It is far beyond the financial means of the typical cultivator in traditional agricultures, and in many cases its adoption might not be profitable with rates of interest ranging up to 50 percent per year and even higher. Thus, the provision of production credit to rank-and-file cultivators at reasonable rates of interest—say, 5 to 10 percent—is a necessary prerequisite to the widespread adoption of the production package. Present costs of credit to most farmers in most developing countries constitute a formidable barrier to modernization.

Finally, if the package is adopted widely and if it succeeds in increasing the output of the crop, or crops, involved by, say, 20 or 50 percent or even possibly 100 percent, what is to become of the surplus production that is so generated? Will there be facilities to handle the product physically? And can the market absorb the surplus, without prices falling to disastrous levels at harvest time? The answer, of course, is that there must be a market which can effectively handle the surplus in physical and economic terms; otherwise the farmers will throw away the new production techniques which are worth less than nothing to them in the absence of such a market, even though the nation may desperately need the increased production. Thus, an effective market is the final required service.

How did the production package under consideration come into being in the first place? Certainly it did not spring full blown from the mind of one man at one point in time. The production package capable of significantly increasing output for a given area will be a complex thing, involving a specific combination of resources that are organized into a sequential set of practices consistent with the conditions of a specific locale. Almost certainly it will have evolved through continuous, incremental, and painstaking research. In other words, the package had to evolve through a systematic process of trial and error at a research station located in, or familiar with, the local area. Thus, before the production package could come into being, a research station had to be in operation somewhere, working on the agricultural production problems of the area.

Sometimes, from the research and experimental results of one area we can guess what the content of a production package for another area should be. And sometimes we are right in such guesses, but more often we are wrong. Hence, systematic research work on the production problems of an area should come first, and the production package for adoption by farmers should come second. An effective modernization program for agriculture thus also implies the existence of a system of research and experimentation to guide the process.

Finally, two more important things must occur in the economic system, if the production package is to be adopted on a wide scale and the agricultural plant is to undergo modernization. First, the new capital inputs—improved seeds, fertilizer, insecticides, irrigation equipment—must be produced somewhere. They can be moved up to the farms and adopted there only to the extent that they are available. And they can be available only to the extent that someone, somewhere, has undertaken to produce them in the quantities required. Second, the labor released as a result of agricultural modernization must seek reemployment, probably in a new geographical location. If this released labor is retrained and reemployed in a more productive job, the economy grows in the process. If it is not reemployed, the economy will grow very slowly, if at all, and serious social and political problems will be created as well. These processes will be explored more thoroughly in Chapter 11; it is sufficient at this point to recognize that they are a concomitant part of modernizing the farm plant.

Production Organization

Some American farm leaders argue that for a modern, scientific agriculture to operate efficiently and productively, it must be organized into adequate-sized, family farm units. An adequate-sized family farm unit is commonly defined as one large enough to use efficiently a conventional line of American farm equipment and on which the farmer and his family make the main production decisions and provide at least half of the labor employed. On the other hand, it is often argued in the Soviet Union and in the developing countries pursuing a socialist form of economic organization

188 THE WORLD FOOD PROBLEM

that a modern, scientific agriculture should be organized into large-scale, collective farms where the principal resources are owned by the state, or by members of the collective, and the family members both work on the collective and share in its managerial decisions. And there are still other experts around the world who argue that land tenure arrangements and decisions in the farm organization must be thus and so, if modern agricultures are to be efficient and productive.

But these dogmatic positions really do not square with the facts. It is correct that the family farm form of organization, supported by a set of government services which includes road systems, research systems, production education, supplementary credit, and alternative markets, has proved to be a highly efficient and productive form of organization in the great central region of the United States—from the Alleghenies to the Rockies and in many different crop and livestock enterprises. But it is also correct that large-scale private farms, now typically with a corporate form of business organization, which employ up to hundreds of hired laborers and rely upon hired management, have proved to be a highly efficient form of farm organization in the production of many different crops, as well as livestock, in California, the Southwest, along the Mississippi Delta, and on the East Coast.

Both of these forms of farm organization, which have enjoyed spectacular successes in the United States, have in some other parts of the world—notably South America—failed to perform spectacularly, or even satisfactorily in the twentieth century. It is no doubt true that other kinds of organizational problems have contributed to the stagnation of agricultural production in South America. But this relates to the point that we will soon be making with regard to production organization. And it is a fact that small family farms and large-scale private farms in South America have not usually been able to override the other barriers to modernization and expand output significantly.

The Israeli kibbutz, which is the nearest thing to pure communism in farm organization yet devised, has met with great success in increasing agricultural production through the adoption of modern, scientific methods. On the typical kibbutz, all decisions are made collectively through democratic procedures; individual members rotate among the jobs to be done, from the most menial task of washing dishes to the management of a processing enterprise; and members truly "work according to their ability and share according to their needs." Somehow under Israeli conditions this pure form of communist organization has resulted in a highly efficient and productive form of farm organization. But large-scale state farms and collective farms in the Soviet Union, with varying combinations of authoritarian and communistic organization, have not done as well in terms of achieving efficient, productive units. This is not to argue that agricultural modernization and development in the Soviet Union have failed in any absolute sense, but that gains in agricultural production in that large country have fallen short of plan expectations and have not met the growth requirements of the overall economy.[8] Less charitable observers contend that the Soviet farms are inefficient by almost any standard of comparison.

To turn to another country, the Japanese have experienced sustained and significant gains in agricultural production for a century or more through intensive cultivation, complementary combinations of enterprises, and the adaptation of modern technologies on very small family-operated farms. The drive, the compulsion to expand production on small-scale Japanese farms, is dramatically described by Kusum Nair in her new book *The Lonely Furrow*. We include here her description of family life and production operations on three small Japanese farms:[9]

In Gumma Prefecture, on the central island of Honshu in Japan, he owns and cultivates in all 0.8 hectare. The land is poor. Nearly 60 percent of it is planted to mulberry; only 20 percent is in paddy; the rest is in upland unirrigated rice.

. . . He lives with his parents. But he is the operator. Father is not home. Mother is in work clothes—navy blue slacks and blouse. . . .

She raised a family on 0.4 hectare of land. They got as much again after the postwar land reform. The most cherished ambition

---

[8] *Soviet Agriculture Today*, Report of 1963 Agricultural Exchange Delegation, USDA, Foreign Agric. Econ. Report No. 13 (December 1963), pp. 1–2, 12–26, 73–75.

[9] A forthcoming comparative study of agricultural development in the U.S., Japan, and India (Ann Arbor, Mich.: University of Michigan Press, 1969).

in her life has been to have a son, see him married, and then retire. "Not from work," she hastens to add. Only from the compulsions and responsibility of work—"to have the freedom of working as and when *I* want to." . . .

They live in a single room, which they share with thousands of crawling silkworms in wooden trays filled with mulberry leaves. Worms occupy most of the space. The family's share of it is exceedingly small, at the kitchen end. . . .

The house is only a couple of hundred yards from the office of the local experiment station. No agricultural extension officer, however, visits him. He does not expect him to do so.

Nevertheless, this farmer is producing nearly half a ton more rice per hectare than is the average for the prefecture. He is applying a great deal of chemical fertilizer—more than is recommended—in addition to the compost he gets from the hogs. *He read about it in a journal.*[10]

• • •

Takeo Kamilkawara . . . has a farm in Iwate Prefecture, in northeastern Tohoku. The region used to be known as the Tibet of Japan —it was so backward.

Forty-nine years old, Takeo wears a grey jacket over an open-collar shirt and grey trousers. . . . He started farming almost three decades ago. In an area noted for inferior volcanic ash soil and a harsh climate, Takeo owns 2.5 hectares of paddy; an upland field of 0.7 hectare; 5 hectares in forest; and 1.0 hectare of pasture. His oldest son Tadayoshi, twenty-nine years old, lives and works with him. In fact, the son is the main operator. Together with their wives they are eight hands on the farm. . . .

According to Takeo and his son, however, "Our income has never been enough." They do not think it is sufficient now. They are not satisfied. They would like to make at least 2 million yen from the farm. But they are unable to figure out how to do it.

They cannot get more land. And since Iwate is situated in the snowy and cold zone of Japan, they can raise only one crop in a year. Tadayoshi therefore goes south every winter, from October till March, and drives a tractor on a daily wage of 1300 yen. Of this, he saves about half to invest on the farm. They have no other off-farm income. They have added a dairy enterprise. "It means more work, yes; but it brings in more cash." They are milking four cows. "Well, what else *can* we do?"

---

[10] Italics are mine.

As for rice, their main crop, Takeo is already producing 570 kilograms per *tan*, which is well above the average. Moreover, he believes that is as high as the yield can be under the existing techniques and know-how. . . . Nevertheless, he and Tadayoshi are trying very hard to improve the yield of rice. "But we are not succeeding. We do not know how we can do it." They are using all the chemical fertilizer they can, as well as stable manure. They think they are doing everything right; exactly as it should be. They keep in close touch with the agricultural extension worker and with the experiment station in Morioka. *They are hoping that scientists can offer yet a higher yielding strain of rice or suggest some new cultural practices that will be more productive.*[11]

• • •

. . . Specialists at the agricultural experiment station in Kyoto had been experimenting with direct sowing of rice for more than three years. They had found no appreciable reduction in yields. The climate here is suitable, and pests and weeds could be controlled effectively by chemicals.

Hatta is farming literally under the shadow of the experiment station in Kameoka. He owns 1 hectare of paddy land and cultivates another 4.5 *tan* in cooperation with two other farmers. Forty-five years old, he has been farming for nearly 30 years. He has 4 workers in the family—his parents, himself, and his wife. His gross income hovers around a million yen from the farm. He has no off-farm income.

On his own land he is growing rice, and barley and wheat in winter. Besides, he raises seedlings of parsley and other green vegetables. An excellent farmer, he has won a prize in rice culture. But he does not sow his rice directly. Nor does he intend to. At first he claims that he does not do it because he is cultivating vegetables as well. Then he explains that he did try it about twenty years ago, but the yields were very low. He has not tried again more recently. Finally, it emerges that "land productivity is still the most important consideration with me and with other farmers. That is why the practice is not spreading."

On the land farmed cooperatively, for example, "We use more chemicals for killing weeds in order to save on labor. But not on my own farm. I am too nervous to experiment." He weeds manually. According to him, the yields on the cooperative farm are lower than on his own. But so too is the cost of production.

[11] Italics are mine.

On his farm, Hatta pays 200,000 yen in wages for help hired for transplanting and harvesting rice. He realizes also that the return on his and the family's labor is dismally low. It is very much lower than in other professions, especially in this, a highly urbanized and industrially developed area.

"But I do not mind," he insists. "Money is not of prime importance to me. I enjoy the work. *I like to work hard.*[12] I *do* work very hard. But then I like it."

• • •

Again, according to Kamio Haruhide, an official appointed by *Shōgun* Yoshimune (1716–1745) to improve the falling revenues of the *bakufu:* "Peasants are like sesame seed. The more you squeeze them the more oil you get." The statement expresses more than the harshness of a stray eccentric, who incidentally, did succeed in collecting more revenue. It reflects the attitude of the times and the tax treatment meted out to the peasantry in Japan for a period of more than three hundred years. Towards the end of the Tokugawa regime when the *bakufu* and most of the *daimyō* were in severe financial straits, it was not unknown for the lord to appropriate 80 percent or more of what was supposed to have been the peasant's produce.

. . . [A]pparently Kamio Haruhide was right. With a draft animal or without, and however tight the squeeze, the Japanese peasant did produce more and more just like the sesame seed.

• • •

According to an FAO study, "notwithstanding the institutional limitations," gross output of agriculture increased by 121 percent between 1878 and 1912 at an annual average rate of 2.7 percent. Per hectare yield of rice in the same period, rose 42 percent at 1.2 percent per year. Between 1913 and 1937 also, according to this study, agricultural production continued to expand by about 40 percent, though the pattern of cropping and growth varied.

The prodigious efforts and magnificent production achievements of Japanese farmers on very small holdings over the past century have more recently been duplicated by the farmers of Taiwan, again on very small average holdings. The story of recent agricul-

---

[12] Italics are mine.

tural developments in Taiwan is masterfully told by Raymond P. Christensen in a recent study[13] from which we quote below:

> Agricultural output per hectare of land averaged 3.2 times as high in 1961–65 as in 1911–15. This increase resulted from increased multiple cropping as well as from higher yields per hectare of crops grown. Growth in productivity per hectare has been especially rapid in the last 15 years. During 1910–39, agricultural output per hectare increased 2.4 percent a year. Output per hectare nearly recovered to the 1939 level in 1951. Since 1951, agricultural output per hectare has gone up 4.4 percent a year.
>
> Expansion in crop production has come from two sources: Increased cultivated area and increased crop production per hectare of cultivated area. Increases in crop production per hectare of cultivated area also have come from two sources: Increased multiple cropping and increased crop production per hectare of crop area. The relative importance of these different sources has changed over time.
>
> From 1911–15 to 1936–40, expansion in cultivated land accounted for about one-fourth and increased crop production per hectare of cultivated land for about three-fourths of the expansion in total crop production. However, from 1951–55 to 1961–65, increased production per cultivated hectare accounted for nearly all of the expansion in crop production. The growth in crop production per hectare of crop area is most remarkable. It has involved shifts to crops that mature in a short time and that have a high value per hectare planted. Shifts in crop pattern to include more vegetables and other high-value crops have contributed to increased crop production per hectare of crop area.
>
> Numbers of farms and farm households in Taiwan went up only 7 percent from 1912 to 1940 [Table 9.1]. . . .
>
> Changes since 1940 have been quite different. The total number of farms has doubled and average size of farms has decreased to 1.05 hectares. The number of people per farm household has decreased slightly. Total cultivated land increased only 4 percent as potentials for bringing additional land under cultivation were gradually exhausted and industrial and urban growth occupied some agricultural land. Agricultural output per farm did not change much, but it is significant that it was maintained in view of the reduction in land area per farm. More intensive use of land brought a doubling in agricultural output per hectare.

[13] *Taiwan's Agricultural Development: Its Relevance for Developing Countries Today*, USDA, ERS, Foreign Agric. Econ. Report No. 39 (April 1968), pp. 18, 20–21, and 39–40.

TABLE 9.1

*Number of Farms, Cultivated Land, Land Per Farm, and
Agricultural Output Per Farm and Per Hectare, Taiwan,
Selected Years, 1912–65*

Year	Number of Farms	Cultivated Land	Cultivated Land Per Farm	Agricultural Output Per Farm	Per Hectare
	Thousand	Thousand Hectares	Hectares	Percent	Percent
1912	401	690	1.72	100	100
1917	415	721	1.74	129	128
1922	385	751	1.95	149	131
1925	394	775	1.97	175	153
1930	411	812	1.97	195	170
1935	420	831	1.98	233	203
1940	430	860	2.00	216	186
1945	501	816	1.63	97	102
1950	638	871	1.37	162	204
1955	733	873	1.19	172	248
1960	786	869	1.11	198	308
1965	847	890	1.05	231	378

SOURCE: *Taiwan's Agricultural Development: Its Relevance for Developing Countries Today,* USDA, ERS, Foreign Agric. Econ. Report No. 39 (April 1968), p. 40.

The development experience of Japan and Taiwan in the field of agriculture is, however, in sharp contrast to that of much of Asia. The very small family farm in the traditional agriculture of South and East Asia, except for Japan and Taiwan, was not an effective unit of modernization in the period 1946–66. For many reasons the very small family farmer in Asia has been slow to adopt new practices and slow to increase the total output of his farm. Turning to Kusum Nair again, she describes in her little classic *Blossoms in the Dust,* the sense of frustration, despair, and failure that engulfs many an Indian farmer.[14]

Gangawati is in the district of Raichur and it has had the good fortune of being irrigated by the Tungabhadra project. . . .

The project is located in Mysore near Hospet and commands a total area of two million acres stretching across into the neighbouring State of Andhra as well, in a belt which has been notorious for

[14] (New York: Frederick A. Praeger, 1962), pp 47–48, 88–91. Reprinted by permission.

centuries for recurring droughts and famines. . . . Like the Lower Bhavani Project, Tungabhadra also is meant primarily for "light irrigation" of dry crops such as *jowar*, groundnut and cotton, which are already under extensive cultivation in this region. In Raichur, *jowar* is the principal cereal crop and also the staple food.

But whereas in Coimbatore the Bhavani waters were taken up as soon as they could reach the fields and there is a clamour for more, in Balappa's village not one single peasant has yet deigned to avail himself of the irrigation facilities from the Tungabhadra. This, even though for the first three years the water is being offered free of any charge.

Meerappa also belongs to this village. Two of his front teeth are missing. He wears a white shirt, *dhoti* and turban. He owns ten acres of land. The irrigation channel passes right through his property. But he lets the water flow by unused.

"It rained last year so I did not take. It has rained this year also so I have not taken. I will take when the rains fail," he concedes, grudgingly, but not very convincingly, because even this year the rains were not regular.

"Have you made the field channels at least?"

"No."

According to an official of the project: "We carry manures and improved seeds in a trailer and offer to deliver them right at the doorstep to induce these cultivators to use them. We offer them loans to buy the seeds and manures. We go to their fields and offer to let in the water for them. We request them to try it out first in two acres only if they are not convinced. They could quadruple their yields if they would only take our advice and at least experiment. Still they are not coming forward."

• • •

It was in what is now known as the State of Bihar that Gautama searched and found the answer to his quest on a full-moon night in the month of *Baisakh*[15] and became the Buddha. . . .

That was 2,500 years ago. Today the landscape survives, but the light has faded from it, and once again the struggle on the socio-economic level appears to be against the identical forces of obscurantism which the Buddha strove to combat on the moral and religious plane.

It is pure obscurantism again which in Bihar, as in most parts of India, continues to prohibit certain upper caste Hindus from

[15] In May.

touching the plough, though these communities are full-time agriculturists and often own, except in predominantly tribal regions, most of the best cultivated land. This has serious economic repercussions.

In the village of Dhobgama, in Darbhanga district, for example, there are several *Brahmin* landowners. Although in most cases their land holdings are small, every one of them has given some land to a *Harijan*, to build his house on and to cultivate it on a crop-sharing basis, or entirely for himself.

I asked these landowners how it was that *Harijans* could get land from them to cultivate, since the present trend generally is not to give any land on lease because of the tenancy laws. At first one of them said: "Well, after all they have to live also. Where will they go if we do not give them land?" When I enquired again if it was only out of altruism that they gave the land, to keep the *Harijans* alive, another reason emerged: "But if they go away, what will we do? Who will work for us?" It is because not one of these *Brahmin* farmers ploughs, or is permitted by caste custom to plough and work on the land.

Jogeshwardas, of another village, admitted frankly: "You see we are *Maithili Brahmins*, so we cannot plough. To bind the *Harijans* to ourselves we give them the land. Then they have to work for us exclusively, and only when we have no work can they work elsewhere. Otherwise, what would we do if they went away? The land would remain unploughed. . . ."

Perhaps many lessons or ideas may be deduced from the observations and experiences outlined above, but to this writer they set in motion the following line of reasoning. Agricultural production under any state of the arts is a highly complex activity; it is a systems concept in which a large number of resources must be combined in relatively precise proportions and a series of productive acts or practices must be undertaken in specific ways and in proper sequence, if there is to be a significant final product. In other words, one combination of resources and set of practices in sequential order maximizes production, and total production will fall and perhaps fall greatly if the resource combination is changed or a practice is altered or a productive act is taken out of sequence.[16]

[16] In a commercial agricultural situation where certain resources are variable in the economic sense, the maximum profit position will be different from and

In a traditional agriculture the productive system evolved out of the distant past, perhaps by accident, perhaps by design, and has been handed down to the present day through tradition, or custom. The present-day cultivator is thus a part of a complex productive system, but he does not understand it or consider manipulating it. He follows the system through tradition; hence the name "traditional agriculture." But modernization means changing the productive system: changing the resource mix, or a production practice, or the sequence of operations, in order to increase production and thereby increase the income of the person involved. Changing the productive system means what it says; changing the resource mix, or a production practice, means that the affected parts of the productive system must be adjusted to that change. If the change in the productive system is an important one, then in all probability many elements of the system will also need to be changed and brought into adjustment with the initiating action. The potential gain in output resulting from the change in one practice, or the adoption of a new technology, will not be fully realized unless the whole productive system is adjusted to and made compatible with the new practice or technology.

This means that when the state of the productive arts in agriculture begins to change as a result of modernization, *management skill* must exist on individual farms, or be available to them, to help formulate and to put into practice the productive system that maximizes output for the new state of the arts and management and labor (perhaps the same person, perhaps not) must have the economic incentive or compulsion to bring that new productive system into operation quickly and properly. In other words, agricultural modernization places a very high premium on management skill and incentives. The fruits of modernization will be lost, or simply will not take place, unless the new and improved technologies and practices can be quickly and purposefully integrated into a produc-

---

less than the maximum output position. But in a subsistence-type agriculture, where most resources are fixed in the enterprise and hence are not variable in the economic sense, all resources will be employed to the fullest extent possible, and the maximum profit position is achieved at the maximum output position. Thus, for the purposes of this analysis, the maximum output position of a farm is assumed to be co-equal with its maximum profit position.

tive system that makes effective use of them. And this, it is argued here, is absolutely dependent upon the existence of management skills commensurate with the task and economic incentives that will induce farmers (or economic compulsions that will force them) to get the new productive system into operation.

In the late 1960's, the large farmers in India and other Asian countries are adopting the newly developed production packages organized around the new, high-yielding varieties of wheat and rice, and they are greatly increasing the total output of their farms—in some cases by as much as 100 percent. They are able to do this because they have the management skills themselves, or have ready access to those skills, to effectively integrate the new production packages into their farm organizations. The small farmers, on the other hand, are not participating so generally and so fully in the revolution in grain production which is sweeping over these countries. They are not doing so because they do not have the necessary management skills themselves and do not have ready access to them. Thus the great issue confronting India and many other Asian countries is whether they will find a way to upgrade the management skills of the small farmers within the next decade and thereby enable those small farmers to participate fully in the agricultural production revolution that is taking place in their countries.

The point of this argument, then, is that there is no one best form of production organization or size of farm for all situations; probably the form of productive organization and size of farm can and should vary with the land base, population density, social mores, and political goals of the society.[17] And a preoccupation with the most desirable form and size of farm organization tends to divert attention away from the really central organizational questions of agricultural development.

The central organizational questions, which must be solved satisfactorily if agriculture is to develop and production increase significantly, are:

---

[17] This is the pragmatic conclusion reached by Kenneth L. Bachman and Raymond P. Christensen in their article, "The Economics of Farm Size," in Herman M. Southworth and Bruce F. Johnson (eds.), *Agricultural Development and Economic Growth* (Ithaca, N.Y.: Cornell University Press, 1967).

1. How is the research on agricultural production to be organized and undertaken, the results of that research adapted to local conditions, and the results of the latter research developed into new and improved technologies (e.g., a new wheat variety) and practices (e.g., a weed control practice) for adoption on farms?

2. How is the production and distribution of the capital inputs called for under the research and development activities to be organized and undertaken so that those capital inputs are available to all farmers, large, medium, and small, at the *time* and *places* they are needed?

3. How can the management skills be developed and made available at the farm level, for the small farmer as well as the large, for combining the new knowledge, new technologies, and new resources into effective productive systems?

4. How can economic incentives (e.g., farm prices relative to input prices), or other forms of incentives (e.g., medals and citations), or economic compulsions (e.g., a land tax that forces the farmer to increase his output to survive) be established to induce managers and workers to put the new production system into operation quickly and properly?

The next chapter will deal with these questions as they relate to economic, social, and political organizations; here we deal with organizational issues that relate to production at the farm level.

The basic organizational problem at the farm level, we have argued, is the establishment of a production system which will yield an output that maximizes profits. Under subsistence conditions, this tends also to be the maximum output position of the farm; under commercial conditions, which is the goal of development, the maximum profit position of the farm will be short of the absolute maximum output position, but it will involve a total production that is much greater than under a traditional state of the agricultural arts. This organizational problem is intensified where the agricultural production research effort is successful and technological development is rapid; then the production system of a farm may need to change annually. The solution to this problem, we have further argued, rests with the development of management skills commensurate with the state of the productive arts and the establishment of a system of incentives or compulsions, which can induce both management and labor to put an effective production system into operation quickly and properly.

The question then arises: How can a developing country obtain the necessary management skills at the farm level? The first answer is that there are no shortcuts, no magic; as with all aspects of development, the process of acquiring the requisite management skills among illiterate peasants is a slow one, although we should recognize that we are not starting from zero. There are some progressive farms, typically the larger ones, with modern management skills in every developing country. Nonetheless, the basic starting point would appear to be universal primary education to achieve literacy among all farm workers, managers, and operators. Effective management in a modern, scientific world requires that all persons who must make decisions, down to those who mix rations for the feeding of livestock and apply fertilizer to crops, be able to read and follow instructions. Thus, literacy among farm workers at all levels is highly desirable if not absolutely necessary for effectuating a scientific agriculture, and universal primary education is the means to that end.

But for those who are already managers, either of a family farm or something larger, there must be an effective system of production education. Such a system might have several or many component parts, but it must be able to reach the farmer-manager with the guidance that he requires to reorganize his production system after each significant technological advance. The components of this system might include: (1) vocational training at the post-primary school level, (2) extension agents who work directly with all farmers—particularly the small ones, (3) production demonstration programs in local areas, (4) special short courses for farmers, (5) agricultural colleges, (6) salesmen and servicemen of private business organizations, and (7) information through printed materials and radio.

Every developing country will not, of course, want to include each of the above activities in its production education program for farmers. But each nation will have to undertake some kind of program with the capacity to reach its farm managers, if it expects to increase farm output significantly and rapidly through modernization. The demands for increased skill in management will not be great where the research effort is weak and unproductive and the rate of technological development slow. Further, it is probably a mistake to mount a major production education effort before research and technological development have begun to produce results. Thus, the production education effort to improve management skills should bear a close relation to the research and technological development effort, with the production education effort following, not preceding, the research and development effort.

As far as incentives are concerned, it is important for developing countries to recognize that farmers (except in special cases such as war or the threat of famine close by) will not attempt to raise more food in response to the exhortation that the country needs more food. Such a call will have little or no meaning to them, first, because under a traditional system they are producing all they know how to produce anyway, and, second, to break with tradition and innovate a new production system involves physical risks (possibly a smaller crop), economic risks (reduced prices if output should increase importantly), and increased out-of-pocket costs to initiate the new system. Stated differently, a farmer will be reluctant to move to a new production system in which there are unknown physical and economic risks which he cannot evaluate, no matter how much his nation needs more food. And he will not move to a new production system, even if he believes that it will expand his output, if he also believes that his cost per unit will be increased and price per unit might decline.

The point of all this is a simple and obvious one, but one which is often ignored in developing countries—namely, that economic incentives must be established at the farm level which are sufficiently strong to override the risks and thereby induce farm decision makers to innovate, adopt new techniques, and establish new and more productive production systems.[18] This means that government policies with respect to consumer price ceilings, farm price

---

[18] Earl O. Heady makes price incentives the central theme of his pamphlet, *A Recipe for Meeting the World Food Crisis*, CAED Report 28, Iowa State University, Ames, Iowa, 1966, and the author of the present volume has stressed time and time again the need for incentive farm prices in his consulting work with the government of India.

guarantees, requisition programs, prices of producer goods, and wage rates must be formulated so as to create a strong incentive— a compulsion if you will—for farmers to adopt new technologies, integrate them into new production systems and, through these processes of modernization, expand production.

The farmer is a decision maker at a key point in the production line. If he *believes* that he can take a new resource, or technology, or practice, and put it together with his other resources in a production system to increase his income by expanding output, he will. The great trick in this development business is to create such a belief in the minds of millions of peasant farmers, for it is at this point that the whole process bears fruit. The research results, the technological development, the newly produced capital items, the production education—all find concrete expression in the *increased food production* resulting from the new production system *instituted by the farmer*. But if the farmer does not believe, and so does not choose to innovate and bring into being a new production system, the whole elaborate and complex process of modernization grinds to a halt. The ultimate decision point in the agricultural development process is the farmer, and his criterion, within the constraints of his management skill and knowledge, is what will happen to his income. If the farmer believes that it will pay to innovate, then the whole complex process moves; if he does not, it stops.

10

Agricultural Development: Organizational and Policy Requirements

IN THIS CHAPTER we shall be concerned with those economic, social, and political organizations beyond the farm enterprise that are prerequisite to agricultural development. We have in mind here those organizations engaged in supplying capital inputs to the farmer, in supplying technical information and production "know-how," and in handling and distributing the products of farmers. Our concept of organization is a commonly accepted one: a specialized unit composed of a few to many persons related to one another by rules and working arrangements that permit the unit to take collective action to achieve a specific purpose. A military unit is a traditional, easily understood form of organization; a private firm producing and distributing automobiles has become an essential form of organization in the economies of the Western world; a unit, or units, bringing farm management skills to illiterate cultivators is the form of organization prerequisite to agricultural development.

Organizations provide a way of taking action and getting things done. If they are strong and effective, then the things that concern them get done efficiently and expeditiously. But if they are weak and ineffective, things don't get done. And all too often organizations, particularly economic organizations, are weak and ineffectual in developing countries. This writer, for example, once defined economic backwardness as "a state of weak and ineffectual orga-

204 THE WORLD FOOD PROBLEM

nizations for promoting development."[1] And with few exceptions, scholars and planners concerned with economic development have neglected the problem of creating effective economic and political organizations to make the process of agricultural development, as well as all other aspects of development, move.

A Progress-Oriented Government

The late John Brewster argued in his last major paper that among the organizational requirements of agricultural development, the most strategic one is a progress-oriented government. In Brewster's words:[2]

. . . Such a government is here recognized as one with sufficient (1) power, (2) perception of the felt wants of people, (3) determination, and (4) professional competence to conceptualize and implement inter-connected institutional and organizational reforms necessary for achieving sustained economic progress. As a very minimum, such reforms presuppose governments capable of formulating and backing up rules that protect all individuals and their possessions against exploiters; rules that give agreements among individuals the dependability of legally enforceable contracts and protection against fraud or swindle; rules that shift resources and jobs from less to more efficient users, and reward people in line with their productive contributions; and tax and public investment rules that generate social overhead services like roads, schools, credit facilities and power installations which people cannot provide for themselves, but which they must have for developing and using their capabilities as fully as possible. Without a whole nation of people being related to each other through such rules it is impossible for increasingly large numbers to combine their behaviors into reciprocally serving activities which are necessary for the creation and widespread use of increasingly productive technologies. And no generator of such large-scale organizing rules of life is conceivable without the emergence of progress-oriented, stable governments.

[1] *Some Notes on the Role of Agriculture in Economic Development*, an address by Willard W. Cochrane to the Food for Freedom Conference, University of Idaho, Moscow, Idaho, April 5, 1967. The address is printed in the conference proceedings, *Food for Freedom*.
[2] "Traditional Social Structures as Barriers to Change," Southwort and Johnson (eds.), *Agricultural Development and Economic Growth* (Ithaca, N.Y.: Cornell University Press, 1967).

In other words, government institutions and agencies should provide as a minimum:

protection of individuals against exploitation, theft, and violence;
protection to individuals in contractual arrangement against fraud and malpractices;
equitable returns to producers and workers;
services such as roads, education, and credit available to all.

But these are minimums. A truly progress-oriented government should want for its people:

public health, medical, and family planning services;
vocational training and production education;
publicly sponsored research and development;
expanding work and enterprise opportunities;
community cultural services and higher educational opportunities.

But then Brewster recognizes, as do all who spend any time overseas on development problems, that a striking feature of most economically backward societies is precisely the absence of such governments. Because of lack of power, perception, determination, or professional competence, or some combination of these inadequacies, governments in developing countries typically cannot "conceptualize and implement inter-connected institutional and organizational reforms necessary for achieving sustained economic progress."

But why? Why cannot the developing countries institute such reforms? Brewster finds an answer, or part of an answer, in strong village loyalties and even stronger kinship bonds, which lead to fear and distrust on the part of the villagers of all things originating outside the village; this in turn builds formidable barriers to the formation of large-scale organizations capable of effective collective action. Thus, mutually beneficial linkages fail to develop between the "simple folk" in the villages and elite groups in the national and provincial capitals; hence, a progress-oriented government cannot emerge.

But sometimes the barriers between the villages and the capital city are overcome and the climate of fear and distrust is dispelled. In such cases a progress-oriented government may come into being. It did, for example, in the case of Japan in the nineteenth century. But it is at this point that the explanations become slippery, and each country that has met with some success in development seems to require a special explanation. In the case of Japan, some scholars believe that the development of a progress-oriented government was due to the ascendancy of the emperor and the development of some kind of a transcendental relationship between the emperor and all the people. But whatever the explanation (and to this writer they all seem fuzzy), it is a fact that a stable government came into being with the Meiji restoration in Japan in 1868, a government relatively free of corruption and with the capacity to make those institutional and organizational reforms necessary to sustain economic development.

Taiwan seems to have found a progress-oriented government when the ruling elite was thrown off the mainland by the Communist revolution, and it came to realize that it no longer had a second chance. If it did not establish a satisfactory governing relationship with the villagers of Taiwan, it would be thrown into the sea as the tide of communism swept over Taiwan as well as the mainland. The Taiwanian case is thus explained on a last-chance principle. The Israeli case is perhaps similar to that of Taiwan. Facing extermination in Europe, surrounded by hostile Arab nations, and benefiting from a heavy immigration of highly skilled and educated persons, the Jews established in Israel during the 1950's and 1960's one of the most effective and progressive societies, as well as governments, that the world has ever seen. Again, a progress-oriented government seems to have emerged from the workings of the last-chance principle.

Thailand, on the other hand, may be one developing country that is establishing a progress-oriented government from a somewhat more rational and transferable set of causes—namely, the free flow of ideas, educational services, people, and trade over a long period of time. The winds of change have blown into Thailand in large measure through international trade and travel; but it is also true that the threat of communism in northeastern Thailand in recent years has spurred the government there to make needed institutional and organizational reforms.

The point to all this is that we know very little, or have little useful knowledge of how a developing country establishes a progress-oriented government. The explanation for those developing countries that have had the greatest success in establishing progress-oriented governments is either shrouded in mystery, or appears accidental. In either case, there is not a body of knowledge that can be used to assist other developing countries. Progress-oriented governments tend to be wherever you happen to find them, and they tend to be there for special and endogenous reasons.

But it is also critically important to recognize at this point that special organizations to support and facilitate agricultural development cannot be effective in the absence of a progress-oriented government. Or, stated differently, special organizations established to undertake developmental activities in the agricultural sector are not likely to be more successful than the general government operation itself. If the government cannot protect its people against exploiters, reward people in line with their productive contributions, maintain reasonable price stability, collect taxes on a reasonably equitable basis, and generate the necessary social overhead services, then it will not be able to sustain a significant increase in food and fiber production through agricultural modernization. In such cases, it is foolish to speak of increasing food production through development, and even more foolish for a developed country to invest in the agricultural development of that country. Significant and sustained agricultural development can take place only to the extent that the governments involved are determined and have the capacity to convert their structures into progress-oriented ones. This must be recognized by political leaders in both the developed and the developing countries.

Granted this conclusion, two policy considerations flow from it. First, general economic aid and technical assistance to increase food and fiber production should be withheld from developing countries that do not have the potential, or are not taking steps, to institute the reforms required by a progress-oriented government. It is not suggested here that a government of a developing country need adopt the Swedish, or British, or United States model. A progress-oriented government could be instituted under a military dictatorship or a complete socialist model. What is important is to establish institutions and organizations that give individuals and groups the inducement and the confidence to take the actions which can lead to the modernization of agriculture.

Second, since we know so little about the forces and actions that lead to progress-oriented governments, much more study and research must be directed to this aspect of development. The volume *The Political Basis of Economic Development*,[3] by Robert Holt and John Turner, sets forth some interesting hypotheses regarding the role of government in initiating and sustaining development, which suggest that centralized planning and decision making have in the past inhibited development. But in general this is a neglected field in which *economists, businessmen, and public leaders tend to assume away the critical issues.* Assuming a progress-oriented government, it is not too difficult to conceive and recommend to that government policies and organizations that will increase food production on a sustained basis. The critical question is: How do progress-oriented governments come into being? Once we know more about this, it should be possible to provide technical assistance to those countries wanting assistance on this kind of political organizational problem. As of 1968, this form of technical assistance is avoided like the plague.

The Political-Economic Model

In theory, a developing country might choose any one of three economic models—free market, mixed-capitalistic, or complete planning—and develop a set of organizations and institutions consistent with that model for directing and operating the economy. But as we observed in Chapter 8, few, if any, developing countries are opting for the free market model; either they don't trust it or they don't believe that it will produce the quick results they seek. On the other hand, few, if any, developing countries have the skilled manpower, the technical information, and the disciplined political and government organizations required by a complete

[3] (Princeton, N.J.: D. Van Nostrand Co. Inc., 1966).

planning model. In practice, the complete planning model has more often led to arbitrary actions and economic chaos than to a rapidly growing economy. Thus, the only real choice open to developing countries is the mixed-capitalistic model.

We shall, therefore, assume in this chapter that the developing countries under consideration have opted for a mixed-capitalistic model. In other words, the organizing principles for allocating resources, integrating productive activities, and distributing the national product among consumers—it is assumed—will be those of a mixed-capitalistic economic system. And we shall be concerned with the development of those specialized organizations required by a modern, scientific agriculture in such a system.

What organizations are required? How should they be structured? And what policies should guide their operations? These are the questions to which we seek answers in the context of a mixed-capitalistic system.

The Organizational Requirements

If the goal of a society is rapid economic development, a rapid increase in real per capita incomes (of which a rapid increase in the per capita production of food must be a part), then it must be the responsibility of the government of that society to bring into being the specific *organizational units* required for that development. A progress-oriented government will take steps to bring such units into being. But taking steps that result in a significant increase in per capita food production implies that the government, first, knows what organizations are required and how they should be structured, and, second, has the power and the skill to bring them into being. Once again we see the significance of a progress-oriented government for development; such a government must have more than good intentions; it must possess the power, the determination, and the knowledge to bring into being those elements required for development—in this case, organizational units.

But a government pursuing a development strategy in the context of a mixed-capitalistic model need not own and operate each organizational unit required by the development process. Its responsibility is to see that such organizations come into being, not to exert property rights over them. Thus, a progress-oriented government might observe that certain organizations required for development were coming into being spontaneously through private or cooperative action and therefore do nothing but observe. Or it might assist private groups in the development of specific organizations by providing credit or technical support. Or it might create government-owned and operated organizations when the private sector failed to do so, or when the private sector was performing poorly.

What organizational units are required by the development process in agriculture, in modernizing the agricultural production plant and in handling and distributing the increased product of that plant? The list, or classification, of organizations will vary somewhat with the analyst but it cannot vary too greatly, for the essential economic functions must all be undertaken in a balanced fashion if agricultural development is to occur at a desired pace.

Our detailed classification of the organizations required by the agricultural development process is as follows:

I. *Farm-related Organizations*

A. *Farm Supply Organizations* to bring new physical inputs and improved farm technologies to the village farmer from distant production points: fertilizers, improved seeds, insecticides, irrigation equipment, farm machinery, and so on.

B. *Farm Product Organizations* to acquire the farmers' surplus product, handle it, process it, and move it toward consumption centers. Such organizations must grade, buy, concentrate, store, process, and distribute farm products.

C. *Production Education Organizations* to convert new scientific knowledge and research findings into farm production practices for use in local situations, and to show farmers how to employ such practices. Such organizations may take many different forms, but they must have the capability of reaching all farmers, large and small.

D. *Irrigation Organizations* to allocate water supplies among local farmers, in accordance with rules of equity and desired agronomic practices. They deal with the allocation of water at the local level, from supplies brought in from central canals and reservoirs constructed by the larger society beyond the village level.

E. *Credit Organizations* to supply farmers with loan funds to purchase the physical inputs and new technologies required. They have the task of supplying credit to farmers at reasonable rates and in the amounts and at the times required by modern production systems, and, of course, they collect the loans.

II. *Farm Input Provisioning Organizations*

A. *Production Organizations* to produce fertilizers, insecticides, improved seeds, and machinery and equipment within the country for the use of farmers.

B. *Importing Organizations* to import such inputs as fertilizers, insecticides, improved seeds, and machinery and equipment when for technological reasons it is necessary, or for economic reasons desirable, to import them rather than produce them domestically.

III. *Food Supply and Distribution Organizations*

A. *Food Produce-Exporting Organizations* to export surplus, or high-valued, products to earn foreign exchange.

B. *Reserve Stock Organizations* to build reserve stocks in surplus areas and times, and release such stocks in deficit areas and times to avoid hunger, famine, and food crises.

C. *Special Food Distribution Organizations* to distribute food to the hungry and needy on special or concessional terms. Such organizations distribute food according to need rather than to market criteria.

D. *Regular Food Distribution Organizations* to distribute food to consumers on a conventional or market basis. The bulk of the food supply will be distributed through these channels.

IV. *Research, Development, and Training Organizations*

A. *Research and Experimental Organizations* to develop the new knowledge of all aspects of agriculture: agronomy, plant pathology, horticulture, economics, veterinary medicine, and so on.

B. *Developmental Organizations* to convert the basic research findings into production technologies and capital inputs—e.g., a plant-breeding experiment into a proven new variety for distribution to farmers, agronomic research into a new fertilizer formula, medical research into a new animal vaccine, and so on.

C. *Personnel Training Organizations* to produce the required skilled manpower, perhaps in the developing country, perhaps in some foreign country. Such organizations might take the form of universities, or special training centers, or apprentice arrangements.

Besides the specialized organizational units described above, which relate directly to the agricultural development process, a progress-oriented government would need to initiate many organizations that are indirectly related to agricultural modernization but basic to the general process of development. Such units would be concerned with primary, secondary, and higher education; central planning and development strategy; transportation and communications; price stability; and police protection.

Two further points should be made about these specialized agricultural organizations. First, the activities of most are interrelated and intertwined. In large measure they provide the personnel, product inputs, sources of funds, and physical linkages for one another. Thus, it is essential that they develop in a balanced fashion. It does no good to produce fertilizer if there is no means of distributing it, if farmers don't know how to use it, and if credit is not available to farmers who would like to use it. Similarly, there is no purpose in undertaking all the actions required to produce a surplus of, say, wheat, if the market cannot handle the product at a favorable price to producers. Agricultural development will take place, and food and fiber production will increase significantly, only where all these organizational units of the puzzle come along together to support and reinforce one another.

Second, the basic criterion for judging the effectiveness of each and every one of these organizations is not whether they are privately owned, or socialistically controlled, or have the best accountability and reporting service in the world, or employ all black men or yellow men or white men. The criterion for judging an organization's effectiveness must be its *performance*. How well did it do in the undertakings assigned to it? Did the credit organization reach all of the farmers in its district with credit in time and at rates that would permit all those farmers to plant the new, higher-yielding variety of seed? That is what counts. And did the seed distribution organizations reach all the farmers who had access to credit with supplies of the new, higher-yielding variety? That again is what counts. It is not the new buildings of the credit association or the seed distribution cooperative that is important, or the glowing reports written about their activities. It is the extension of credit and the distribution of seeds on time that is important; it is *performance* that is important. And this is a lesson that all developing countries must learn.

Some Organizational Examples

Production and Distribution of Improved Seeds

It is one thing to breed a new variety of wheat, or rice, or millet; it is quite another to produce the seed of that new variety in quantity, certified to yield the variety in question and to contain a minimum of foreign materials, including weeds, and then to distribute that certified seed to farmer producers at the proper time. Because new plant varieties are typically developed in public, or quasi-public, research stations, and because many developing countries are distrustful of private enterprise, it is common for developing countries to turn over the production and distribution of certified seed to a government agency. This is perhaps a good first step, for it gives the government experience with the problems of producing certified seeds. But government agencies are notoriously slow and ponderous in operation, and ineffective in pushing a product at the local customer level. Thus, the production and distribution of certified seeds often languishes or proceeds unevenly when undertaken by government agencies alone.

What government agencies require for a businesslike production and distribution of seed is *competition*. Thus, in this field of endeavor it would seem wise for developing countries to invite private seed companies from Western Europe and North America to come into the countries with their expertise, and produce and distribute the seeds of desired varieties in competition with the government agencies.

The number of private seed companies to be invited into a particular country cannot be prescribed here. It should vary with the size of the potential market and with technological and financial conditions. But enough should be invited to ensure strong competition in the production and distribution of seed. The battle for the market, and the profits that go to the successful firms, can provide the force that is needed but is so often lacking to achieve a widespread adoption of a new, improved variety.

Without doubt Jonathan Garst overstates the case when he argues:[4]

> The salesman is, more than anyone else, the key man in promoting change in the American scene. He can be a huckster or an instructor or a combination of both. He is best when he has this combination of showmanship and knowledge. Academic education, research, technical information operate on a different time scale. Studies deal with the past or the future. The present is in the hands of the salesman.

But there is much to be said for his argument that new practices and new farm inputs—such as the seeds of improved plant varieties and fertilizers—must be pushed, and pushed hard, upon the conservative, illiterate peasant farmer, by men with a strong incentive for doing so, if the adoption of the new practice or input is to be rapid and widespread. Thus, there is merit in Garst's argument when he says:[5]

> Here is the road to progress: millions of little salesmen, millions and millions of small sales to small poor operators, financed in all sorts of petty ways. Their ways, not our ways.

The role of government is altered in such an organizational scheme, but it remains an important one. A government agency could and should continue to serve as one important production and distribution agency; as an effective distributive outlet for the new variety it could ensure fair prices to farmers. But the govern-

4 *No Need for Hunger* (New York: Random House, Inc., 1963), p. 19.
5 *Ibid.*, p. 108.

ment would have other missions to perform. Some agency of government would need to provide seed inspection services and make sure that all seeds measured up to the certification under which they were sold. And finally, the government would have to work out the arrangements under which the private firms entered into business in the country; there would have to be adequate inducements and adequate safeguards to protect all parties concerned. The role of government is not eliminated here; it is altered to create an effective overall organization for producing and distributing seeds. And an important ingredient of this effectiveness is competition.

Provision of Production Credit to Farmers

The problem of providing production credit to farmers in the typical developing country is almost the obverse of providing certified seeds. Credit to farmers in developing countries is typically extended by small private moneylenders who lend from one crop period to the next at exorbitant rates running as high as 100 percent per year. What is needed in this situation, once again, is competition. But this time the competitive force must be provided by government. Government agencies must, through competition, force these loan rates down to, say, 5 to 10 percent; for at private moneylender rates farmers cannot in most situations borrow and invest in new capital goods with the expectation of a profitable return. Hence, the improved production practice involving new capital inputs is not adopted.

Many developing countries have already recognized this need and are attempting, through cooperative credit associations, or direct government agencies, to extend credit to farmers in competition with private moneylenders. In this competitive credit game, the collective agencies often are not successful for a number of reasons: (1) graft and corruption—the managers and clerks in the collective agencies turn out to be no different from the private moneylenders; (2) the rules governing the extension of credit are so rigid and so inflexible that the collective agencies cannot meet the varied and specific needs of local borrowers; and (3) the private moneylender is known, he is not an outlander, and his paperwork is simple; the borrower can get the loan in the same hour that he applies for it.

It should be recognized, however, that the government credit agencies and cooperatives may in many cases be performing effectively in a competitive role even though they are not making the loans. The presence and activity of the collective credit agencies may force the private moneylenders to lower their interest rates in order to continue to make most of the loans to farmers. And the important consideration in this context is not who is making the loans, but what is happening to the loan rate on farm production credit.

But for government credit agencies and cooperatives to be effective in extending credit to farmers in competition with private moneylenders, they must succeed in doing three important things: (1) rid themselves of graft and corruption where the managers and clerks regularly take bribes for making loans; (2) introduce flexibility into the operation of credit agencies, wherein managers can make loans tailored to the credit needs of local farmers rather than to a set of nationally prescribed rules; and (3) simplify the process of granting of loans—this is essential. A farmer will not wait three months and make ten trips to the office, when he can get the money he needs in three hours from a private moneylender (albeit at a much higher rate).

How are such reforms to be brought about? Once again we are driven back upon the need for a progress-oriented government. If the ruling elite, for whatever reason—fear for their personal survival, or enlightenment achieved through trade, travel, and education—believes that a progress-oriented government is necessary, then the kinds of reforms indicated above for credit agencies will *begin* to take place. But if the ruling elite has no concept of a progress-oriented government, then the kinds of credit agency reforms outlined above have no chance of occurring.

Farmers in the developing countries desperately need credit at reasonable interest rates to modernize their units. But such credit is dependent upon the successful intrusion of government into that field to create effective competition for the private moneylenders. The establishment of this competition is, in turn, dependent upon effective government action—upon the emergence of a progress-oriented government.

Establishment of an Effective Market
for the Surplus Products of Farmers

Even in the many developing countries pursuing socialistic economic policies, or attempting to implement the complete planning model, the local grain merchant continues to play a leading role and often constitutes the only market available to farmers. In some local markets there are many grain merchants and the competition is strong; in others, there is only one. In some cases, the local grain merchant is also the miller; in other cases, he sells to a mill. But it is the local grain merchant who typically buys from farmers, concentrates the grain, stores it, sometimes mills it, and moves it toward the consuming center.

The local grain merchant is much maligned in most less developed countries, but there are some good studies which suggest that middleman costs are not unduly high, given the high risks to which such operations are subject.[6] No doubt the local merchant cheats on weights and measures as much as he is able and gives out misleading price information whenever he can. But there is sufficient competition in most cases to eliminate the worst trade practices and to yield the farmer something approaching a competitive price and return for his product.

But the local grain merchant is typically a small operator, with limited capital and storage space. Thus he does not provide a good market for farmers at harvest time or a good source of supply to urban-consuming centers at the hungry time before the harvest. Grain prices to farmers fall badly at harvest when the crop is just a little larger than normal, and prices to consumers rise sharply when supplies become a little short. This does not happen because the middlemen are all "bad guys who wear black hats." It happens

[6] One such study is that done by Louis F. Herrmann, as consultant to the Ford Foundation for the government of India, entitled *Considerations Relating to Agricultural Price Policy in India, with Special Reference to Rice and other Food Grains* (August 1964). Another such study is Ralph Waldo Cumming, Jr.'s *The Structure and Functioning of the Indian Wheat Market with Special Reference to Khanna, Punjab, 1956–57 through 1963–64* (dissertation submitted to the University of Michigan in 1965 in partial fulfillment of the requirements for the Ph.D. degree).

because the distribution system lacks the handling and storage capacity to move a large crop or to carry the reserves necessary to protect against short crops.

To even out supplies over the crop cycle and stabilize prices to both producers and consumers, there is need in most developing countries for a government grain-marketing organization. Such an organization would have the responsibility of acquiring stocks in periods of large crops by purchasing grain from farmers at a previously announced minimum price and of storing that grain for use in periods of short supply. During periods of short supply such a grain-marketing organization would pour that grain into the market to moderate retail or consumer prices. In other words, in most developing countries the government should provide a balance wheel type of grain-marketing organization which accumulates stocks in good crop years, thereby stabilizing prices to farmers, and releases supplies in deficit periods, thereby stabilizing prices to consumers.

The private grain-marketing system cannot do this. It lacks the necessary operating funds and the necessary storage space. Further, the achievement of price stabilization in no way contributes to increased private profits. Thus the government grain-marketing organization must supplement and reinforce the private organization —if low prices to producers in good crop years and skyrocketing prices to consumers in poor crop years are to be avoided. In this scheme of things, the private sector might handle 80 to 90 percent of the product going to market, and the government organization only 10 to 20 percent of the domestic supply. But by handling this relatively small proportion of the crop, the government grain-marketing organization could perform its supply-balancing role and even out prices to producers and consumers within years and between years.

Research for Agricultural Development

Research is the engine of agricultural modernization. From successful research come the new ideas, practices, and technologies that can transform a traditional agriculture into a modern, scientific agriculture. Once they begin to roll out of the research stations, the transformation of agriculture can occur at a rapid, even revolutionary pace. But the building of a research organization capable of turning out production-increasing practices and technologies in a sustained flow is typically slow and fraught with untold difficulties. Further, the payoff in terms of research results and technological developments is (1) highly uncertain in its occurrence, (2) generally distantly removed from the time of the original input of research resources, and (3) not easily captured in a monetary return by the investors of the original research inputs. Thus, private enterprise is not inclined to undertake the kinds of basic and applied research required in agricultural development. In this situation, government must build and man the agricultural research organization. Private firms will undertake specific pieces of developmental research, the results of which can be captured in a monetary return by the investing firms (e.g., a particular model of farm machinery or a formula weed killer). But the broad, pervasive research on hybridization, plant protection, and animal diseases must be undertaken by agencies supported by society itself.

There is wide experience with the development of effective agricultural research organizations in the Western world which has not been utilized to the extent possible, or needed, in the less developed world. A desirable pattern of organization for the early stages of agricultural research might well be the following: The developing country enters into a cooperative arrangement with a private foundation, a university, or government agency of a developed country, or with an international agency, to build an agricultural research organization in which the administration and the actual research work are shared between local and foreign personnel.

There is much to be said for such a cooperative arrangement. The introduction of experienced Western research workers into the research organization from the beginning means that some work on the agricultural production problems of the country would be started quickly. There would be no need to wait until country nationals have been trained for research work. If partially trained nationals work alongside experienced Westerners in an apprentice arrangement—both in administration and in the research itself— errors, false starts, and mistakes in judgment on the part of nationals will be minimized and the effectiveness of the organization in turning out relevant research results speeded up. And when highly skilled Western researchers work alongside the people of the country, who are aware of the local problems and the characteristics of the local people, the research is given a problem orientation, and hence a greater relevance, in terms of the developing country's research needs.

The Rockefeller Foundation pattern of agricultural research organization, which was pioneered in Mexico, is currently spreading through South America, and is beginning to take shape in Asia, would seem to be the ideal pattern. A cooperative arrangement is made between an agricultural research organization in the developing country and the Rockefeller Foundation, in which the Rockefeller scientists share in the administration and the research work of the organization.[7] The inhabitants of the country then learn by sharing in administrative decisions and in the research work of the organization. At first, the Foundation may provide most of the leadership in administration and research, but the objective is to train administrators and research workers eventually to take over the leadership in both these areas. And that is the way the cooperative program has worked out in Mexico. Mexicans have learned the mysteries of doing research and administering research work and are now running their own show, as well as working with Rockefeller research teams in the Far East.

The pattern for developing effective agricultural research organizations in the less developed world has been established. It takes time, perhaps twenty years, and the sharing of responsibility and work is always awkward. But basically this is the way the *art* of doing scientific research is taught in the United States in professor-graduate student relationships. And it can be made to work fruitfully with skilled Western researchers and willing nationals. But again a progress-oriented government must initiate and support such cooperative relationships.

[7] The experience of the Rockefeller Foundation in developing an agricultural research organization is described briefly in *The World Food Problem*, A *Report of the President's Science Advisory Committee*, Vol. II, The White House, Washington, D.C. (May 1967), pp. 628–629. A fuller and more exciting treatment of the Rockefeller Foundation research operations around the world in agriculture is found in *Progress Report: Toward the Conquest of Hunger, 1965–1966*, Program in the Agricultural Sciences, The Rockefeller Foundation, New York (December 1966).

Relationships to Farmers

The purpose of the organizational activity described above is to convey ideas, skills, technologies, and physical inputs to farmers and thereby assist them to modernize their plants on the one hand and to purchase, concentrate, handle, process, and distribute the product of those farmers at reasonable prices on the other. But in performing these functions, an important procedural issue arises. How directly should such organizations interject themselves into the daily operations of farmers?

There is a strong tendency under the complete planning model, and there remains a tendency under the mixed-capitalistic model, for government-sponsored or owned organizations to tell the peasant farmer exactly how to undertake each farming operation (e.g., rates of fertilizer application, plant spacing, water application, and so on). In other words, there is a tendency to direct the operations of each farmer according to some fixed and general formula.

But such a policy can only lead to production trouble. No matter how small or how large, each farm is different: the soil, the topography, the labor supply, the consumption needs of the family, and the financial position of each farmer are all different. Thus, a general rule promulgated for the district or state level regarding the amount of money that can be loaned per hectare, or the application of nitrogen per hectare, will fit the requirements of very few farmers, if any. It will be too generous in one situation and too skimpy in another. General rules promulgated on high will almost certainly create more problems than they solve.

As we saw in the previous chapter, the illiterate peasant involved in farm modernization desperately needs good and relevant production education, but he needs it to enable him to fashion a production system that *fits his farming unit.* We are not, then, arguing against good and relevant production education, but against farming by government edict and general formula. Farming by a general formula leads to an unending series of disproportionate situations on individual farms in which there is always a little too much of one resource and not enough of another, with the consequent adverse effects on production.

The goal of organizations working with individual farmers should be to *liberate* their production talents rather than circumscribe them. This means, first, that organizations should provide farmers with the production education that upgrades their management skills; second, that they should present to farmers alternative courses of action with respect to production methods and the consequences of those different courses; and, third, that they must recognize the need for flexibility in dealing with farmers and permit farmers to pursue different options with regard to the use of services, credits, and resources. In this context the farmer ceases to be a prisoner of tradition, and he does not immediately become the prisoner of government regulations; he is provided with the opportunity to develop into a skilled manager in a modern, scientific agriculture. It is this kind of farmer, capable of formulating a production system consistent with the conditions of his farm and locale, and making use of proven new practices and technologies for his area, who can and will significantly increase the production of food and fiber.

Policies for Development

Up to this point, the discussion has been concerned with the need for specialized organizations to undertake specific functions in the development process. But if these organizations are to achieve the goals assigned to them, their operations must be guided and directed by realistic, relevant policies. Organizations do as they are directed. Thus it is appropriate here to pay some attention to the content of the policies that guide and direct the organizational units required in development.

Certainly the process of policy formation will vary from country to country, and the forces involved will be as varied and as unique by time and place as we find in the developed countries. The art of policymaking is as varied and unique as the art of politics. But the content of the operating policies of specific organizations can be analyzed. And that will be our procedure here. We will analyze the policy requirements of the same group of organizational units as we analyzed earlier for structure.

Production and Distribution of Improved Seeds

The organizational units involved will obviously aim to reach as many farmers as possible with seeds of improved varieties. And they will probably have some sort of an operational target of reaching, say, half the farmers in a district, or province, within a three-year period. But how is this target to be achieved? How will the organizations operate and what must they do to realize their purpose?

First, farmers must be informed about the new variety; they must see it grow and produce; they must come to believe in it. Thus, the organization must have an overt and effective policy of demonstrating to farmers what this new variety can do. This, in turn, must mean the formulation and pursuit of a means of working with the production educational organizations to demonstrate to farmers under field conditions how this plant variety performs. In other words, a demonstration program must be carried to the village level.

Second, the farmer must have an economic incentive to adopt the new variety. If the cost of producing and distributing the new variety is high relative to the prospective price of its product, then the farmer will not adopt it. Thus, it may be necessary for the government to subsidize the production and distribution of a plant variety in the early years of its use, and by that means reduce the cost of the seed to farmers. (Alternatively the price of the farm product might be increased, but this will not be discussed here for lack of space.) How large a subsidy should be on a given plant variety is a question related to the prices of other inputs, as well as to the price of the product and to the speed of adoption sought. But it is obvious that the subsidy should be paid through both private and government distribution units, if both are operating. The purpose of such a subsidy should not be to aid one kind of organization at the expense of others. The purpose of the policy of subsidizing the sales price of a new plant variety is to make the price more attractive and therefore speed its adoption among farmers.

Third, if farmers have been accustomed to growing and planting their own seed, it might be necessary to assist them to purchase this new off-farm input through the provision of new or additional credit. Thus, a policy might have to be conceived and pursued to extend credit to farmers for an entirely new purpose—the purchase of certified seed. This might mean, in turn, that representatives from the seed organizational units would have to sit down with representatives from the credit organizations and devise a program to make credit available to farmers at reasonable rates for the purpose of purchasing certified seed.

So it could well be that the seed-producing and distribution organization units would have to formulate and execute policies of production education, pricing, and credit before they were able to achieve any significant adoption of their new farm input—certified seed of an improved plant variety. And the formulation of these policies and programs would require that the seed organization units work out satisfactory and effective arrangements with educational organizations, governmental fiscal units, and farm credit organizations.

Provision of Production Credit to Farmers

If a credit organization is to reach farmers with loan funds, it must be physically accessible to them. Thus, a credit organization that has the overt goal of pulling interest rates down to a range of, say, 5 to 10 percent must obviously make itself physically accessible to farmers. This might mean the development of an operating program with credit offices located in the larger villages and towns, with one office for, say, every thousand farmers. This might or might not be a desirable ratio; manpower capabilities, desired rate of modernization, and experience all will be involved in finding the proper ratio. But there can be no question about the need for such a policy. If the credit organization really wants to affect the interest rate to farmers, it must be prepared to maintain credit offices within easy reach.

There is also a whole set of policies related to the administration of a farm credit program that would have to be initiated and faithfully executed. These administrative-type policies might include: (1) a rule stipulating that each application for credit must be acted upon, say, within two weeks; (2) an information policy under which the interest rates for each type of loan (e.g., seed loan, loan to purchase land) is announced publicly; and (3) a policy of vigorous prosecution, with heavy fines and penalties, of employees charged with accepting bribes in the granting of loans. All these administrative policies would be aimed at improving the effectiveness of the program and reducing the graft and corruption associated with it.

In a major credit program aimed at reducing the effective rates of interest to all farmers, the central government, too, would have to make some important policy decisions. With the heavy demands on it from all sides, how much of the government's limited financial resources should be devoted to agricultural credit and to the modernization of the agricultural plant? If too great a proportion of its financial resources were devoted to agricultural production credit, the development of other sectors would be inclined to lag. It would be bad policy, for example, to restrict the availability of credit to industries producing fertilizer, pesticides, and irrigation pumps and equipment, while credit was being pumped out to farmers. Such credit to farmers would be wasted as they bid against one another for limited production supplies coming from the nonfarm sector. Thus, some very careful policy decisions would have to be made at the national level with regard to the allocation of financial resources among different sectors. Agriculture should receive and extend to farmers an amount sufficient to enable farmers to put into operation the modernizing inputs flowing to them, but not more. These strategic decisions are of great importance in the general development process.

Establishment of an Effective Market for the Surplus Product of Farmers

Many of the organizational units included under this heading would be privately owned, and their merchandising policies would be the direct result of private competition and the induced result of government policies (e.g., reserve stock policies, price-supporting actions). But the progress-oriented government of a developing country must have a clear and articulated policy for the operation of marketing organizations in the private sector. This policy must include, as a minimum, three basic points: (1) the establishment of rules and regulations governing trading operations that increase the efficiency of markets (e.g., realistic grades and standards for the basic commodities, by which they are regularly traded); (2) the provision of technical assistance and credit to private marketing firms to increase their operating efficiency (e.g., building modern storage facilities); and (3) the taking of actions to strengthen competition in local markets (e.g., helping establish effective cooperative marketing organizations). The vigorous pursuit of these policy lines in the private marketing sector is essential to the establishment of an effective market for the surplus products of farmers in almost every developing country.

Turning specifically to the operation of a national grain-marketing organization acting as the agent of government, there are a host of operating policy issues to be resolved. How should the farmer be paid at harvest time—at one time, or throughout the marketing period? How should the product be priced to farmers with respect to location? Where should the grain be stored? What grain-freshening policy should be pursued? What extraction rates should be used in processing? How should the byproducts be priced? And so on.

If, however, the developing nation has two great stabilization goals—(1) to keep farm prices from falling disastrously at harvest time, and (2) to keep food prices from skyrocketing in the hungry time prior to harvest—then its agent, the national grain-marketing organization, must have two overriding operational policies. First, it must be prepared to step into the market and purchase all grain offered by farmers, *everywhere*, at a previously announced price. It won't get all the grain offered; the private merchants, if they are to remain in the business of handling grain, will continue to acquire most of it. But by standing ready to buy it from any farmer anywhere, this policy puts an effective price floor under the commodity at harvest time. The policy must include a publicly announced floor, or minimum price with reasonable location differentials, *with an absolute guarantee on the part of the national grain-marketing organization to purchase the grain of each and every farmer at the announced minimum price. Such a pricing policy will hold market prices at or above the announced minimum price, and encourage farmers to produce a surplus of grain for the market.*

Second, the organization must be prepared to sell its reserve stocks in consuming centers whenever prices in the market begin to move above an agreed-upon level. If the government is in a strong reserve stock position, it would be helpful to all persons operating in the market to know exactly at what prices the organization would begin selling and what its price stabilization goals are. But if it is in a weak stock position, the organization must be careful about announcing its pricing plans. Once a price stabilization organization fails to achieve its announced objective, public confidence in the market drains away fast.

An organization concerned with stabilizing farm and food prices must (1) *be prepared to purchase any and all supplies offered to it at a previously announced price,* and (2) *have a release and selling formula for moderating price rises that is consistent with its reserve stock position.* This is the heart of the matter; if an organization concerned with stabilization cannot hold to these two policy positions, it will quickly receive a vote of no confidence from all parties concerned.

Research for Agricultural Development

The central goal of an agricultural research organization is obviously to create new knowledge and develop new technologies which farmers can use to increase their production. But this goal will be achieved only as men are trained in the agricultural sciences (including the social sciences) and then set to work on relevant and specific agricultural production problems. Thus, it is clear that the research organization for the agricultural sector must develop and pursue a manpower policy which guides and directs, first, the training of agricultural scientists and, second, their employment on research projects and programs.

Whether agricultural scientists and skilled technicians should be trained (1) abroad in the developed countries, (2) abroad in regional centers located in the developing countries, or (3) locally in research stations that are receiving technical assistance from a developed country can be debated endlessly. There are good arguments for and against each approach, so we can expect that all three approaches will continue to be used in varying combinations. But it is critically important for the developing country involved to have a systematic policy on these approaches, as well as on the numbers of men to be trained, methods of selection, and fields of training, and then adhere to that policy until a flow of skilled manpower into the agricultural research stations of the country has been established. It is the failure to establish and hold to a realistic manpower policy for training agricultural scientists that is the downfall of many developing countries. The new nations often do not appreciate that skilled manpower is a resource that must be trained and developed, and that this training and development takes time—a very long time. Research scientists and technicians cannot be gathered like wild berries in the fall as part of nature's bounty; they must, like hybrid tea roses, be nurtured over a long period under special conditions.

The second aspect of manpower policy in this area must be concerned to seek out the trained agricultural scientists and technicians of the developing country and employ them in the kinds of jobs for which they have been trained, under conditions that are conducive to productive research and with adequate monetary rewards. Too often newly trained agricultural scientists have not returned to their own country, or have left it at the first opportunity, because there was no policy for using their talents in research work or for providing them with an income commensurate with their training. A trained plant breeder, or agricultural engineer, will not long be happy running an elevator or serving as a receptionist in a government building of his home country.

Finally, when the two aspects of manpower policy outlined above have been implemented, there must be a policy for guiding the broad directions of agricultural research. Few countries, even in the developed world, are rich enough to do research in depth on every agricultural problem. Thus, a developing country must select carefully the areas in which it invests its skilled human resources and limited physical resources. The areas selected for intensive research should be consistent with the country's development strategy. If that strategy calls for an expansion in the production and export of such commodities as cotton and jute, and the importation of increased quantities of food grains, agricultural research should then be directed toward the production and handling problems of cotton and jute. But if the country is trying to cut down on the importation of food grains, then its agricultural research program should be directed toward the production problems of the cereals.

Obviously, the agricultural research program should not wander aimlessly in accordance with the whim of each new researcher employed; each developing country should have a research policy that focuses its meager research resources on its relevant agricultural and economic problems.

Some Concluding Remarks

The four areas of food and agriculture which we have analyzed for organizational structure and policies were not selected because they are necessarily the most important, or the only, areas meriting analysis. They were selected and analyzed here to represent the varied kinds of organizational questions in food and agriculture that must confront developing nations and to illustrate the kinds of policy considerations that must be explored and resolved in some way.

The organizational requirements in *each area* of food and agriculture must be analyzed and later developed in a comparable way *by each* developing country. Of course, that development will vary in accordance with the goals, mores, and resources of the country concerned. But each developing country must in some way bring into being organizations with the capacity—the structure and policies—to undertake successfully all the activities categorized earlier in this chapter for food and agriculture. The four areas examined here in some depth have suggested the kinds of organizational questions and ways of resolving them that must be taken into consideration by the developing nations along with the many other aspects of agricultural development.

11

Food, Agriculture, and Economic Development

As THE TITLE IMPLIES, this chapter will deal with the relationships among the three basic elements of this analysis: the food problem itself, agricultural development, and the general process of economic development. It is our thesis that these problematic elements cannot be analyzed separately with productive results, and they certainly cannot be solved without reference to one another in practical developmental situations. If this volume is to make a contribution to the solution of the world food problem, it must therefore develop in a meaningful and fruitful way the interrelations among these three elements. This we shall do in terms of a conceptual model for a hypothetical developing country.

The Conceptual Model

The model we have in mind assumes a hypothetical developing country that is overpopulated, predominantly rural, with a tradition-bound agriculture, low worker productivity, mass poverty, and widespread undernourishment and malnutrition, *but* with a progress-oriented government that seeks to increase the real income of the masses of its people. Our shorthand description of this hypothetical developing country is "an overpopulated, traditional agricultural economy."[1]

[1] Those interested in the economic theory of the development process in such an economy should turn to three excellent readings: John C. H. Fei and Gustav Ranis, *Development of the Labor Surplus Economy: Theory and Policy,*

230

There have been, and will be, countries that do not fit this short-hand description—countries with special food problems (e.g., among the ethnic minority groups in the United States), countries with stubborn agricultural development problems (e.g., the Soviet Union), and countries with general development problems (e.g., Argentina). But the model of an overpopulated, traditional agricultural economy aptly describes those areas of the world with acute and massive food problems: East Asia, South Asia, most of West Asia, and the upland areas of Latin America. These countries have a food problem because they are overpopulated in relation to the available conventional resources, their agricultures are bound by tradition, and worker productivity is very low. And the food problem takes a modern twist—e.g., food prices are rising and the shelves of government food shops are bare, because the countries are attempting to develop. Thus, the model is an appropriate one for our purposes—that is, it can be used to describe the interrelation between the food problem, agricultural development, and general economic development in those developing countries that are experiencing acute and massive food problems.

It is characteristic of countries represented by this model that agricultural worker productivity is very low. Some economists hold that the productivity of the marginal farm worker is zero—that is, the contributions of the last worker added, or the last 1,000 workers, or the last 1,000,000 workers, depending upon the situation, have no effect on the total volume of production. In other words, given the limited and antiquated capital resources available to the additional workers and the restricted land base on which they work, the efforts of the last worker, or last 1,000 workers, or last 1,000,000 workers, depending upon the situation, do not result in any additional output. Other economists hold that the productivity of the marginal agricultural worker in an overpopulated, traditional agri-

---

(Homewood, Ill.: Richard D. Irwin, Inc., 1964); William H. Nicholls, "An 'Agricultural Surplus' as a Factor in Economic Development," *The Journal of Political Economy,* Vol. LXXI, No. 1 (February 1963); and N. Georgescu-Roegen, "Economic Theory and Agrarian Economics," *Oxford Economic Papers,* new series, Vol. 12, No. 1 (February 1960). The present writer accepts many of the theoretical formulations presented in these readings and adds his experience in developing countries to obtain the model and analysis outlined here.

cultural economy rarely falls to zero, but that it is typically lower, measured in value terms, than the cost of subsistence of the worker. This is the conception of the worker's productivity that we shall accept here. In this overpopulated, traditional agricultural economy, agricultural production is organized and directed by tradition, and the population is so dense in relation to the existing land and capital resources that the productivity of the marginal worker, or workers, remains below the subsistence level. It is, further, our opinion that this relationship holds for much of developing areas of Asia, the Middle East, and the uplands of Latin America.

But as Georgescu-Roegen has pointed out in his penetrating essay "Economic Theory and Agrarian Economics,"[2] such low-level productivity on the part of the worker is not devastating in its effects in a truly agrarian society. In such a society, the total product of society is distributed among its members in accordance with social status or family relationships (as in the case of feudal Europe or the extended family in the village life of Asia), rather than with the productivity of specific workers. In such cases, any additional product contributed by the marginal worker adds to the total product of the society to be shared among its members in accordance with status and family relationships; hence, the well-being of society is improved over what it would have been if the marginal worker sat under a tree and produced nothing. In other words, in an agrarian society, where *all* members share in the total product in accordance with status or family relationships, the average share of each member will be increased when the product of the marginal worker is added to the total, even though his marginal product is less than the cost of his subsistence. Thus, we see women and children in such societies gleaning the field after the harvest to maximize the total social product, even though the gleaning operation yields little additional product.

But once modernization begins to take place in agrarian societies and contractual relations are substituted for familial and status relationships, economic difficulties also begin to arise for the marginal workers. Assuming that the product contribution of the marginal worker is less than his subsistence, perhaps even zero, the farmer-

2 *Op. cit.*

entrepreneur cannot afford to pay the marginal worker a subsistence wage because the worker does not earn one; and the marginal worker cannot afford to accept what he earns as a wage, because it is less than his subsistence requirement. In the context of modernization and development, then, marginal agricultural workers in overpopulated countries are cut adrift to wander as landless agricultural labor or to settle in squalor around the larger cities. The process of modernization and development in overpopulated agricultural societies unfortunately tends to sort out and isolate specific groups, marginal farm workers, who in fact become surplus members of the economic society.

In theory it should be possible to transfer these surplus workers out of the agricultural sector, place them in nonfarm jobs, and thereby enable them to contribute to the development of the country.[3] Let us consider the simple case where the productivity of the marginal farm workers is zero. (The logic of the case where the productivity of the marginal workers is greater than zero but less than subsistence is essentially the same, but somewhat more difficult to explain since the losses to total agricultural output must be taken into account when such surplus laborers transfer out of agriculture.)[4]

In this case, since the product of the surplus agricultural workers is zero, nothing is lost from total agricultural production by transferring them out of agriculture and into the nonfarm economy. Further, in one sense there is a "surplus" of agricultural products that could be tapped to feed and clothe the surplus workers and their families after they have made the jump into the nonfarm sector; this "surplus" may be conceived as being that share of food and clothing which was used to sustain these workers and their families under the older sharing relationships of the agrarian so-

[3] For a full development of this idea see the article by W. Arthur Lewis, "Economic Development with Unlimited Supplies of Labor," *The Manchester School* (May 1954), reprinted in *The Economics of Development* (New York: Oxford University Press, 1963).

[4] Gunnar Myrdal, in his *Asian Drama: An Inquiry in the Poverty of Nations,* finds this "modern approach" to the development of densely populated countries invalid for various institutional reasons (see particularly Chapter 21). Although we too find the approach analytically inadequate, we do believe that it serves as a useful point of departure for our development problem.

ciety. The food and clothing allocated to the workers and their families through status or family arrangements in the agrarian society is still in being somewhere in the rural sector, even though the surplus workers have transferred out of it. Now, assuming that this food and clothing "surplus" is somehow transferred along with the surplus labor, this labor could be sustained in new nonfarm jobs—building roads, irrigation works, houses, and other public structures, working in factories, and providing various kinds of services.

To the extent that these former agricultural workers, who were surplus and produced nothing, are now employed in producing goods and services required by the developing country, the development process will have been enhanced and the total product of the economy will have been increased, although nothing in the reasoning to this point has led to an increase in food production. Further, to the extent that the transferred workers are now being employed in jobs involving greater amounts of capital, and improved capital, their productivity and real incomes will have increased significantly, probably to well above the subsistence level.

But will these transferred workers in fact have more capital to work with? And if so, where will it have come from? The analysis has not so far supplied the answer. It has suggested only where the daily sustenance of these workers might be found.

There are, however, several sources that might provide the capital to be combined with these workers. The first such source to be considered is a "boot-strap" operation in which these workers create their own capital with their bare hands, and then in a later stage use that capital. This capital formation process may be conceptualized as follows: the transferred surplus agricultural workers are first employed making picks, shovels, sledges, and baskets for carrying dirt and gravel, which, in turn, are used to build roads and irrigation works. This is a slow process, but it was a common one in the pioneering and settlement stages in North America. In more recent years, Communist China appears to have made extensive use of this boot-strap form of capital formation; the surplus agricultural labor was available and China has used the hand and foot power of these workers to create capital.

A second source of capital to be combined with the transferred workers is foreign, external capital, obtained through loans or grants. This, of course, is the quick way to obtain capital, if it is available: borrow it, or receive it as a gift, from the more developed countries. But despite exhortations from all sides to the developed countries to provide more of such capital, efforts in this direction have fallen far short of the needs of the developing countries.

The third source of capital, and probably the most important over the long run, is to squeeze it out of the share of production going to landlords from farming operations. In a modern contractual society, the share going to landlords will increase as more and more workers are added to the farm land base and their wage rate declines with their productivity, even though total production increases. In an overpopulated agrarian society, where labor productivity falls below the level of worker subsistence, the landlord's share will be consumed by the surplus labor under established family and social distributive arrangements. Even then, however, the landlord's share will be positive and therefore constitute a source of capital to be combined with the surplus labor transferred to the nonfarm sector, except in one special case—that of a maximum surplus population, where the total product of agriculture is exhausted in order to sustain that population at a subsistence level. Short of this extreme, there will exist a *surplus* of agricultural products in landlords' hands that represents potential capital which can be employed by the developing country.[5]

This is not to suggest, however, that it is an easy task to extract the available surplus in landlords' hands for use in production in the nonfarm sector. Traditionally, such surpluses have been hoarded in the form of gold or used in displays of conspicuous consumption— for example, expensive weddings, jewelry, or trips to Paris. But the fact remains that the share of production going to landlords represents a surplus that *could* be used to produce or purchase capital goods, if it were squeezed out of the hands of the landlords.

There are two principal ways for this squeeze to occur: (1) the government could tax away such surpluses and use the revenues so obtained to purchase or produce the needed capital items, and (2) private agents could borrow such surpluses and transfer them into the nonfarm sector to purchase or produce capital items in demand in the private sectors. These private transfer agents might, in fact,

[5] For a technical discussion of these marginal relationships, see Nicholls, "An 'Agricultural Surplus' as a Factor in Economic Development."

be landlords with one foot in the farm sector and one in the newly developing nonfarm sector; in this dual role they would draw the surplus out of agriculture and reinvest it in profitable nonfarm enterprises.

Chroniclers of Japanese development in the nineteenth century emphasize the squeeze that was applied to Japanese agriculture to provide a product surplus, or savings, to be used to supply capital to the private nonfarm sector, to build an economic infrastructure, and so create new capital to flow back into agriculture. Fei and Ranis stress the dynamic role of the dual landlord as the transfer agent of private funds in this process,[6] and Kusum Nair emphasizes the relentless pressure of taxes on the peasant as a means of acquiring a surplus to produce or purchase capital goods for the developing economy.[7] Thus, although the means may be debated, there is no debating the fact that a surplus was squeezed out of the overpopulated Japanese agricultural economy of the nineteenth century to provide capital for the development of its nonfarm economy. The Japanese somehow managed to squeeze "the last unit" of surplus product out of the agricultural sector to support the development process.

The model of an overpopulated, traditional agricultural economy has now produced a surplus labor supply for work in the nonfarm sector, the food and fiber supply required to sustain these workers and their families, and (with or without external assistance) a product surplus to be used to produce or purchase capital goods to combine with the surplus workers. This is a remarkable achievement, happening, so to speak, out of thin air. But it is an achievement that is logically possible and has the historical basis of the Japanese experience.

Once these elements of the development puzzle have come into being in a reasonable sequence, the development process of the hypothetical country can get under way. Workers, daily bread, and capital can be combined to produce roads and schoolhouses in the public sector; cotton textiles, bicycles, and bricks for the private nonfarm sector; and fertilizers and tube-well equipment to flow

---

[6] *Op. cit.*, pp. 164–179.
[7] *The Lonely Furrow* (Ann Arbor, Mich.: University of Michigan Press, 1969).

back into the farm sector. The productivity of the once surplus agricultural workers will have increased greatly as they work in combination with capital goods to produce the products listed above and many, many others. In this context the natural forces of development, together with the assistance of a progress-oriented government, will increase money wages and the effective demand of these workers for the products of both the farm and nonfarm sectors. Finally, the real income of these and all other workers in the economy will have increased and a balanced development will have been set in motion.

Whether this miracle of development can be sustained depends upon a host of considerations: whether production in agriculture increases in response to rising farm prices through investment in new technologies and capital goods (e.g., fertilizer and tube wells); whether businessmen see the opportunity to invest further in new plant and equipment and are encouraged to do so by the same progress-oriented government that helped wages catch up with worker productivity; whether government has the power and capacity to collect taxes and maintain law and order, and the wisdom to avoid costly edifice building (e.g., steel mills and great dams) and external wars; and whether the masses of the people can discipline themselves to live with modest real income gains, while much of the increased product of the development effort is siphoned off to support further development—in a national educational system, research stations, and plant and equipment. Development, the people of the developing nations must learn, is an insatiable consumer of capital.

If the decisions made by this hypothetical country on all of these problems are the correct ones, the development process will be sustained. The product stream—the flow of goods and services—will widen with the increased employment of workers and application of capital; and the capital goods flow will be allocated among competing demands according to its most productive and efficient uses. The income stream will be allocated among consumers in ways that will guarantee *to all* a minimum level of living, and among consumption uses and savings in ways that will sustain the economic growth process. Government fiscal operations will contribute to price stability. The manpower policy and research and development policy will contribute to the increased productivity of labor and capital, which, in turn, will contribute to a widening of the goods stream and money stream, and so to increased real incomes for all. Food production and trade in agricultural products will have increased sufficiently to permit an important increase in per capita food consumption. Thus, undernourishment and malnutrition, which were commonplace in this once overpopulated country, will have receded before rising real incomes, and the food problem will have disappeared. In the conceptual model, the food problem of the developing world is resolved to the extent, and only to the extent, that development—i.e., rising real incomes—supplants underdevelopment—i.e., rural poverty. The food problem is solved by successful general development.

The Model and Reality

In our analysis of development in the model of an overpopulated, traditional agricultural economy, we assumed, first, that the food and clothing consumed by the surplus workers in agriculture would somehow be transferred with them to the nonfarm sector, and, second, that a surplus would be squeezed out of the landlords in agriculture, or would be forthcoming from external sources, to provide capital for use by those workers in their new nonfarm jobs. Given these and some other heroic assumptions, we can postulate a situation in which the development process begins to pick up momentum; economic development is under way.

But this is not the way things generally happen in the real world. It is extremely difficult to capture through collective means the food and fiber formerly consumed by surplus workers in an agrarian setting, and transfer that food and clothing along with them to the nonfarm sector. Taxation is the only realistic means available to a developing society, and it is not an effective means in a diffuse, agrarian setting. Further, the quantities of food and clothing made available to the surplus workers and their families to provide them with subsistence, given the familial and societal obligations of an agrarian society, have a way of disappearing when the surplus workers move away to urban areas; probably those quantities of food and clothing are used to increase the consumption of the people who remain on the land. In any event, those supplies don't move easily and readily to urban centers with the released surplus agricultural workers; they tend to disappear in rural areas.

In the more typical case, as the onset of commercialization and modernization loosens social and family ties, surplus agricultural workers become rootless in rural areas and drift to the cities and towns. These rootless, landless ex-agricultural workers congregate on the fringes of the larger towns and cities, living in shacks and on the streets, and are sustained on various kinds of relief programs and make-work projects under which the head of the family receives a very small daily money payment or wage. These money wages are then spent in private food shops, or government stores, for basic food products. But there are no additional food supplies in the urban food shops, since the food supplies previously consumed by them did not move to town with them. In this context, the increased money purchasing power of these uprooted farm workers flows against a fixed supply. Food prices then begin to rise in the private shops, and the shelves in the fixed-price government shops become barer and barer. The increased competition for a fixed food supply in the cities and towns forces food prices to rise, food inventories to be drawn down, and hoarding to become a regular practice among the upper income groups. These are the overt symptoms of the modern world food problem—a problem that is part and parcel of economic development in the world of reality.

This unhappy situation can be alleviated to some degree if the struggling underdeveloped country is receiving foreign economic assistance. If, for example, the foreign assistance takes the form of food aid, the food supplies received as assistance can be moved to the cities, distributed through fixed-price government food stores, and the increased demand for food satisfied. By augmenting food supplies in urban areas with foreign food aid, the food price inflation is averted and the food problem of the country *temporarily* solved. This is precisely the way in which food aid from the United States has been used in many developing countries, and it is an example of foreign aid in action that is easy to visualize.

The example of *general* foreign economic assistance is perhaps more difficult to visualize; but since it is probably more important and more likely to lead to a permanently improved situation, we should take the time to understand it. Foreign economic assistance in the form of free foreign exchange means that the country can import additional resources up to the amount of the assistance in whatever product form it deems most advantageous. Food products could be imported with such foreign assistance, but if the country is following an effective strategy of development, and the food problem has not become unmanageable, it is more likely to import metal products, trucks, motors, pipes, cement, fertilizer, fabricating machinery, and spare parts. These kinds of resources, when employed with labor, make the arm of each laborer longer and stronger. And these kinds of resources can be combined with the surplus agricultural workers now ringing each town and city, as well as other workers, to produce new and additional products for sale in the export market, to produce new capital goods required on modernized farms, and to produce more food and fiber on those farms. By these productive processes the new urban worker will have an increased real product to exchange for food, both in the domestic and the foreign market. At the same time, more food will be produced on farms, a part of which must move to the city in exchange for the producer goods obtained by farmers from the city.

But the struggling country that is not receiving foreign assistance will have great difficulty obtaining capital resources to combine with the surplus agricultural workers, who, having drifted to the urban centers, are now "unemployed" in the modern industrial sense (or if they are not technically unemployed, are unproductively employed, providing those unneeded services that abound in developing countries—e.g., car watchers, shoeshiners, and parcel carriers). To construct capital by a slow and grinding "boot-strap" operation, or to extract the agricultural surplus in the hands of the landlords to purchase or build capital goods, requires more political power and more organizational know-how than most governments in developing countries possess. Thus, the capital needed to increase the productivity of the released agricultural workers in the urban setting is not created or found within the domestic economy, and the inflationary pressures described earlier are not moderated. Thus, the surplus and released agricultural workers are not productively employed in nonfarm enterprises which could have increased the national product and their real incomes at one and the same time;

instead, they remain surplus to the economy, unemployed, and dependent on private or government charity for their subsistence. The surplus population has migrated from the farm to the nonfarm sector, but it remains surplus, and will continue to remain so until investments have been made in new productive enterprises, private and public, which can employ them. *The investment capital to employ them and to combine with them is the critical missing piece of the development puzzle.*

But as the landless and the rootless flock to the cities and towns, and as responsible governments attempt to satisfy their most basic needs through welfare payments and "make-work" projects, the money-purchasing power so generated drives the prices of food products skyward, and food products move out of the shops into private hoards. The surplus agricultural workers have produced no new additional product since they joined the nonfarm sector; hence there is no additional product in the towns and cities to be used to exchange for food. An incomplete development process has led to a food crisis in the cities that threatens the overall development process.

At this point, the government of this struggling, overpopulated country should recognize that it must take two important sets of actions if it is to develop without outside economic aid. First, it must begin to take all those actions described in Chapters 9 and 10 to increase its agricultural output significantly. Second, it must find ways to capture those gains in agricultural output in order to (1) feed the unemployed and underemployed ringing each city and town, and (2) sell, in part, in the export market so that it can earn the foreign exchange with which to purchase the capital items needed to combine in productive enterprises with the unemployed and the underemployed at home.

But governments of countries characterized by "overpopulated, traditional agricultural economies" typically have not been inclined, even when they could see and feel the modern food problem, to take those actions required to modernize their agricultural plants. They have failed to do this for at least two reasons. First, they have most often not understood the complexity of the agricultural production problem; they have not understood that they were dealing with a systems problem that must be attacked in a full and systematic way, if a significant increase in output is to be achieved in a short time. Hence these governments have not appreciated the nature of the effort required of them. Second, even where the governments did appreciate the stubbornness of the agricultural production problem, and had some understanding of the costs involved in terms of resources and time, they often failed to take the actions required because they were appalled by the enormity of the task confronting them. Satisfying the exacting demands of a modern productive agriculture meant sacrificing cherished plans for education, public health, public transportation, and other development needs; so the specific demands of agriculture were pushed aside.

The struggling, overpopulated country seeking to develop economically is unwilling, or more probably, unable to take the disciplined actions required, first, by agricultural modernization and, second, in capturing the fruits of the increased productivity. So it is forced to gamble—to gamble on cheap solutions. The solutions most fervently hoped for, or sought after, depending on the nature of the food and agriculture problem, are (1) good weather and (2) PL 480 food shipments from the United States. The first costs nothing, but there is no control over it. The second costs little, but is dependent upon political conditions.

But sooner or later such gambles must fail. Either the rains fail or Washington fails. In any event, available food supplies are reduced in the country, and the familiar pattern of rising food prices, empty food shops, and private hoarding becomes the norm. And should the country's food problem result from a bad crop, the incidence is likely to spread beyond the towns and cities to encompass the rural areas as well. Then the phenomenon of the modern food problem, which grows out of a malfunctioning development process, will have metamorphosed into an old-fashioned countrywide famine, unless help is forthcoming from the outside as it was in India in 1965–66. In other words, when an overpopulated developing country tries to sustain its development process by gambling on the continuance of good weather or large food aid shipments, the consequences will be particularly devastating if the gamble fails to pay off. The food situation is likely to move quickly from a problem stage to a crisis stage.

But at this point the Hegelian dialectic may achieve what advice and logic could not. A desperate food situation that leads to widespread rioting, starvation, and death may demonstrate to the political leaders of the country, as nothing else can, the fallacies in their previous development policies. The stocktaking that results from desperation may, and we shall assume here that it will, cause the political leaders of the country to recognize that they must create a modern, scientific agriculture capable of increasing food production significantly. But the pursuit of such a policy costs money and takes time. How, then, is the country to obtain these financial resources, and can it buy the time?

The resources to finance and support the costly process of agricultural modernization can be obtained in one of three basic ways: (1) by squeezing more of the agricultural surplus, over and above the subsistence requirement, out of the farm operators and landlords; (2) by slowing down the rate of investment in the nonfarm sector and in social overhead services (e.g., roads, schools, and hospitals); and (3) by obtaining foreign loans and grants to be used to increase agricultural productivity. The last source is, of course, the most advantageous, or least costly, if it is available. The first two sources imply the acceptance of a social and political discipline that was not possible earlier, but may be possible with the new social attitudes born of desperation. But the use of any one or some combination of all three, to finance the development of a modern, scientific agriculture with its increased food-producing potential, *means that other aspects of the country's development will have been slowed down.* In this view of the national development process, agriculture is recognized to be a stubborn obstacle to development, and investment in agricultural development is given top priority, until such time as increases in food supplies match increases in food demands. Again, the direction of this investment in agriculture with respect to both manpower and physical resources should be that traced out in Chapters 9 and 10.

But it still takes time, often a long time, to get agriculture moving. How is this time to be bought? It can and properly should be bought with foreign food aid. It is a mistake, indeed it is courting political and economic disaster, to substitute food aid for the development decisions that lead to increased agricultural productivity in the overpopulated, traditional agricultural economy. But foreign food aid can make an important contribution by filling in the gap in food supplies in countries that are beginning to modernize their agricultural plants, but whose programs have not yet reached fruition. A program to increase the production of fertilizer or to develop a more productive variety of grains may, as we have seen, require five to ten years after the investment decisions have been made before the full payoff is realized. In the interim, an increased supply of food is required.

Food aid, then, does have a legitimate role in the development process. This role is to buy time, where the decisions which can lead to sustained development have, in fact, been made.

At some stage in the development of our hypothetical country, the myriad of new production practices and technologies will catch hold in a new, modern system of agricultural production, and an increased product will begin to pour forth. This will probably occur in a period of favorable weather, so that a bumper crop, or series of bumper crops, will be harvested. If, by the time these bountiful harvests appear on the scene, an effective marketing organization, made up of both private and public elements, has not been developed, the result will certainly be a disastrous decline in farm prices. Such a price decline will then choke off, first,technological advances and investment in agriculture and, second, the flow of savings out of agriculture for investment in the nonfarm sector. Thus, price and income gyrations in agriculture, arising partly out of variations in the weather and partly out of the unpredictability of technological advance on farms, where the developing country is predominantly agricultural, could set in motion an uneven, teeter-totter-like development effort.

Success on the agricultural front means, once again, that there must be a series of development decisions with respect to agriculture that act to gear the rate of growth in farm production to the demands of the overall economy. The export policy for agricultural products, the rate of investment in agriculture, food storage policy, farm price stabilization policy, and manpower policy—all must be integrated into a *national development policy* that does not necessarily aim for maximum production or a maximum exodus of people from agriculture, but rather, at an expanding flow of food and fiber products that parallels the growth in demand.

As our thinking shifts from food shortages to agricultural surpluses in terms of the analytical model, there is need to reflect on the food problem and its solution in greater depth. It is one thing to meet and satisfy the calorie, or undernourishment, problem with an expanded production of food grains and other crops; it is quite another to meet and satisfy the fat and animal protein deficiency problems. But as development progresses, the food and agricultural problem shifts from the first form to the second. It does so because, as consumers experience rising real incomes, they seek an improved and higher quality diet, involving a greater consumption of fats and animal products and a reduction in the consumption of grains and root crops.

However, the conversion of excess grain production capacity into the production of increased amounts of fats and animal products is not an easy task. The technical problems of a scientific animal agriculture are much more complex than those of a crop agriculture; the resource adjustment is more difficult to program over time, and hence more risky, and the capital requirements are greatly increased. The conversion is thus not likely to go smoothly. Countries in this stage of economic development are likely to find themselves faced with severe shortages and high retail prices in the animal products, and burdensome surpluses and low farm prices in the grains. The "second" modernization of their agricultural plants to meet the changing food demands of their peoples (a shift away from grains and carbohydrate foods to fats and animal protein foods resulting from increased real per capita incomes) will turn out to be more complex than the "first" modernization and fraught with as many or more problems—but very different ones.

In terms of our analytical model, the place and role of agriculture in the general development process has shifted once again. The problem is no longer to push and drive the laggard element, total agricultural production, to new and higher levels of output. Once agriculture gets moving in a modern, scientific sense, the period of pushing, which had seemed unending, is over. In the more advanced stages of economic development, the problem is to achieve a balanced rate of growth between the farm sector and the nonfarm sector (as it was in the early phases, too), by gearing the now fast-moving agriculture to a rate of growth in the *total* demand for food which is slowing down; and within the context of a slowing aggregate demand, adjust productive resources to meet changes in *specific* food demands, e.g., an *increased* demand for meat and milk and a *decreased* demand for grain products and potatoes. This, of course, is the *farm* problem which plagues the Western developed countries, and although a less terrifying problem than the *food* problem of the developing countries, it is no less tractable. It is hard to break the chains of tradition and get agriculture moving; and it is equally difficult to adjust a swiftly moving scientific agriculture to a declining rate of increase in the aggregate demand for food in developed countries.

But our hypothetical developing country is not yet "out of the woods" as far as balanced growth or the food problem are concerned. Investment in the nonfarm sector, both public and private, was reduced to obtain the resources to modernize the agricultural plant. Thus, it is probable that the nonfarm sector has experienced a slower rate of growth than would be considered desirable for a good number of years. It is also probable that industrial production has grown slowly, that the provision of essential public services has lagged, that the absorption of displaced agricultural workers has been unsatisfactory (i.e., unemployment is high in urban areas), and that the incidence of undernourishment and malnutrition is still widespread in urban areas.

Given this state of affairs, together with an agriculture that is regularly producing a surplus over domestic requirements, at least in the basic crops, the country must now find a solution to the growth problem of the nonfarm sector. The answer here is less difficult than that of getting agriculture moving, for a number of reasons. First, the gnawing fear of hunger and starvation has been eliminated. Second, the agricultural surplus exists to eradicate undernourishment and malnutrition in the population, if suitable distributive arrangements can be established or unemployment reduced. Third, the nation now has an agricultural surplus which it can sell to earn foreign exchange in order to purchase needed physical resources. Fourth, the high levels of production and increased incomes already generated in agriculture will be exerting a demand pull on the nonfarm sector for both consumer and producer goods. Important forces are now working to support the nonfarm sector.

Besides foreign grants and loans, which are always welcome but not always available, two sources of capital are open to this developing country for investments in the nonfarm sector. First, the expanding agricultural surplus can be acquired through taxation or borrowing to provide capital resources. Second, the country should now be able to reduce the volume of investment in agriculture and transfer the funds so released to the nonfarm sector. In other words, having established a surplus in agriculture, the country should now be able to increase the rate of capital formation in the nonfarm sector, both public and private, either by capturing a part of the agricultural surplus for investment in the nonfarm sector, or by diverting a part of the investment flow away from agriculture. But regardless of the means, *the existence of a marketable surplus in agriculture provides a resource base out of which to make investments in the nonfarm sector.* This is the important point of this analysis.

Whether investments in the nonfarm sector will be wisely made is another issue. There is, as we observed earlier, a propensity in the developing world to invest in ostentatious structures (e.g., great dams). Further, it must be recognized that investments in public services, such as education, have a slow payoff. But in the main, industrial activity is directly related to the volume of investment. Thus, it is reasonable to conclude that industrial production and employment would increase directly and readily with an increased flow of investment. With this increased investment in the nonfarm sector, the real incomes of nonfarm workers would increase and make possible the increased consumption of food by them.

The modern food problem, born of a discontinuity in, or malfunctioning of, the development process thus finds a solution in the achievement of a balanced growing economy. It is resolved as the surplus agricultural workers who have migrated from farm to city are able to find productive employment in an expanding nonfarm sector of the economy. In the real world of "overpopulated, traditional agricultural economies," the task of converting millions of surplus agricultural workers to productive urban workers is a formidable one; without large amounts of external economic assistance, it can be achieved only through iron discipline and wise development decisions.

Some Quantitative Relations

It is exceedingly difficult to describe, by any form of exposition, the total growth process of an economy—particularly an overpopulated agrarian one heavily weighted by tradition. Dale Jorgenson has expressed the pure economic relations of the development process in a mathematical model;[8] Fei and Ranis have presented the basic economic relationship of the development process, together with the important institutional considerations, in a prose-graphic model;[9] and I have just attempted to sketch the sequential steps of the development process, as it relates particularly to food and agriculture, in terms of the key economic, social, and political variables. But no one to my knowledge has succeeded in putting together a complete description of the development process in terms of all the social and technical variables involved. Probably no one ever will, because the task defies the imagination.

It is possible, however, to relate in a meaningful way some of the more important variables in the food, agriculture, and development complex. John Mellor, in his comprehensive treatment of the agricultural development problem, presents an arithmetic tableau which sets forth the effect of different rates of increase in food production upon farm prices, with various hypothetical demand assumptions.[10] To facilitate the exposition, we have modified some of the data assumed by Mellor and present these modified quantitative relations in Table 11.1.

The basic assumptions for a hypothetical developing country with a high rate of population growth (Table 11.1, Case I) are as follows: (1) a rate of population growth of 3 percent per year; (2) a rate of growth in per capita nonfarm income of 4 percent per year; (3) a population distribution of 70 percent in agriculture and 30 percent in urban areas; (4) an income elasticity of the demand for food products of +0.8, meaning that, with a 10 percent

[8] Working Paper No. 66, *Subsistence, Agriculture and Economic Growth* (Berkeley, Calif.: Institute of Business and Economic Research, University of California, April 1965).

[9] *Op. cit.*

[10] *The Economics of Agricultural Development* (Ithaca, N.Y.: Cornell University Press, 1966), p. 75.

increase in per capita income, expenditures for food increase by 8 percent; and (5) a price elasticity for food of −0.9, meaning that, with a 9 percent increase in the supply of food products, the farm price of food products will decline by 10 percent.

These assumptions are generally consistent with the demographic and economic conditions of the overpopulated, traditional agricultural economy undergoing development. The income elasticity assumption may be a little low, and the price elasticity assumption a little high, which taken together have the effect of dampening down food price fluctuations; but they are not far from what one would expect in this kind of situation. And the population assumption seems highly representative. Thus, the quantitative analysis in Case I of Table 11.1 should be generally representative of developments in the situation under consideration.

We observe that food production must rise to an annual rate of increase of 5 percent per year before farm food prices stabilize. In other words, with a rate of population increase of 3 percent per year and the economic relationships assumed here, increases in the demand for food exceed the rates of increase in the supplies of food, with price-increasing consequences, until an annual rate of increase in food production of 5 percent is achieved. The agricultural development task for this hypothetical country is thus clearly defined— and it is a very large task.

If we assume a somewhat lower rate of population growth, as is done in Case II of Table 11.1, the pressure to increase food production is, of course, moderated. With a rate of population growth of 2 percent per year, and all other assumptions unchanged, the rate of increase in food production need rise to only 4 percent per year to bring about stability in food prices. The rates of increase in the demand for food and the production of food are roughly in balance at 4 percent, and the food problem associated with unbalanced development is under control.

But if we make some further assumptions (not shown in Table 11.1) associated with a slightly more advanced stage of development, then the need to step up the rate of food production arises again. Assume two additional changes in the assumptions from Case II: (1) the rate of increase in per capita nonagricultural income rises to 6 percent, and (2) the proportion of the population

250

TABLE 11.1

The Effect of Different Rates of Increase in Food Production Upon Farm Prices, with Various Hypothetical Demand Assumptions

		Annual Rate of Growth in:					Income Elasticity of Demand for Food Products	Rate of Growth in Demand for Food Products	Price Elasticity of Demand for Food Products	Rate of Increase in Farm Prices
Food Production	Population	Per Capita Agricultural Income	Per Capita Nonagricultural Income	Proportion of Population in Agriculture	Rate of Growth of Overall Average Income Per Capita					
Q	P_o	$g_a = Q - P_o$	g_n	d	$g = \dfrac{g_a(d) + g_n(100 - d)}{100}$	n	$D = P_o + ng$	e	$Pr = \dfrac{Q - D}{e}$
					CASE I—HIGH POPULATION GROWTH RATE				
1	3	−2	4.0	70	−.20	0.8	2.8	−0.9	2.0
2	3	−1	4.0	70	+0.50	0.8	3.4	−0.9	1.6
3	3	0	4.0	70	+1.20	0.8	4.0	−0.9	1.1
4	3	1	4.0	70	+1.90	0.8	4.5	−0.9	0.6
5	3	2	4.0	70	+2.60	0.8	5.1	−0.9	0.1
6	3	3	4.0	70	+3.30	0.8	5.6	−0.9	−0.4
					CASE II—MODERATE POPULATION GROWTH RATE				
1	2	−1	4.0	70	+0.50	0.8	2.4	−0.9	1.6
2	2	0	4.0	70	+1.20	0.8	3.0	−0.9	1.1
3	2	1	4.0	70	+1.90	0.8	3.5	−0.9	0.6
4	2	2	4.0	70	+2.60	0.8	4.1	−0.9	0.1
5	2	3	4.0	70	+3.30	0.8	4.6	−0.9	−0.4
6	2	4	4.0	70	+4.00	0.8	5.2	−0.9	−0.9

SOURCE: Adapted from John W. Mellor, The Economics of Agricultural Development (Ithaca, N.Y.: Cornell University Press, 1966). p. 75, Table 9.

in agriculture falls to 60 percent. In this event, the annual rate of food production must rise once again to almost 5 percent to bring the rates of increase in demand and production into balance. Thus we see that, as a country continues to develop, more people transfer out of agriculture, and nonfarm incomes rise, the rate of increase in food production must also increase to avoid a recurrence of the food problem, one symptom of which is rising food prices.

As more advanced stages of economic development are realized (as, for example, in the Western world of the 1960's), rates of population increase are likely to fall to 1 percent or even less, and the income elasticity for farm food products is likely to fall to 0.3 or 0.2; given these developments, the rate of increase in the demand for food will fall to 1 or 2 percent per year, reducing the growth requirement in food production to 1 or 2 percent per year. But in the early and middle stages of economic development—when population growth rates are high and the income elasticity of demand for food products is high—rates of increase in food production must rise to 4 percent, and possibly 5 percent, per year. These heavy demands on the agricultural sector of developing countries are made clear in Table 11.1.

Development Strategy and the Food Problem

In theory, a country described as an overpopulated, traditional agricultural economy can achieve a sustained rate of economic development without foreign assistance; the Japanese appear to have done just this in the nineteenth and early twentieth centuries. But not many countries answering such a description have achieved a sustained rate of economic development without a large amount of external assistance. This is so because the demands of the development process are so formidable. Manpower must be trained; improved production practices and technologies must be developed and mass produced; labor and product markets must be functioning reasonably smoothly; investment capital must be squeezed out of the masses of farm operators and landlords; the requisite business, economic, and political organizations must be brought into being; and a progress-oriented government must come to power, with a rational concept of development to guide its decision making. This is a demanding set of requirements, most often not satisfied. Hence, successful economic development springing completely from indigenous sources is a rare phenomenon.

The typical developing country requires external assistance, and large amounts of it. Such assistance will most certainly involve investment capital and technical aid, and most likely organizational assistance and food aid. But even where foreign assistance is forthcoming in adequate amounts (which usually is not the case), agriculture is likely to be a serious stumbling block to balanced and sustained national economic development. Agriculture is slow to get moving because the complex production units of millions of small farmers must be transformed from units organized by custom and tradition to units organized on modern scientific principles. This is a reorganization problem of enormous proportions.

To add to the development burden, once the agriculture of a developing country is moving, its annual rate of production increase must be raised to a very high level in the early stages to meet its expanding food requirements. Once development is under way, food requirements begin to soar as, first, population increases; second, the nonfood-producing urban population expands; and third, the money incomes generated by the development process rise. If food production does not increase sufficiently to meet these requirements, food prices begin to rise, private hoarding sets in, food shops run out of supplies, and, of course, the poor go hungry. Here are all the elements of the modern food problem. And should it continue and intensify, rioting will become commonplace, the development effort will be choked off, and governments may fall.

In this view, it is a mistake to depend upon a development process centered in urban areas to *pull* forth the required increases in food production. The pull on agriculture expressed through the normal market mechanism of higher prices will not succeed. Agriculture must be *pushed*, and pushed hard, from the inception of the development process. And the strategy of pushing agriculture hard from the earliest stages of development must involve the spectrum of activities discussed in Chapters 9 and 10—new farm practices, new producer goods, production education, effective credit, public research, effective markets, incentive prices, and on, and on, and on.

We are not saying that economic development involves only agricultural development. We are saying that the agricultural sector must increase its production significantly in the early stages of development to yield a surplus which can satisfy the expanding food requirements arising out of population increases, an expanding nonfarm population, and rising money incomes. We are saying, further, that agriculture cannot and will not modernize itself and increase its production importantly in any automatic sense. It must be *pushed* into this new and expanded production role by wise and resolute public, or government, actions, which tear away the crust of tradition and then substitute new practices, new production organizations, and new producer goods for the old. A development strategy which fails to incorporate within its structure a hard, broad, determined push for agriculture will almost certainly lead the country involved first into a food crisis; then into a breakdown of the development process; and finally into political upheaval.

But achieving a high rate of food production will not in itself solve the food problem; it is only the first necessary step. Next, industrial production and public services and infrastructure must be expanded to sustain the agricultural development, to provide vital nonfood goods and services, and to provide jobs—millions of jobs—for the surplus agricultural population. With a decline in urban unemployment, the circle of development is closed: workers have the real purchasing power to acquire the expanding flow of agricultural products and, in so doing, eradicate the modern food problem—widespread undernourishment and malnutrition among the surplus population that has moved to the towns and cities.

III

Recommendations and Summary

12

Policies for the Developed Countries

IN THIS CHAPTER we turn to the question: What policies should the developed countries adopt toward resolving the world food problem, which in effect means: What policies should the developed countries adopt toward the economic development of the densely populated, less developed countries of the world? There may be some who would argue that the developed countries of the West have no special responsibility for the successful development of the less developed countries, and therefore no reason to pursue special policies toward them. But this is really a very shortsighted view.

It should be clear to all who are willing to look that failure on the part of the developing countries to achieve satisfactory rates of economic growth must lead to food shortages, dashed expectations, social and political upheaval, and wars from within or without. These kinds of international developments have a way of involving the developed nations—perhaps only in a philanthropic program, but more likely in a power struggle among rival developed nations. The interdependence of nations in the modern world commonly leads to power struggles when one country in that interdependency gets into serious political difficulty. Thus, enlightened self-interest on the part of the developed nations, if their motives are basically peaceful, dictates the need for an attitude of international responsibility toward the developing countries. Given this attitude of international responsibility, it is incumbent upon the developed nations to accept and pursue policies that contribute to the successful economic development of less developed countries. And a satisfactory resolution of the food and agricultural problems of such countries must, as we know, be an integral part of their successful development.

The question therefore now assumes a special form. It is: What developmental policies should the developed nations adopt toward the less developed countries, where the former recognize their responsibility to the latter?

National Attitude toward Development

The first point that we wish to make is not, strictly speaking, concerned with policy; it is concerned with the attitude of developed nations toward the economic development of the less developed countries. When Americans discovered the less developed part of the world following World War II, and acquired a sense of responsibility toward it, neither they nor their leaders seemed to understand that the successful development of "an overpopulated, traditional agricultural economy" is a long, hard, slow process. From their own experience with pockets of economic backwardness, particularly in the rural South, Americans should have appreciated the great obstacles to achieving and sustaining satisfactory economic growth rates in the developing countries. But they did not then, and they do not now, seem to grasp the requirements of, and the difficulties in, the development process.

Americans approached the development problems of the less developed countries in 1948, and each year since, as though they were fighting an old-fashioned shooting war: call out the troops, vote the money, fight the enemy, win the war, and then come home with the victory. But developing an overpopulated, traditional agricultural economy does not work that way. Development requires staying power on the part of both the countries receiving assistance and the countries providing assistance. It takes time to build an economic infrastructure, to educate the masses, to build a research base, and to accumulate the savings required by modern heavy industry. Even with abundant natural resources, a growing but not dense population, and a stable government, it took the United

States roughly 100 years, from 1850 to 1950, to build a modern economy. How, then, are overpopulated, traditional agricultural economies to work the miracle of becoming developed countries in a few years, or even a few decades?

They can't. And the developed nations of the West must come to recognize that they can't; the development process, in which most of the less developed countries are engaged, is a 50- to a 100-year process. Given sustained development, it will most likely be that long before the common man of a developing nation has achieved the level of living to which he aspires today.

This means that the Western developed nations must be prepared to work with and to assist the developing countries over a very long period. Crash programs, passionate pleas, and quick victories do not meet the requirements of economic development. These requirements include educating the masses, accumulating the capital for a modern industrial plant, building a national research system, and training millions of farmers to employ new and improved technological methods. And satisfying these requirements takes time and staying power. This the developed nations of the West must come to understand and act upon.

Economic Assistance Goals

The fifteen Western nations[1] that make up the Development Assistance Committee (DAC) have talked about the desirability of allocating 1 percent of their respective national incomes to economic assistance for the developing countries during the 1960's. And, as we observed in Chapter 8, most countries have come reasonably close to achieving this goal of economic assistance. The United States, however, under the stress of the Vietnam war, has fallen short of that goal. But even if the United States had held to a level of foreign economic assistance equal to 1 percent of its national income, the total economic assistance available to the developing countries would have been far below the assistance needed. Further, picking an arbitrary target of 1 percent of national income for each

[1] Australia, Austria, Belgium, Canada, Denmark, France, Germany, Italy, Japan, the Netherlands, Norway, Portugal, Sweden, the United Kingdom, and the United States.

developed country's contribution to economic assistance can hardly be considered a rational approach to the problem.

The proper approach for determining the foreign economic assistance requirements of the developing world for the 1970's might be as follows. The United Nations might appoint a special commission, or designate the World Bank, to make a thorough study of the economic assistance needs of the developing world— indicating the total amount and categories of economic aid required to yield satisfactory growth rates in the developing countries. Once determined on the basis of study and reason, the dollar total of the economic assistance bill could be converted to a percentage of the GNP of, say, the 15 DAC countries. It might turn out, on the basis of this study, that the economic assistance bill was double, triple, or quadruple the present level (i.e., as much as 2, 3, or 4 percent of the national income of each country, which for the United States in 1967 would have been about $13 billion, $19 billion, or $26 billion).

Achieving such levels of foreign economic assistance in the developed countries will not be easy, but it will not amount to a disaster for the developed countries; whereas failure to achieve these levels could lead to disaster in the developing countries. Interruptions and slowdowns in the development process and the social and political upheavals that must follow, as night follows day, will in the longer run spell trouble for the developed countries. Expectation gaps, food shortages, riots, and civil strife, which are the direct consequences of sputtering developmental processes and too slow rates of real income growth, also lead to Cuban crises and Vietnam wars with their terrifying and costly implications. Thus, the developed countries do not come off free when there are failures and revolutions in the developing world.

The argument being made here, then, is that the wise course of action for the developed countries is to provide an adequate flow of economic assistance to the developing countries. Such a flow of assistance is likely to exceed considerably the present target of 1 percent of their respective GNP's. But such a level of assistance is cheap compared with the loss of life and financial costs of even limited wars. In short, an adequate flow of economic aid to the developing world is simply one part of the cost of maintaining reasonable order in the world.

As we said earlier in this chapter, this is not a short-term cost. Citizens of the developed countries can expect to pay the economic assistance bill annually for the next 50 years at least, and possibly longer. This is a long-term problem, and no amount of wishing will make it go away. In fact, too much wishful thinking has intensified the problem of development across the developing world during the 1960's.

But some readers will be thinking, and others muttering: "Why all this concern with development? Our problem is one of producing enough food. Why don't we discuss the point at issue—producing and distributing food?" The answer to that question is that there has already been too much discussion of the world food problem as an isolated phenomenon; the food problem of the developing countries cannot be solved in isolation. Food production will be increased, and that increase will be distributed effectively in economically backward countries, only as: (1) new production practices are researched and developed; (2) new and additional capital inputs are produced and made available to farmers (e.g., fertilizer, tube well equipment); (3) surplus agricultural labor is siphoned out of rural areas and put to work in new and more productive jobs; (4) the new agricultural surplus is moved through the distribution system at remunerative prices; and (5) a flow of savings is effected which can support these developments. Until all these parts of the development puzzle are brought into being and put together in the proper sequence, more food cannot be produced and distributed. And these pieces are only a part of the total development puzzle— the ones visible in the food and agricultural sector. Increased food production, and its more effective distribution, are integral parts of the total development process. The development process cannot succeed without the proper integration of the food and agricultural processes; and the required food production cannot be achieved without a satisfactory state of overall economic development.

It is senseless to talk of solving the world food problem in isolation. It will be solved only as the individual less developed countries achieve satisfactory rates of economic development. And we are concerned here with the level and duration of economic assistance required to achieve those income growth rates.

Technical Assistance Strategy

Most developed countries of the West have been engaged in some technical assistance work in the less developed world during the past two decades. It is not the purpose here to evaluate the technical assistance of different developed countries, but it can perhaps be said that the projects of the smaller developed countries, which have been small in scope and have emphasized intimate personal contact and intensive technical training, have proved more successful than the projects of the great powers (e.g., the Soviet Union and the United States), which are larger and have emphasized fast action and edifice building.

In the case of the United States, it is possible to find dedicated, hardworking men and women assigned to technical assistance projects in every developing country in which we have an AID program. It is also possible to point to highly successful projects in most of these countries. Still the technical assistance programs of the United States have failed to make the contribution to world development that most professional observers feel they should. This is not to place the blame on the policy leadership in AID or the technical workers in the field. At least since David Bell became the administrator of AID, the policy leadership in that agency has known how to improve the effectiveness of our technical assistance programs. And the workers in the field have been representative of American levels of professional competence from the very beginning. The problem is one of building the kind of overseas technical assistance programs that policy leaders know should be built and the American professionals are capable of building, when the American body politic operating through the Congress impatiently calls for crash programs and quick victories.

The first element of a successful strategy of technical assistance to the developing world must be a *long-term commitment* to technical assistance work. In this context, both donor and recipient countries will be able to make the decisions to establish institutions, train manpower, and make those investments which will have a significant payoff only after long periods of time. It takes years to build and man a research station with the capacity to widen the field of knowledge consistently and produce new and relevant technologies in the field of agriculture. The same generalization also holds in such diverse fields as transportation, electrical equipment, and business management. Thus, it is senseless to undertake technical assistance work on a short-term basis when all experience points to the long-term requirement.

The second element of a successful strategy of technical assistance must be the willingness to participate in the building of *institutions* in the less developed countries. And here we have in mind a wide range of institutions: universities, research laboratories, credit organizations, private and cooperative marketing organizations, planning commissions, fertilizer factories, secondary vocational schools, a ministry of transport, a public health service, a family planning service, an export marketing board, and many more.

In the initial phase of institution building, the assisting country may need to provide leadership as well as technical workers and financial support. But such projects are doomed to failure, quickly or slowly, unless there is from the outset a substantial component of leadership from the recipient country, as well as technical workers, no matter how poorly trained they may be. One measure of success of the institution-building project will, of course, be the product it turns out, whether that product be university graduates, a new high-yielding variety of rice, or a successful plan of development. But a more important measure will be the extent to which leaders and technical workers are trained to take over eventually the full management and operation of the institution. Thus, the basic objective of institution building must be the training of leaders and the training of staff with the competence to manage and operate the institution when the foreign technical assistance workers go home. This kind of institution building is often slow going, but the goal of staffing the institution with country nationals from top to bottom must be kept in mind from the very beginning and striven for day after day, if a viable, productive institution is ever to come into being.

One key concept that must be transferred to and embedded in the attitudes, thought processes, and value systems of the nationals being trained to man the new institutions is that it is *performance* that counts, not *form*. It is not the form of the experiment that is important, but the result; it is not the shape of the building that is important, but the work that is being undertaken there. This is not an easy message to convey in a society where status and appearances are all-important. But it can be done, and probably the best way is to have young, inexperienced nationals working alongside competent foreign technical workers. Doing things, producing things, accomplishing things can be rewarding and infectious.

Institution building, then, involves many things: training managers, teaching technical skills, imparting new values, and, of course, constructing some buildings and installing some equipment. But the last part is the easy part. Finally, the assisting country must be willing to accept and live with adversity, social and political upheavals, and slow progress, for these, too, are a part of the process of building institutions in a developing country.

The third element for a successful strategy of technical assistance must be effective resource support in the developed country providing the assistance. This support will take many outward forms, but it involves three principal activities: (1) training technical assistance workers to work in less developed countries; (2) doing research and scholarly work on problems of development; and (3) training nationals from the less developed countries.

The fact that a technical worker, whether employed in a developed country or an underdeveloped one, must have technical skill is so obvious that the need for a technical education for such workers has never been debated. But for a long time it was not recognized that the technical worker going to a less developed country to ply his trade needs two additional kinds of formal training or education: (1) some adaptation of Western technical skills to the problems of the less developed world; and (2) some knowledge of the way of life (including the language) of the less developed country to which he is going. It is probably correct to say, as of 1968, that some recognition is now being given to these two requirements, but the training actually provided is very uneven and often informal. The press of time and limited funds often result in the neglect or oversight of these kinds of training. Thus, technical assistance workers from the United States are often poorly prepared to cope with the professional problems and the living problems they will encounter in their careers abroad.

We have also recognized, from the inception of technical assistance work after World War II, the need to provide formal training and higher education for potential leaders and professional workers in the developing countries. This, again, is an obvious requirement if the developing countries are to acquire the administrators, managers, professional workers, and technical workers needed to make a modern society and economy function. To this end, thousands of young men and women have been brought to the United States with all degrees of financial aid to obtain undergraduate and graduate collegiate training. But in keeping with the traditions and manpower objectives of the United States, we have too often produced and sent back to the developing countries more theoretical physicists, theoretical economists, and specialized medical researchers than we have men who could manage a rat-extermination program, breed a new variety of rice, or combat a disease epidemic in humans, cattle, or wheat. In short, we have not in the United States made a serious effort to provide the kind of training most urgently needed by students from developing countries; we have provided students from the less developed world with the same kind of educational experience that we have given our own students. In the main, this is high-quality training and education, but it is not focused on the manpower requirements of the less developed countries.

This educational policy, or lack of policy, for training students from the less developed world must be corrected. One way of doing it would be to develop special courses of study in American colleges and universities. A second, perhaps more productive way would be to develop major training centers in "third" countries like Mexico or the Philippines, where students from developing countries could study in a situation and on problems more comparable to their own. But no matter which way is chosen—and the magnitude of the problem may dictate that both ways be employed—money and leadership from the developed countries will be required to implement the new policy. Both of these ingredients have been largely lacking in the past, and both must be supplied in generous quantities if the education and training of students from the less developed world are to be made relevant to the needs of their countries.

In the general area of resource support from the country giving technical assistance, there has been a great unevenness in research and scholarly work on the problems of development. In the fields of economic development, birth control, and public health, a great deal of research and scholarly work has been done in the United States that relates directly to the problems of the less developed countries. This work has produced relevant materials and methods for the technical assistance worker to use when he goes abroad; it has provided research projects on which he may work and to which he may contribute on his return from a tour of duty abroad; and it has contributed to a rich and exciting educational experience at American universities for students from less developed countries. But in such broad fields as agriculture, engineering, and education, very little research work is under way in American institutions which focuses directly on the problems of the developing world. Thus, a resource base is not provided in American research institutions in the above three fields to support the technical assistance worker abroad.

This, too, must be corrected if the technical assistance work of the United States is to be made more effective in the less developed world. The technical assistance worker from the United States working on an agricultural development problem in a less developed country must have technical support from "home," and he needs a "home" to which he can return and make use of his overseas experience. This means that there must be an active research program under way in the United States in each field in which technical assistance is being provided, and this program must be effectively related to the technical assistance worker overseas. Otherwise, his work will tend to be mechanical, barren, and lacking in content. He will be in the position of a salesman without a product.

Considering again the three principal activities involved in resource support—training technical assistance workers to work in less developed countries, doing research and scholarly work on the problems of development, and training foreign nationals from the less developed countries—it is clear that these activities are closely related. A solution to one contributes to the solution of the other two; and a failure to solve one will have an adverse effect on the other two. It is impossible, for example, to have a first-rate training and educational program for students from the developing countries without a concomitant productive research program on development problems in the fields concerned and a high-quality course of study for Americans interested in technical assistance careers abroad. These activities go hand in hand, and they are a part of the mission of a modern American university. Thus, a solution to these resource support problems must in large measure be found in the American university system as far as the technical assistance program of the United States is concerned.

American universities generally are prepared to deal with these problems, if they have the financial resources. The leadership in the universities is aware of these problems and has given much thought to their resolution. But the missing piece in this puzzle is financial resources. State and local groups do not in the main see foreign technical assistance as their responsibility, and the federal government has thus far been unwilling or unable to provide American universities with the funding required on a sustained basis. Thus, the solution to the problem of providing the kinds and quantities of resource support necessary for effective technical assistance work in the developing world awaits financing. And without question this financing must come from the federal government.

Export Markets

Most developing countries export primary products: agricultural products, forestry products, and minerals. These tend also to be the *leading* export commodities of the developing countries and are destined in the most part for the developed countries of the West. Since most of the developing countries lie in the tropics, and their products move to the developed countries in the temperate zone, there would seem to be a natural complementarity in trade between the two regions and therefore a flourishing trade between the two. In fact, there *is* an important flow of trade between the two regions; but there are also some exceedingly difficult problems associated with that trade that have damaging consequences for the developing countries.

Three of the more important trade problems are the following.

First, the producers of such tropical products as coffee, cocoa, and bananas are constantly oversupplying the international market, thereby driving the prices of these products down and shifting the terms of trade against themselves. Second, in the case of certain other commodities commonly produced in hot climates—sugar, cotton, and rubber—the developed countries of the temperate zone have acquired the technology for producing these products, or close substitutes for them, almost as efficiently as they can be produced in the tropics (and sometimes more efficiently), thereby squeezing these raw products from the tropics out of the markets of the developed countries. Third, many, if not most, of the developed countries maintain significant import restrictions and duties on processed primary products, thereby denying the developing countries the opportunity to develop processing industries in connection with their export trade.

All of these problems work in the same direction, namely, to reduce the export earnings of the developing countries. As a result, the amount of foreign exchange that could be used to finance the importation of needed producer goods is reduced, and the development process is held to a slower pace than might otherwise be the case. In this context, the slogan "trade not aid" has little meaning. Trade cannot supplant aid in financing development when that trade is suffering from low prices and restricted volume. What is needed is "trade *and* aid." And we are concerned at this point with what the developed nations can do to widen the export markets of the developing countries.

There is no easy solution to the first problem of chronic overproduction in such products as coffee, cocoa, and bananas. Certainly it is not to be found in international commodity arrangements which rely upon production controls at the farmer level in the developing countries; even the developed countries with their opulent treasuries and efficient bureaucracies have found this to be a difficult and rocky policy route. And probably it is not to be found in international arrangements which rely on storage programs to handle the surplus. Surplus products have a way of flowing endlessly into the storage bins, but rarely is there an opportunity for them to flow out; thus surplus stocks accumulate, hang over the market, and finally spoilage and exorbitant carrying charges wreck the program.

The solution may be found in international arrangements which depend upon rigorous grading to control the flow of products into the commercial market; the high-quality produce is sold on the international market, the low-quality produce is destroyed or fed to animals (depending on the nature of the product). Under this kind of arrangement the price of the commodity is maintained in the international market, the producers of high-quality products are rewarded by receiving a good price for most or all of their produce, and the producers of low-quality products are discouraged by receiving a very low price for most or all of their produce.

This type of international commodity program is not likely to encounter smooth sailing in its operations. In the first place, the discipline required to administer such a program within a producing country is beyond the capability of many, if not most, developing countries. In the second place, the requirements of cooperation and fair dealing among producing nations in the arrangement are highly demanding. In the third place, individual nations from the developed world are not likely to want to participate in, or to help manage, an international commodity arrangement which has the objective of raising the level of prices to themselves. Thus there are many handicaps to overcome, even where the structure and purpose of the arrangements make a successful operation seem feasible.

But, one institutional arrangement removed, it is possible for the developed nations to assist the developing nations to cope with their surplus problem in international trade. The vehicle is the United Nations. Agencies of the United Nations, supported in large measure by the developed nations, can and should assist the developing nations to formulate and administer international marketing arrangements to combat the price-depressing effects of surplus production in such commodities as coffee, cocoa, and bananas. As we have suggested, it is easy, even seductive, to concoct international commodity arrangements which cannot possibly operate successfully. And it may be that the developing nations will have to suffer through several program failures before they can force themselves to adopt a program which can operate successfully. But at some point in time, some of the agencies of the United Nations should be able to provide the leadership, and perhaps the secretariat, for bringing into being an international commodity arrangement which can stabilize international prices at a reasonable level.

A solution to the second problem is harder to find. Competition to natural cotton and rubber from the synthetics, based on technological advance in the developed countries, is going to continue and become more intense. The outcome of this competitive struggle is beyond our knowledge at this time, but we can be sure that the competitive struggle will be intensified, that the boundaries of science and technology will be rolled back still further, and that natural cotton and rubber will find it increasingly difficult to hold onto their traditional markets.

Sugar is a different story. But as one studies the politics of sugar in Europe and the United States over the last 200 years, there is little to suggest that sugar production and marketing problems will be settled on either rational or economic grounds. They will be settled in the arena of cold, hard politics.

In this context, is it likely that the beet producers of the temperate zone, who through much research are approaching the production efficiency of the cane producers in the tropics, are going to cut back production in order to give markets to those producers? It seems highly unlikely that they will. It is probably wise national security policy for each temperate zone country to produce some part of its national sugar requirement—perhaps 30, 40, or even 50 percent. But to produce more than this amount by means of sugar beets, as many temperate zone countries are now doing,[2] is, first, to rely on a relatively high cost source of production and, second, to deny the developing countries a market for a product that most of them can produce abundantly and at lower cost than the temperate zone countries. In terms of economic rationality, the tropical countries should produce and export sugar to the temperate zone developed countries in exchange for fabricated producer goods (e.g., fertilizer and steel products).

Thus, it is argued here that the developed nations of Europe and the United States should reserve, on the average, 60 percent of their domestic sugar market for producers from less developed tropical countries. This should become a goal of the developed nations when formulating practices and programs for assisting the developing countries.

[2] France is 100 percent self-sufficient in sugar production, West Germany is 80 to 90 percent self-sufficient, and Northern Europe on the whole is about 75 percent self-sufficient.

The marketing and trading of primary products in the less developed countries may also have to be approached from an entirely new direction. Perhaps the solution to the foreign trade and export earnings problem lies in deemphasizing the production and export of traditional primary products (e.g., cotton, sugar, cocoa, and coffee) and exploring new and diverse patterns of resource use and production (e.g., moving in the direction of greater meat production and export in South America and Africa, and increased manufacturing unrelated to primary products in South Asia, as has occurred in Japan). But this kind of diversification is generally dependent upon expanding the technological frontiers of production in the developing countries. And such an expansion is in turn dependent upon the whole complex of modernization and general economic development, including scientific research and experimentation, product development, and improved commercial practices and business management. This is not a magical approach to the trade problems of the less developed countries, but it does suggest the direction in which they must move—away from such great emphasis on production and trade in primary products and toward increased diversification.

But the great opportunity for the developed nations to assist the developing nations expand their merchandise exports, and thereby increase their rates of economic development, is related to the solution to the third problem. If the developed nations would lower their tariff barriers and eliminate their import quotas on processed and semi-processed primary products, the economies of the less developed countries would be immeasurably helped. If the less developed countries could export and sell to the developed nations their sugar, vegetable oils, cotton, lumber, rubber, and mineral products in a finished, or even semi-processed, form, a chain of desirable consequences could be set in motion. First, their processing industries would create new and more productive jobs and raise real incomes. Second, the value added in processing would increase importantly the value of merchandise exports. Third, the increased foreign exchange earned from the sale of these more highly processed products would enable the developing countries to increase their purchases of machinery and equipment, steel, and fertilizer from the developed nations and thereby increase their rates of economic development.

The Committee for Economic Development (CED) argues the case as follows:[3]

Without in any way minimizing the importance of primary products, we must recognize that the establishment of an increasing range of manufacturing industry is an essential feature of economic development. For some low-income countries, not well endowed with natural resources, the export of manufactures is indeed the only way of expanding their earnings of foreign exchange enough to pay for the imports of goods and services that their economic growth requires and to pay for the servicing of their external debt. Given the slow growth of the world market for primary products the expansion of their exports of manufactures is necessary for the exporters of primary products too, if they are in the long run to share in general prosperity and to pay their way in the world.

In the high-income countries the typical pattern of protection is one in which the more the basic material has been processed or fabricated, the higher the tariff. Raw materials usually enter with a low level of restriction or none at all, processed materials encounter moderate tariffs, whereas final products, particularly consumer goods, encounter the highest degree of protection.[4] But even moderate tariffs on materials that have been through the early stage of processing often result in a high degree of effective protection for the processing industry itself. This is because the tariff is levied on the total value of the processed product but the value added in the processing industries is only a small percentage of this total value.[5]

[3] *Trade Policy Toward Low-Income Countries*, A Statement by the Research and Policy Committee (June 1967), pp. 19, 20.

[4] Thus the level of the common external tariff of the EEC, which will come into force July 1, 1968, is set at zero for hides and skins and 10 percent for most leather, whereas the duties on leather manufactures range between 14 and 19 percent; and the tariff is 6.7 percent on cocoa beans (reduced to 5.4 percent until 1969), 20 percent on cocoa butter, 25 percent on cocoa paste, and 27 percent on cocoa powder. There are many similar examples in the tariffs of other high-income countries such as Britain and the United States.

[5] For example, suppose that the world price of a certain type of leather is $100 and the cost of the hides to make the leather is $70. Then the "value added" by the foreign producer is $30. Now assume that imports of hides into the EEC are duty-free, but that imports of leather are subject to a 10 percent tariff. The tanner in the EEC is, therefore, in a position to charge $110 for the leather. But the $10 duty protects not the cost of producing hides, which can be imported free of duty, but only the "value added" in tanning the hides which amounts to $30. Thus, a nominal tariff of 10 percent on leather gives effective protection to the tanning industry equivalent to 33⅓ percent by permitting the domestic producer to incur higher costs to that extent on his processing operation.

For some products the early stages of processing are the natural first steps for the entry of low-income countries into manufacturing and in such cases it is clearly important to reduce or eliminate even low tariffs on the processed product.

Recent studies have also shown that the effective protection of the manufacture of highly fabricated products is for similar reasons often substantially greater than the stated tariff.[6] The final stages of processing some products involve a great deal of hand labor and constitute precisely the kinds of manufacturing most suited to newly-developing countries. Thus, a reduction in tariffs on manufactured products, even when they appear to have been fixed at moderate levels, can in certain cases be crucial for the export prospects of developing countries.

This is where the developed nations of the world could help the less developed countries in an important way. Such a foreign trade policy on the part of the developed nations would entail some unpleasant production adjustments in the developed countries: activity in the processing of primary products would decline and activity in the more sophisticated fabricating industries would expand. But these adjustments would not seriously disrupt the economies of the developed nations; they move in the direction of the established patterns of economic growth in the developed nations, and they would contribute to an increase in total production and trade in the world economy.

Will the developed nations have the courage and the wisdom to take the lead in bringing such a trade policy into being? To date, special interests in the developed countries have blocked any significant move to lower tariff barriers and eliminate import quotas on processed and semi-processed primary products. We can only hope that enlightened national self-interest in an aggregate sense will override the special interests in the developed countries in the 1970's and support a reformation of trade policy with respect to

[6] For example, in the United States the nominal tariff on shoes is 16.6 percent but it has been calculated that the effective protection is 25.3 percent. Likewise in the EEC the nominal tariff is 19.9 percent and the effective protection 33.0 percent; in Japan the nominal tariff is 29.5 percent and the effective protection 45.1 percent; in Britain, the nominal tariff is 24.0 percent and the effective protection 36.2 percent. The source of these estimates is an article by Bela Balassa, "Tariff Protection in Industrial Countries," *Journal of Political Economy*, Chicago, December 1965.

processed and manufactured primary products. Perhaps this book can make a small contribution to that policy reformation.

The Reformation of Development Strategies

By "development strategy" we mean a set of agreed-upon courses of economic and social action capable of achieving the development goals of the nation. The typical developing country has a development strategy, or set of strategies, with regard to such things as economic planning, product pricing and wage policy, tax policy, investment outlays, institution building, land tenure, trade policies, and education and manpower policies. Often these strategies are over-ambitious in terms of what they seek to achieve; are dictated, as in most countries, in large measure by special and regional interests; and are sometimes just plain wrong (i.e., obstruct or inhibit development rather than contribute to it). But the formulation of an overall development strategy, together with the necessary substrategies, goes to the heart of the social and political processes. To an important degree, this is what politics in the new developing countries is all about.

The issue before us here, therefore, is *not* how to initiate national strategies of development; for the most part they already exist in one form or another. The issue is: *How* can the developed countries assist particular developing countries to rework and reformulate their development strategies so as to achieve their development goals? More specifically, how can the developed countries best assist the developing countries in making investment decisions; in pursuing a wage, price, and tax policy; in building educational, research, and marketing institutions; and in training and employing its manpower so that programs are executed, political stability is realized, and economic development actually occurs on a broad base (i.e., the real incomes of the masses are raised)?

Although almost every developing country desperately needs help in establishing a national development strategy that has the capacity to do what the nation wants and expects of it, we must note again that the content of such a strategy is dependent upon political decisions of great import to the nation. Much of the political activity of newly established nations is concerned with fixing the content of their development strategy. Thus, it is clear that a new, developing nation will not invite a large, powerful developed nation to participate in its councils and to assist in the formulation of its strategy of economic development unless its trust of the developed nation is complete. In short, rarely will a developing country want to entrust the formulation or reformulation of its development strategy to a single developed country. The risks are too great. The chances of falling under the political or economic control of the developed country are too great. Thus, a bilateral approach to dealing with this kind of problem is not likely to be either acceptable or productive.

If the great developed nations of the West are not to perform this function, then what agency can or should? It has been suggested that a large private foundation, such as the Ford Foundation, might undertake this kind of development assistance. To some degree the Ford Foundation has already been involved in this work in both India and Pakistan. But it lacks the resources to provide all the assistance needed in this endeavor for a huge country like India, and certainly it could not begin to provide such assistance around the world. Further, there is the problem of the acceptability of a large private foundation from one country. Often a private foundation will be identified with its parent country in a developing country; hence its assistance will be rejected.

The most probable, and perhaps the only practical, solution to the provision of this kind of foreign assistance on the part of the developed countries is through the United Nations. It might be provided by one or several of the specialized agencies of the U.N. (for example, the World Bank and the Food and Agricultural Organization), or by a newly created agency of the U.N., comparable for example to the Special Fund. The developing nations in the main trust the U.N. and its specialized agencies, and the bulk of the budget for the U.N. and the specialized agencies comes from the developed nations. Thus, the U.N. in fact offers a way for the developed nations to assist the developing nations in this sensitive area.

But turning to the U.N. or one of its specialized agencies to provide assistance to individual developing countries in the reformulation of their development strategies is not a perfect solution. In the first place, with the possible exception of the World Bank, no agency in the U.N. family now possesses the capability of providing this kind of assistance; it would have to be developed. In the second place, bureaucratic strife among U.N. agencies and political struggles emanating from member nations have seriously reduced the effectiveness of some U.N. agencies in the development and administration of substantive programs. In the third place, because of the pressure for a "fair" representation on the secretariat, or staffs, of U.N. agencies by member countries, the competence of the staffs of some U.N. agencies leaves much to be desired. For these reasons then, a particular U.N. agency, although acceptable to the developing country involved, might have considerable difficulty providing the high-quality technical assistance required in this sensitive area.

We are not suggesting that the form of assistance under consideration here should lead to more planning. It could be that the development strategy that emerged for a particular developing country would call for less detailed planning and greater reliance on the play of market forces. We are, however, suggesting that most developing countries need assistance in formulating policies and making decisions that are consistent with, and contribute to, the achievement of their objectives for economic growth. Given the country's development objectives, given its institutional goals and social mores, and given its resource limitations, what kind of public investments should it make, what kind of manpower policies should it pursue, what kind of wage, price, and trade policies should it follow, and which institutions should it build first and where? These are the kinds of strategic questions confronting every new developing nation. And almost all lack the skilled manpower to develop answers to these questions that will contribute to consistent and overall growth.

A densely populated developing country cannot, for example, solve its food problem by first calling for more food production and then holding farm prices down to low incentive levels in order to provide cheap food to its urban consumers. Neither can it increase food production by increasing its capacity to produce fertilizer, on the one hand, and taking actions which restrict credit to farmers, on the other. The many and varied actions of government must be internally consistent and rational in terms of its development objectives. If they are not, economic chaos will result, not rapid economic growth. And this has been the outcome in all too many cases in the developing world in the past two decades.

So a development strategy which produces internally consistent economic measures on the part of government and which is consistent with the resource capabilities of the country, is an absolute prerequisite to sustained economic growth—to a rise in per capita real income and an increase in the per capita availability of food. The developed nations can assist the developing nations to formulate such development strategies, if a mechanism can be developed for reducing the risk of the developed nations meddling in, and gaining control over, the affairs of the developing nations through such efforts. This mechanism would seem to exist in the form of the United Nations Organization. Let us, therefore, ask for and expect to receive more creative leadership from the U.N. in this respect.

13

Policies for the Developing Countries[1]

IN CONSIDERING policies for the developing countries, it would be a mistake to visualize a set of countries with stagnant economies, starting out from zero in their development efforts. The statistical data presented in Chapters 1 and 8 on rates of growth in GNP and per capita incomes make clear that this is not so. Most developing countries have achieved respectable rates of growth in national income by almost any standard of comparison, and some have outstanding records. The problem is not the absolute performance of the economies of the developing countries; it is the gap between the *actual* levels of per capita real incomes that they are generating and the *expectations* of their people for improved levels of living.

The situation is somewhat comparable for agricultural development and food production. It has not been uncommon for developing countries, even the densely populated ones, to achieve rates of increase in food production (or cereal production) of between 2 and 3 percent per year in the late 1950's and 1960's. And a few countries have achieved rates of increase running up to and above 5 percent per year (see Tables 4.1, 4.2, and 4.3). These good-to-excellent records in food production have been achieved in part through an expansion in the area under cultivation and in part through modernization—that is, the adoption of new and improved technologies on farms, with the latter means becoming increasingly

[1] This chapter focuses on agricultural and general developmental issues, not on population policies. See Chapter 6 for a discussion of emerging and desirable population policies for the developing countries.

important in the 1960's as land available for cultivation has become increasingly scarce.

The problem in food and agriculture in the developing world, as we have seen, is to increase rates of food production for many countries from a level of 2 to 3 percent per year to 4 to 5 percent per year. These higher rates of increase are necessary to satisfy the increasing demand for food and to stabilize food prices in the densely populated countries that are experiencing both rapid rates of population growth and rising personal incomes. But the achievement of these higher rates of increase in food production no longer seems faraway or impossible to attain. The revolution in food grain production that is sweeping across West Asia, South Asia, and East Asia is significantly increasing the outturn of these crops in the late 1960's.[2] This production revolution revolves around the new, high-yielding varieties of wheat and rice, but it involves more than new plant varieties. It involves a *new production package*, which includes the new varieties, improved water management, increased applications of fertilizer, and improved control of plant diseases, insects, and weeds. And most important, this production package is being adopted widely *on farms* across Asia.

But the problems of agricultural development are endless. The large increases in food grain output that are occurring in 1968–69 are giving rise to difficult marketing and pricing problems. The production areas experiencing the large increases in grain output are also experiencing great difficulty in physically handling the product, avoiding increased waste, and protecting farmers against sharp and large price declines. Thus, the developing countries are destined to find that sustaining rates of food production increase of 4 to 5 percent per year is almost as difficult as reaching those rates in the first place. Further, where those new higher levels of food production are realized principally through increases in cereal production, as is the case in the late 1960's, the countries involved will almost certainly be forced to convert a part of the increased grain production into animal products rather than having it all consumed directly as grain by humans. And this further conversion of the

---

[2] The story of this production revolution is well told by Lester R. Brown in his article, "The Agricultural Revolution in Asia," *Foreign Affairs: An American Quarterly Review*, Vol. XLVI, No. 4 (July 1968), pp. 688–698.

agricultural plant will entail new and additional production and distribution problems.

Nonetheless, much is taking place in agricultural production in the developing world in the late 1960's. Where there was despair in 1966, there is great hope in 1968. But problems continue to abound—shifting in emphasis from the pure technology of production to marketing, pricing, and the distribution of the gains of development. Thus, the new great questions take the following forms: Can the countries participating in the food grain production revolution protect that production against disease epidemics? Can they effectively market the increased output and maintain incentive prices to producers? Can they begin to shift their plants in the direction of greater animal product production and thereby sustain the agricultural development process in their countries?

National Attitudes

As we stressed in Chapter 1, the average man in the developing world expects very great increases in his material level of living in the next decade or two. Improved diets, improved housing, improved education for his children, improved health services, and at least a motor bike are a part of his expectations. His political leaders tell him that he deserves all of these things and that he can have them if he follows the "right" leaders and makes the "right" political decisions. Thus, hope is fanned into unbridled expectation.

Associated with the expectation of the masses is the hope (perhaps a belief in some cases) on the part of national leaders of the developing countries that large amounts of economic assistance and trade concessions will be forthcoming from the developed countries. But in light of developments in the 1960's, these hopes or beliefs are certainly unfounded. Economic aid has not increased and does not give promise of increasing on any important scale; and trade concessions that are not in the interests of the developed nations have failed to materialize. The developing nations, for example, won practically no concessions from the developed nations at the much advertised United Nations Conference on Trade and Development held in New Delhi in the spring of 1968.

Concomitant with these false expectations and hopes has been the formulation and promulgation of unrealistic production goals and targets by the planners and bureaucrats in the developing world. Caught up in the process of escalating expectations, the planners and bureaucrats have attempted to substitute unrealistically optimistic production goals and targets for the real thing, which is simply the production of more goods and services. Buoyed up by unrealistic hopes and expectations, the planning process in many developing countries has lost contact with reality. Dreams and hopes have been converted into production targets, and these in turn have served to raise the level of expectation of the masses still further.

If a broadly based development process, which includes a solution to the food problem, is to be properly sustained in the densely populated developing countries, this expectation spiral must be slowed down, even halted for a time. This is necessary, first, because failure to satisfy surging expectations will certainly lead to discontent, political instability, and social upheaval; and, second, because the irrational decisions taken in an attempt to attain spiraling expectations will lead to economic chaos, not sustained development.

Something must be substituted for the expectation spiral—something which does not destroy all hope in the average man and turn him into either a raging rioter or a dumb beast. That something, it is argued here, is a set of attitudes that includes a willingness to work hard, a dedication to the achievement of realistic social and production goals, and self-discipline. The attitude that the good life for everyone cannot be achieved today or even tomorrow must be fostered; that it can be achieved in fact only over a long period of time through disciplined actions, which include hard work, education, savings, and reinvestment in improved methods.

But how is this set of attitudes to be fostered in a developing country? It can supplant the complex of false hopes and unbridled expectations only where the political leaders are willing and able to thrust aside, or cut through, the false hopes and unbridled expectations that blanket most developing nations, and dramatize to their people the strength and power of reality. Somehow the masses must be convinced by their political leaders that national strength and increased national well-being are to be found in work, savings, and investment in realistic projects, not in grandiose promises and spiraling expectations. This may come about through a communistic dictatorship, or through a military dictatorship, as it has in a few cases. Or it might come about through a combination of education and charismatic leadership in an open society, as it has in a few cases. But come it must, if the developing countries are to escape economic chaos and social upheaval in the immediate years ahead. And the responsibility for halting the expectation spiral and substituting reality rests squarely on the shoulders of the more informed, more articulate political leaders of the developing countries. Further, if the current leaders don't do this in the relative calm that pervades most developing countries today, another set of political leaders will have to face up to the task, once they emerge out of the ruins that will follow the collapse of the present-day expectation spiral. One way or another, the dream world of the developing nations must reestablish contact with reality.

According to Gunnar Myrdal, the greatest political and social liability of the developing countries of South Asia is the "soft state," which must be replaced with the "disciplined state" if development is to occur at satisfactory rates. But this replacement is no easy task. He writes:[3]

> When we characterize these countries as "soft states" we mean that, throughout the region, national governments require extraordinarily little of their citizens. There are few obligations either to do things in the interest of the community or to avoid actions opposed to that interest. Even those obligations that do exist are enforced inadequately if at all. This low level of social discipline is one of the most fundamental differences between the South Asian countries today and Western countries at the beginning of their industrialization.
>
> From a Western point of view, the obvious solution to widespread and serious indiscipline might seem to be that the government should rapidly establish a rational system of community rules and see to it that they are properly enforced. Indeed this would appear to be the most essential element in planning for development. There are, however, a number of reasons why such advice is difficult or impossible to follow in South Asia. First, there is the historical legacy. The colonial period destroyed the old structure of village "integration"; the fight for independence, and the fact of foreign government itself, set in motion attitudes of resistance to authority. The inauguration of the "strong state"—which in principle, of

[3] *Asian Drama: An Inquiry into the Poverty of Nations* (New York: Twentieth Century Fund, 1968), Vol. II, pp. 895–899.

course, could be democratic—is handicapped not only by the attitudes and institutions in the villages, but also by inhibitions of the rulers. Moreover, no South Asian country has an administration prepared to enforce new rules, even when these rules are not very revolutionary. Corruption, rampant at least on the lower levels even in colonial times, is generally increasing and takes the edge off commands from the central government. There is also an important ideological element among the inhibitions. As we have said, these new countries have generally accepted the egalitarian ideals of the Western democratic welfare state and the Communist countries. The fact that reforms in the interest of the under-privileged strata are largely thwarted on the level of both legislation and implementation must make precisely those members of the government and the intellectual elite who are most devoted to the egalitarian ideals wary of measures that would demand performance from the masses of poor people. Nonetheless, it is beyond doubt that *rapid development will be exceedingly difficult to engender without an increase in social discipline in all strata and even in the villages.*

General Policy Recommendations

Investment Capital Policies

If the developing countries, particularly the densely populated ones, are to achieve rates of economic growth more rapid than they have in the past, they must increase the flow of capital available for investment into their economies. This increased flow might come from any one, or some combination, of four sources: (1) governments of the Western democracies; (2) governments of the developed Communist nations; (3) private investors in the developed nations; and (4) taxpayers and lenders in their own countries (i.e., a greater financial squeeze on their own people).

It is anyone's guess what the capital giving and loaning propensities of the governments of the Western democracies and developed Communist nations in the years to come will be. But if the immediate past is any guide to the future, neither of these sources is likely to increase their total flow of investment funds to the developing countries in the years ahead. Further, that flow is likely to be highly dependent upon political considerations. Thus, it is our judgment that these two sources of investment capital are not likely to yield an increased flow and are always likely to remain closely related to political considerations.

The record of developing countries in squeezing investment capital out of their own citizens or providing an economic climate favorable to investment of foreign capital is uniformly bad. There is a chronic unwillingness to tax the wealthy and the high income earners (i.e., the larger farmers and landlords and the larger and successful business firms); this is a manifestation of the "soft state" again. And there is, for political reasons, a persistent tendency to whip the foreign investor with words, regulations, and taxes. Consequently, the typical developing country is desperately short on investment capital.

This is something that the developing countries can correct, and something that each country which is truly determined to develop must correct. A substantial flow of surplus funds moves annually from each less developed country into ostentatious living (e.g., weddings and foreign travel, trinkets and jewelry, and Swiss banks). These flows, if captured by progress-oriented governments, could go a long way toward providing the financial resources required to support school systems, power grids, road systems, research stations, and the importation of producer goods—all so desperately needed by these countries. The policy position on this point is clear: if a country really wants to modernize itself, increase per capita real incomes, and solve its food problem, it must be prepared to tax the high income earners among its citizenry; it must be prepared to acquire through taxation a substantial portion of the large incomes received by its moderately rich and exceedingly rich citizens.

Providing a favorable economic climate for foreign private investment, and thereby increasing the flow of investment capital into the developing country, is really not a formidable task. Generally it will involve no real costs to the country. Even the rabble-rousing political speeches directed against foreign investors need not be foregone.

The steps that must be taken to increase foreign private investment in a developing country are really three in all—one general policy step and two procedural steps. First, the countries involved must decide at the policy (political) level that they want an increase in investment in their country by private foreign firms and individuals, and resolve to take those actions necessary to attract that capital. Second, the bureaucratic and discretionary regulations on investment decisions and business operations, which are often oppressive in the developing countries, must be reduced to a level where foreign private firms are willing to enter the field. Third, some kind of effective guarantee must be given to foreign private investors against the expropriation of their invested capital.

Admittedly, the last two procedural steps are not easy for a newly developing country that may only recently have won its independence from a colonial power and may be embarked upon a broad course of socialism to take. But countries seeking to develop rapidly and on a broad base cannot "have their cake and eat it too." Rapid economic development requires, among other things, heavy invest- ments in social overhead services and industrial plant and equip- ment. If the funds required for those investments cannot be squeezed out of the domestic economy in sufficient amounts, or found in grants from friendly developed nations, then the develop- ing nations will be forced either to reduce their economic growth targets or to take action to attract foreign private capital. If they choose the second course, they must take actions which lead to less binding regulations, fewer discretionary controls, and some guar- antee of property. The larger international business firms have had too much experience to be attracted by vague political promises.

In sum, general economic development is geared directly to cap- ital formation; it can occur no more rapidly than the input of capital to provide social overhead services and industrial plants and equipment, although it may occur more slowly if certain other requisite conditions are not met. Thus, capital must be found and invested. And it is the judgment of this writer that important in- creases in the flow of investment capital into the developing world must in the future come from two principal sources: savings and tax revenues derived from the populations of the countries them- selves; and private foreign business firms.

Manpower Policies

There is much talk about manpower policies around the world these days, both in the literature of development and in technical assistance work. But little is being done in the developing world either to formulate operational policies or to implement them. The sons and daughters of the rich continue to go abroad, as they have for decades, to be educated in the fields of their interest. The sons and daughters of the near-rich, government workers, and the intellectuals all clamor for educational opportunities at home to escape from menial jobs and poverty; these educational opportunities, however, usually turn out to be in the humanities or social sciences. As for the poor, who make up the overwhelming part of the population, they are largely ignored, except as primary education is beginning to take hold in some countries. But the connection between trained manpower and economic development is only tenuously understood.

The need for trained manpower is well known by national leaders in a country like India, but the implementation of policies to produce and utilize that trained manpower is fragile and ineffective even there. In the newer developing countries, higher education and advanced training is more often viewed as a luxury; the connection between education and training on the one hand, and economic development on the other, is simply not understood. Thus, the idea must be fostered and then acted upon in the developing world that a modern-industrial-commercial-scientific society capable of high levels of production can be built and maintained only by a highly trained and skilled labor force.

This means that a developing nation that is serious about modernization, and becoming increasingly productive in agriculture, manufacturing, and the distributive trades, must embark upon a two-pronged approach to education and training. One approach must be concerned with extending primary education to the masses to provide, first, a literate working force capable of understanding and following complex instructions and, second, a broad base of candidates for vocational or possibly advanced training. The other approach must be concerned with all aspects of providing advanced technical training and higher education to fit the development needs of the nation.

There is not too much to be said about the first of these approaches. Either a nation is willing to build the schools, train the teachers, and produce the teaching materials to extend primary education to all of its people, or it is not. It can hold taxes to low levels and minimize the level of government expenditures by failing to provide primary education for the masses. By such a policy it is spared today the heavy costs of building an educational system for its masses; but it cannot become a highly developed, highly productive economy in the long run, because it will lack the literate and trained labor force upon which all such economies are based.

A program of advanced technical training and higher education in a developing country must be concerned with a series of related issues: (1) decisions as to the number of individuals to be trained to what levels in what fields; (2) the establishment of equitable and productive processes for selecting persons to be trained; (3) the provision of training at home, in a developed country, or in a country of intermediate development; (4) the implementation of policies to bring the trained personnel home; and (5) the employment of the trained personnel in fields related to their training and at salary levels commensurate with their training.

Instead of dealing with point 3 above in a haphazard fashion, as usually happens, the manpower policy of a developing nation must deal with all five points systematically. The content of the solutions can, and probably should, vary from one country to the next. One country may want to emphasize agricultural and medical training, for example, in the early stages of its economic development, and another may want to emphasize engineering and public administration. But certainly a manpower training program is worth less than nothing to a country if it concentrates on points 1 through 3 above, and then fails to bring its trained manpower home, or permits it to remain unemployed upon return.

The most precious resource in a developing country, or any country for that matter, is trained manpower. Trained manpower is absolutely vital to build, maintain, and administer a modern-industrial-commercial-scientific economy. Thus, every developing country which seeks to achieve a broadly based and rapid rate of economic growth must have as an operational goal a rational program of manpower training and employment.

Pricing, Wage, and Fiscal Policies

In their drive for greater social equity, or perhaps a more egalitarian society, many developing nations have forgotten that prices and wages have the role of allocating resources as well as producing income. Fertilizer prices, set at high levels by a government agency to cover high costs of production in inefficient plants, will certainly act to hold the use of fertilizer to low levels on farms, especially where farm product prices are being depressed again by government procurement actions. And it will be difficult to induce college-trained men and women to become primary schoolteachers, regardless of the political exhortations, if teachers' salaries are below those received by government clerks, tourist guides, and salesmen. Scarce transportation services will be used to the breaking point if those services are provided at low-cost, subsidized rates. In sum, a product or a service will be underutilized when its price is held high relative to the price of alternative goods and services, regardless of the essential goodness or badness of the purpose of the action; and it will be overutilized, or exhausted, when its price is held low relative to the prices of product and service substitutes.

This means that developing countries with weak administrative structures should not generally attempt to achieve equity, or social goals, through price and wage manipulations. Such manipulations are likely to produce strange and unwelcome results, such as a surplus of government clerks and a shortage of primary schoolteachers, or a surplus of sophisticated farm machinery and a shortage of fertilizer. A classic example of this occurred in India in the early 1960's. In an effort to hold food prices to "fair" levels for urban consumers as food production lagged, farm prices were depressed by government-requisitioning procedures; hence the incentive to increase food production was depressed. The effort to achieve an equity goal—namely, low food prices for urban consumers—acted to dampen down food production at the very time that an expansion was desperately needed.

In our view, prices and wages should be employed in the main to guide the production and distribution of goods and services—that is, to allocate productive resources—in the developing countries. This may mean a reliance on free market prices, if the government is too weak to manipulate the forces of supply and demand which generate those prices. Or it may mean a manipulation of the forces of supply and demand to achieve some production or distribution objective. But if this latter policy is pursued, it should be recognized by the country involved that the actions taken to manage either the supply or demand of a product, hence its price, will in turn influence its use in other areas. In other words, the price and wage objectives of government operations must fit—must be integrated—into the national production plan or development strategy.

An individual price or wage cannot be treated in isolation. If the economy is to run smoothly and efficiently, wages and prices must be set at levels that yield the supply of the products or services required in the next stage of production or distribution. Prices must be set so as to avoid a surplus in one product and a shortage in another. The free market system, of course, does this automatically. But a free market system may not produce and distribute the quantities of different goods and services called for in the national plan. Thus, a nation committed to national planning will be required to manage its price and wage system. But that nation must, if it is more than playing at planning, manage its product prices and wages in a total and integrated manner so that it produces and distributes the kinds and quantities of goods and services called for by the plan.

We may then ask: If the price system is not used to achieve particular equity and social objectives, how is a developing country to build and operate public school systems and public health and family planning systems, and assist the very poor to obtain better housing and improved diets? The answer is that every sovereign nation has the power to levy taxes and use the revenues produced by those taxes to achieve equity and social objectives.

The problem in many, if not most, developing nations is that their governments behave as if taxing the wealthy and the large income earners was a positive evil. Thus, the revenues needed are simply not forthcoming. This being so, developing countries often try to achieve their objectives by (1) manipulating particular product or input prices, and/or (2) running the printing presses (creating paper money) to obtain public funds. The first tends, as we have already pointed out, to create difficult resource allocation problems in which needed products like food are not produced in adequate supply, and unneeded products like fountain pens and jewelry are in surplus everywhere. The second leads to national inflation which in turn tends to choke off investment in productive enterprises, and so acts to destroy or erode the national will to develop.

Both of these cheap political solutions lead to trouble; both inhibit, derail, or destroy the process of general economic development. The achievement of a broadly based, reasonably rapid rate of economic development, and of particular equity and social objectives within the overall process of development, are absolutely dependent upon a nation's will and courage to tax its citizens. There is no way around this fiscal requirement, except insofar as foreign loans, public or private, are available; and there have been and will continue to be extreme shortages of these foreign resources relative to need. Each developing country that is serious about modernizing itself and raising the real incomes of its masses through economic development, as well as achieving specific welfare objectives, must develop and impose a taxing system that is capable of raising the revenues required for its development and social objectives. This really means instituting a tax system that reaches into the pockets of the wealthy and large income earners of the national societies. If they can't or won't do this, then they can't or won't develop economically. Development is not a game; it is a process that consumes resources on a massive scale. And those that can't or won't provide the resources must fall by the wayside.

Policy Recommendations for Food and Agriculture

Research and Development

As we said earlier, the engine of agricultural development is research and development. The achievement of a highly productive, modern, scientific agriculture is dependent on research, first, to discover and formalize scientific relationships and, second, to convert those scientific relationships into techniques and technologies to be adopted and employed on farms. We argued further, in the previous chapter, that the developed nations must therefore assist the developing nations to bring into being rational, long-range programs of research and development in agriculture.

We argue now that the first, basic step in modernizing a traditional agriculture is the establishment of a program of research and development with the capability of effecting such modernization. This means that each developing country must cooperate with the technical assistance efforts of the developed countries, provide additional resources of its own, and, with advice and counsel, assume responsibility for establishing a systematic program of research and development for agriculture. In a cooperative effort—where the developing nations provide primarily bricks, mortar, land, and men and women for training and the developed nations provide primarily scientific equipment and materials, trained personnel, and administrative leadership—these partners must build in each viable developing nation: (1) a system of physical structures—research centers and experiment stations; (2) a cadre of trained research workers and administrative personnel from the nation involved; (3) a systematic, long-range program of research and development; and (4) a spirit of scientific achievement and performance that will produce useful and relevant results when the foreign advisers are gone.

Happily for the developing world, an important beginning has been made in a limited number of countries. Now there is a need to widen and deepen the effort. But in so doing, the effort must be a cooperative one, if the program is to be established and produce results on a sustained basis and at a pace required by the development plan or strategy. It must be a cooperative effort, in which the major scientific input and administration is provided by the developed nations in the early stages, but the input of technical work, leadership, and general administration is taken over by the host developing country step by step. Thus, the most concerned partner in this cooperative effort—the developing country—must, with all the wisdom and determination it can muster, see to it that this cooperative effort is mounted and carried through to a self-sustaining stage.

Provision of Producer Goods and Services

Once the program of research and development is in motion and the new production technologies are flowing forth—new plant varieties, new fertilizer recommendations, new water management practices, and new plant disease and pest control practices—a means for providing the producer goods, for distributing them, and for showing farmers how to use them must be brought into being and made to function effectively. To do this, many pieces of the production process must be related and phased together. First, these activities must be a part of the development plan or strategy. Second, trained manpower must be allocated to them. Third, pricing decisions in food, agriculture, and agro-service industries must facilitate the production and distribution of the requisite goods and materials. Fourth, financial resources must be found and allocated either to the production of the producer goods at home or to their purchase abroad. Finally, programs, private or public, must be conceived and put into operation to produce or acquire the necessary producer goods, distribute them, and show farmers how to use them.

It is futile to establish a production educational service for farmers before there are new practices and technologies to extend. It is frustrating to produce, or acquire, critical producer goods and have no effective means of distributing them to farmers. And it is nonsense to produce and distribute new technologies to farmers without an effective means of educating farmers in their proper use. So the second critical step in agricultural development is to provide new techniques and producer goods to farmers under conditions which lead to their effective use. And this step each developing country must find a way of taking.

A Sane Farm-Food Price Policy

The producer goods and materials described must somehow be produced in the "right" quantities and distributed to farmers. Farmers must take those producer goods, combine them with land, labor, and other capital goods, and somehow produce the "right" quantity of food and fiber products. The marketing system, public or private, must take those farm products and distribute them among domestic consumers and foreign purchasers in some "right" way. And "right" in this context means everywhere an operating condition in which there are not crucial product shortages and surpluses created by the production-distribution system.

It may be possible to guide the total food supply of a nation through its diverse and elaborate production and distribution structure by means of a set of man-made rules and man-made quantitative decisions. But we know of no modern society where this has happened. Certainly the developed modern economies, whether communistic or capitalist, rely to an important extent upon a price system to guide the use of resources in the production and distribution of goods and services. The communist economies may rely more heavily on a managed price system, and the capitalist economies more heavily on a free market price system. But both depend upon a price system—a set of prices in a rational ordering—to guide the use of resources in producing and distributing goods and services. By "guiding" we mean that a plant manager in seeking a profitable operation will have to decide whether to use more or less of a resource in accordance with its price relative to the prices of substitute resources, and a consumer in seeking to maximize his, or his family's satisfactions, will have to decide to use more or less of a product in accordance with its price relative to product substitutes.

The point we are stressing is this: if a developing nation wants to modernize its agricultural plant, increase food production, and move that increased production into consumption, it must adopt a farm-food policy which facilitates that development. More specifically, it must establish a system of prices, from the production of farm producer goods (e.g., fertilizer, pesticides) to the production of farm-food products, to the wholesale distribution and retail dispersion of food products, which will induce producers and distributors at each stage to undertake the necessary production and distribution activities. The final result of this rational price system— rational in the sense that it induces the production and distribution sought in the development plan or strategy—might well be a set of food prices which creates hardships for the very poor. If this is the case, then the government in turn must subsidize the food consumption of these very poor people.

But the key point is that the very poor cannot possibly improve their diets unless the food is first produced and made available. And a rational farm-food policy is a prerequisite to getting that food produced and distributed in a modern, commercial economy. This the developing nations must recognize.

Toward a More Efficient Marketing System

The food marketing systems of countries in an early stage of economic development tend to be primitive and highly limited in the functions they can undertake. In the main, they are concerned with moving ungraded, unprocessed farm-food products from the countryside to nearby market towns and selling them to local consumers. In somewhat more advanced stages of development, the marketing system will undertake some storage, transport, processing and, where cash crops are involved, probably some exporting and importing. But the typical less developed country is not prepared to move the large surpluses of a highly productive agriculture long distances to large centers of urban population and undertake all the intermediate functions of grading, storing, processing, and retail distribution that may be involved. Such a complex process is alien because, until recently, there existed no need for marketing systems with such capabilities.

But with development—with the growth in urban populations, rising real incomes, and modernization of traditional agricultures— the need for a good marketing system able to handle large volumes efficiently becomes acute. And a good number of developing countries have now reached a stage where they urgently need such an efficient marketing system—India and Pakistan, for example. Without this system, food products are wasted, farmers receive a low return on their products, and consumers are confronted with periodic market gluts and shortages. Stated differently, the urban consumer in a large metropolitan area cannot enjoy an adequate food supply, and the commercial farmer in a surplus-producing region cannot enjoy a satisfactory economic return, unless these two groups are bound together by an efficient marketing system.

What steps, then, must a developing country take to bring a modern, efficient marketing system into being? First, it must recognize that marketing is a legitimate and necessary activity and stop treating every marketer as if he were a thief and a villain. Second (a corollary of the first point), the myriad rules and regulations that attempt to control and direct every move of marketers and traders must be eliminated as far as possible and the rules themselves liberalized to permit flexibility. Third, marketers and middlemen must be provided with technical assistance and credit comparable to the assistance given farmers. Here technical and financial assistance to cooperative marketing and purchasing organizations is highly desirable, if it is aimed at independent, viable business organizations; and the development of an adequate system of product grades and standards is imperative. Fourth, it will probably be both necessary and desirable for government to establish and operate some sort of national marketing organization in the basic crops (e.g., grains, oils, cotton) to cope with heavy surpluses in years of bumper crops and provide needed stocks in years of short supply. Such a balance-wheel operation on the part of the government may be necessary to even out supplies over time and stabilize prices to both farmers and consumers.

Providing for a modern, efficient marketing system is not the first or even second priority in the strategy of agricultural development. On the other hand, it cannot be delayed too long, or the delay will act as a deterrent to agricultural development. It is too late, once the new, high-yielding varieties are in full production and surpluses in the major producing areas begin to mount. And we know that the new, high-yielding varieties of rice and wheat are being widely adopted throughout West, South, and East Asia in the late 1960's, creating surpluses in the better producing areas. Those surpluses will cause farm prices to fall disastrously and the incidence of spoilage and waste to increase sharply. It may be that visible surplus problems are a necessary prerequisite to the establishment of modern marketing systems. But if this is so, it is a costly strategy of economic development.

The agricultural development strategy of each developing country should thus include a course of action for bringing into being an efficient food marketing system in the proper time sequence. This system must have the capacity to handle efficiently the surplus production of each principal producing area, store it, transport it, process it, and distribute it over time to the deficit areas as required. But such a system, working in reasonable harmony, will not come into being any more easily without the assistance of government than did the modern agricultural producing plant. Both require a scientific research base, improved techniques, new and additional resources, and skilled manpower. To think of a modern marketing system without thinking about the satisfactions of these requirements is to think wishfully. The government of a developing country must assist with the building of a modern, efficient marketing system in ways comparable to the building of a modern, scientific agriculture.

Help for the Small Farmer and Surplus Agricultural Labor

Development in agriculture is not likely to be even and equally beneficent. It will probably occur first on the larger farms, where the operator is literate, his "connections" good, and his financial resources strong, and it will move fastest on such farms. Conversely, it is likely to lag on very small farms, where the operator is more likely to be illiterate, his accessibility to new ideas limited, and his financial resources weak; the small farmer could well be "gobbled up" in the process by his economically stronger and more advanced neighbor. Agricultural modernization is also likely to reduce labor requirements on farms as machinery and equipment are substituted for hand labor. Thus, the force of agricultural development is likely to lead to increased amounts of surplus agricultural labor in rural areas.

A nation that ignores this rise in surplus agricultural labor is likely to find itself in trouble. Such surplus labor may drift to the cities and form a ring of unemployed around those cities, or it may float in aimless fashion in rural areas. But whether this surplus labor has migrated to the cities or remained in rural areas, it will be destitute, hungry, and ripe for radical action. Such people will pursue revolutionary courses of action, if those courses promise an improved life —why shouldn't they?

Stated differently, agricultural development creates social problems as well as real income benefits. The social problems arise out of the costs of adjustment, which tend to fall with greatest severity on the very small farmers and the landless labor. These are the agricultural workers who first become surplus as modernization occurs in agriculture. These are the workers who must adjust and move as modern techniques and technologies substitute for them.

The happy solution to this problem is, of course, industrial and commercial development in urban areas to provide more productive and more remunerative jobs for these displaced agricultural laborers in the cities. If this occurs, the national development process is working as it was hoped, even planned, that it would; the gross domestic product is increasing and is being spread in a reasonably equitable fashion over the available working force.

But if the displaced agricultural workers are not reemployed in the development process, it may be necessary for the national government to employ them in public works projects. These might include road building, irrigation maintenance and construction, and dam and levee building. Such projects would serve two purposes: (1) providing employment for destitute surplus agricultural labor; and (2) creating infrastructural facilities necessary for the general development of the country.

Further, by wise and aggressive programs of assistance to small farmers, developing nations can reduce the casualty rate and thereby minimize the flow of these people into the landless labor force. Some countries seem to have been exceedingly successful in assisting the very small farmer to participate fully in the development process; Taiwan is one such developing country.[4] Every effort should be made to convert the small traditional farmer into a viable, efficient modern farmer. This goal should have a high priority in agricultural development strategy. But insofar as the surplus agricultural labor force is augmented by the development process itself (and this is happening in many developing countries), those same countries must be prepared to deal with the expanding unemployment problem. In our view, a practical and productive means of dealing with this problem is to be found in a public works program.

The Hard Line Revisited

Most of the ideas presented in this chapter are not new. They have been discussed and written about a great deal during the 1960's, but very often they do not get beyond the idea stage in developing countries. Where they do become incorporated into policies, those policies often are not vigorously implemented and the program results are meager.

The ideas are not wanting. What is wanting is the hard work, the self-discipline, and the financial resources to carry them out. The point we wish to make here is that the additional financial

[4] *Taiwan's Agricultural Development: Its Relevance for Developing Countries Today*, ERS, USDA, Foreign Agric. Econ. Report No. 39 (April 1968), esp. pp. 39–48.

resources required to implement these ideas will not generally be forthcoming from the developed nations—whether capitalist or communistic. Those countries have their own internal and external ambitions to further, all of which cost more than they feel they can adequately support. Economic aid to the developing world in the late 1960's takes the form of charity, and thin charity at that. The financial resources required to implement the development policies, agricultural and general, described in this chapter must come largely from hard work and savings on the part of the developing countries themselves. Such hard work and resultant savings will occur only if there is self-discipline on the part of all members of those societies.

If this diagnosis is correct, the political leaders of the developing countries must stop fanning the income expectations of their people and start extolling the virtues of hard work and savings. In short, the politicians must find a way, if they really seek development for their countries, to substitute self-discipline for rising expectations in the daily thinking of their people.

14

Summary and Conclusions

IT HAS BEEN THE BASIC THESIS of this study that population growth has not run away from food production in the developing world; we believe that a careful review of the recent historical records supports this thesis. Population growth, it is true, has been rapid and shows no signs of slowing down in the near future; but rates of increase in food production have been equally rapid. Both population growth and agricultural development have been, and continue to be, highly dynamic factors in the developing world.

The demand for food, compounded of population growth and rising money incomes, did increase more rapidly than food production in some important developing countries in the early 1960's. This pressure of demand on food supplies led in turn to a tightening of food supplies, rising food prices, and considerable political discontent. The gravity of the situation was complicated by a partial failure of the monsoon, and a bad crop year, in South Asia in 1965–66. These factors, in conjunction with a rediscovery by the West of the surge in population growth in the developing world in the 1960's, led to wild speculation about world famine and dark despair for the future.

But the rains returned, and the development efforts in agriculture in the densely populated regions of Asia began to pay off in the period 1967–69. New, high-yielding varieties of wheat and rice became available to farmers in West, South, and East Asia, and were widely adopted; increased supplies of fertilizer became available to farmers, as well as increased supplies of other producer goods needed (e.g., pesticides, tube well equipment), so that the out-turn of these grains increased dramatically. Thus, at the end of the 1960's it appears possible that increases in food production will match and exceed increases in food demand in the developing world in the foreseeable future.

But these dramatic developments in the *production* of food grains do not alone solve the food problem of the developing countries. The forces of development—political, social, and economic— in large measure created the modern food problem, and only through successful general development will it be solved. The modern world food problem, as we know, has three principal components. First, some 2 billion people in the world are living in countries and regions where most of the inhabitants suffer from undernourishment or malnutrition, or both; and many experience outright hunger. Second, the total demand for food in the world and in several important regions of the less developed world has been increasing more rapidly than food supplies in the past decade. This pressure of demand on food supplies leads to a serious economic problem that takes the form of rising food prices, empty food shops, or a combination of both. Third, given the expectation of rising levels of living (including improved diets) in the developing countries, short supplies, empty food shops, and rising food prices result in disappointment and dashed hopes and thus in social and political unrest; in extreme cases, rioting and the overturning of governments follow. Thus, in the context of modernization and development with the concomitant expectation of rising real incomes, the food problem takes a modern twist: *it is the failure to achieve improved levels of food consumption, not starvation, that leads to social unrest and political upheaval*.

The obvious solution to the world food problem is to produce more food and thereby increase the supplies available per capita. Much is being achieved in this direction. But before we discuss this solution in some detail, let us consider another equally obvious solution. It is to reduce the rate of population growth in the developing world and thereby have fewer mouths to feed. Strenuous efforts are being made in some developing countries to moderate rates of population growth through birth control, and some successes are being achieved. But the consensus among demographers is that rates of population growth in the developing world will not abate significantly in the next two decades, but will continue at or about 2.5 percent per year throughout the 1970's and only slightly less than that in the 1980's.

Realistically, then, it does not appear that a solution to the world food problem will occur through declining birth rates in the next two decades; the solution must come in the form of increased production of the kinds of foods that the populations of the developing world both require and want. In the next half-dozen years, this clearly means placing the greatest emphasis on increasing the output of food grains in most developing countries. But in the late 1970's this probably implies that it will be necessary to transform the agricultures of many developing countries once again. This second transformation will move in the direction of producing more animal products, with all the attendant problems that entails.

Because of the scarcity of land that can be readily converted into tillable acres, it is unlikely that further increases in food production will occur to any important degree in the next two decades through expansion of the areas now under cultivation. The increases in production will have to come through the modernization of agricultural plants in the developing world—the conversion of traditional agricultures into modern, scientific agricultures. Through such modernization—the development of new production techniques and their adoption on farms—food production in the typical developing country must be increased from between 2 and 3 percent per year to 4 or 5 percent per year. This is the magnitude of the problem.

The specific actions required to increase agricultural production and distribute the product in a reasonably efficient and equitable manner have been summarized as follows: (1) establish research stations, acquire new scientific knowledge, and develop new production practices and technologies; (2) introduce these new practices and technologies to farmers; (3) produce and distribute the production inputs required by the new practices (e.g., fertilizers and insecticides); (4) make credit available to farmers so that they have the financial resources to acquire the new production inputs; (5) set up a marketing system that can efficiently concentrate, store, move, process, and distribute surplus products from the better producing areas; at present such systems are generally nonexistent;

(6) maintain product prices to farmers at incentive levels; (7) ensure a national reserve stock operation in the basic commodities to enable these countries to pass through periods of seasonal shortages and poor crop years with stable food prices and reasonably adequate supplies for consumers; and (8) organize special food programs to reach the poorest and most vulnerable groups (children and nursing mothers).

These are the actions which must be taken to increase food production further, sustain those increases, and ensure a reasonably efficient and equitable distribution of supplies. Some important successes have been achieved in at least the first three specific actions described above—namely, the development of new, high-yielding varieties of wheat, rice, and other grains; the extension of these new varieties to the larger, more aggressive farmers; and the increased availability of such production inputs as fertilizers and insecticides.

But the eight specific actions outlined above, which, if effectively carried out, would significantly increase the availability of food in the developing countries, *cannot be carried out in isolation.* All of them imply at least five additional related actions throughout the economy: (1) transfer of farm labor made surplus by the agricultural modernization process into nonfarm occupations, to provide those people with a respectable livelihood and increase the total product of the country; (2) feed the labor transferred from agriculture to the nonfarm sector with the help of a food surplus either generated in the domestic economy or acquired from foreign sources; (3) accumulate capital to be combined with the labor transferred into the nonfarm sector and to provide for the greater use of producer goods in the farm sector; (4) either produce the increased volume of goods needed in agriculture in the nonfarm sector of the developing country or acquire it from abroad; and (5) make sure that the marketing system, the stabilization stock operation, and the feeding programs described above reach into the nonfarm sector and compete successfully with other nonfarm enterprises for resources required by the development process.

In short, the actions required directly in the agriculture sector to increase food output and to distribute it efficiently and equitably entail a second set of actions in the general economy. If this second set of actions is not effectuated, the first will become simply a set of good intentions.

In other words, the new, high-yielding varieties of wheat that are sweeping across South Asia from west to east, and the new, high-yielding varieties of rice that are sweeping across Asia from east to west, will not continue to produce high yields over the long run if (1) the knowledge and materials are not available to combat the disease epidemics that are also certain to follow these varieties across Asia; (2) incentive prices to producers are not maintained so that farmers can and are willing to purchase the necessary tube well equipment and fertilizers; and (3) a marketing system is not developed which is capable of physically handling the surpluses produced in the more progressive areas. Further, if ways are not found to assist the small farmer to participate in the production revolution in food grains, that revolution will be aborted, and new and greater social problems will be created as the small farmers are "gobbled up" by the larger, more aggressive farmers. Thus, the agricultural development process creates all kinds of economic and organizational problems which must be resolved if the development process is to be sustained and food production is to be increased in the kinds of commodities demanded by urban populations experiencing rising incomes.

We can now ask: Will all of the requisite direct actions in agriculture and all of the secondary actions in the general economy actually take place? No one knows the answer in any certain sense. In some countries the general development process, with its infinite complexities and subtleties, seems to be moving forward satisfactorily. In others it is in a state of chaos and responsible officials and citizens are frustrated beyond description.

Three further conditions must be satisfied if these numerous requisite actions in agriculture and in the general economy are to be undertaken with any hope of success: (1) the required investment funds must be obtained in adequate amounts, perhaps from foreign governments as grants or loans, perhaps from foreign private investors, or perhaps from taxes and savings squeezed out of the domestic populations. *But they must be obtained.* Development is a voracious consumer of capital, and it can proceed only to the extent that capital is available; (2) manpower must be trained and employed in the work required by the development process. A modern, scientific agricultural economy is absolutely dependent upon skilled manpower for its research and development, its farm management, and its general administration; (3) a development strategy which coordinates and knits together into a productive whole all these direct and secondary actions, as well as pricing, fiscal, and manpower policies, is absolutely essential. These various actions must be taken in the proper sequence and must be consistent with one another in scale and objective, if the economy is to grow and lift the rate of increase in food production to required levels. And this is the task and responsibility of a national development strategy.

One such development strategy might be the adoption and pursuit of a free market; but few developing countries have opted for this. Most developing countries seem to feel that government intervention, comprehensive planning, and socialism will result in more rapid rates of economic growth, along the lines that they wish to grow, than any variation of a free market. But the acceptance of planning ideology means that intervention in one sector of the economy must be followed by consistent and rational interventions in related sectors, if economic chaos is to be avoided. Such a sequence of steps generally leads to attempts at detailed planning and regulation of every sector of the economy. Unfortunately, a developing country with limited productive resources, even more limited skilled manpower, and a chronic unwillingness to impose obligations on its people (e.g., collect taxes) will find it practically impossible to formulate and execute such a detailed plan of economic development. For this reason, it has been suggested in this study that developing countries should pursue a mixed economic policy—involving some planning and some free market measures—and formulate a development strategy that is consistent with such a general economic policy. The scope and objectives of the strategy must, of course, be consistent with the resources and capability of the country concerned.

How can we be sure that these basic conditions will be satisfied? The answer is that we cannot, and all too often they have not been satisfied. Hence, the development process, including agricultural development, has disintegrated in particular developing countries. Basically the satisfaction of these conditions rests upon the existence of a progress-oriented government which has the vision to take the actions required by the development process, the wisdom to limit its development activities to those it can execute with a reasonable chance of success, the ambition to improve the economic well-being of *all* of its people, and the will to impose obligations on its people to achieve its objectives. In other words, the "soft state" which promises everything to its people and requires little or nothing of them must give way to the "disciplined, progress-oriented state" which works realistically, is concerned with performance, and understands the costs of performance. Only this kind of state can satisfy the basic conditions of development and take the actions in the general economy and in the food and agricultural sectors to sustain a rapid rate of increase in food production over the next decades.

Disciplined, progress-oriented governments depend in turn upon the ambitions and actions of their political leaders and intellectual elites. If the masses are told that their countries will develop and that they will realize greatly increased levels of living without cost or heavy obligations to themselves, they will want to believe this, and will in fact do so. In this context, their expectations soar, while development lags. The gap between expectation and consumption realization widens, and social and political unrest is the predictable result.

This study therefore concludes that successful development, including a solution to the food problem, rests squarely on the political and intellectual leaders of each developing country. If the leadership can establish a disciplined, progress-oriented government, modernization will occur as the actions required to make it occur are taken; real incomes will increase, and the food problem will be solved. This conclusion is based on an assumption we believe to be valid—that the technical knowledge can be created and adapted to the development requirements of almost every developing country. The problems arise and seem unending with respect to establishing the *organizations* that can effectively develop and employ that technology, acquiring the *financial resources* to support the activities and projects needed, and above all establishing in the hearts and minds of the people an *attitude of responsibility* toward the national development effort—a willingness to save, to forego immediate gains, and to accept a realistic tax structure.

The developed countries, too, have a responsibility to the developing world. Wise and consistent technical assistance on their part can render each of the actions required in agriculture and in the general economy more effective. Financial assistance, wisely and consistently given, can speed the development process and solve the food problem in each developing country, all other things being equal. A reduction in the developed countries of trade barriers for the products of the developing countries can assist those countries to build viable and productive economies. The developed nations that really want levels of living raised in the developing world and social and political tensions lessened have an obligation to keep technical and financial assistance flowing to those developing countries that are making a determined effort to help themselves, as well as to liberalize their trade policies toward the developing world.

Perhaps at this point, perhaps earlier, the reader is saying to himself: "This is too complex. Why don't we simply help farmers in the developing world produce more food?" The answer is that we (the United States and other developed nations) are trying to help the developing world produce more food, although those efforts have been a bit uncertain at times; but transforming a traditional agriculture in a densely populated country into a modern, scientific agriculture is a complex, difficult process. And, as we have said many times in this volume, it cannot take place in isolation. It can take place only through a series of interrelated actions within the framework of general economic development.

Or the reader may be saying to himself: "It is too complex; it can't be done." But it has been done in the past. It happened over a long period of time under reasonably favorable circumstances, through trial and error, in Western Europe and North America. It occurred in Japan under less favorable circumstances in a shorter period of time with more government guidance. And currently good-to-excellent progress is being made in such countries as Taiwan, the Philippines, Thailand, and Israel. The governments of these countries are behaving in an enlightened manner, development is taking place, food production is increasing, and the food problem is being solved. The general process is not simple and it is never achieved without mistakes and problems. But it can be done, given the right set of circumstances.

In sum, we are saying that the development problem and the food problem are technically solvable. Further, important steps are now being undertaken throughout the developing world to solve them. But the organizational and attitudinal aspects of these problems have a record of frustration, many failures, and too few successes. It is difficult to predict when, or if, a particular developing nation will establish the necessary organizational arrangements for a successful development effort and instill the social attitudes needed to encourage the actions that make the process work. All we can say is: "It has been done before. It can be done in the future."

So we conclude that, even with the rapid rates of population increase that seem to be in store for the developing world for the next decade or two, the technical capability exists, or can be brought into being, to produce the kinds and quantities of food that will be demanded and in this way solve the most serious aspects of the world food problem. But whether the governments of the developing countries will take the organizational and disciplining steps required is another matter. The long-term solution to the world food problem is, however, absolutely dependent upon the ability of the developing world, with crucial help from the developed world, to take these organizational and disciplining steps.

Appendix A

Definition of Regions
and Subregions

Subregions

Countries and territories were grouped into 22 subregions. Criteria for the groupings included geographic proximity and similarities in food production and use. Some countries constituted separate subregions themselves because of size and variation from nearby countries.

Western Hemisphere

1. United States (excluding Alaska and Hawaii)
2. Canada
3. Mexico
4. Central America and the Caribbean—Cuba, Haiti, Guatemala, Dominican Republic, El Salvador, Honduras, Jamaica, Nicaragua, Costa Rica, Panama, Trinidad and Tobago, British Honduras. *Others:*[1] Puerto Rico, Windward Islands, Leeward Islands, Bahamas, Bermuda, Virgin Islands
5. Brazil
6. River Plate—Argentina, Uruguay
7. Other South America—Colombia, Peru, Chile, Venezuela, Ecuador, Bolivia, Paraguay. *Others:* British Guiana, Surinam, French Guiana

[1] Individual food balance sheets were not constructed for those countries listed under *Others* for this subregion and the subregions that follow in the U.S. Department of Agriculture study reported in *The World Food Budget 1970,* from which these materials were taken.

Europe

8. Northern Europe—West Germany, the United Kingdom, France, the Netherlands, Belgium-Luxembourg, Sweden, Austria, Switzerland, Denmark, Finland, Norway, Ireland. *Others:* Iceland, Greenland
9. Southern Europe—Italy, Spain, Portugal, Greece. *Others:* Malta, Gozo
10. Eastern Europe—Poland, Yugoslavia, Rumania, East Germany, Czechoslovakia, Hungary, Bulgaria. *Other:* Albania
11. U.S.S.R.

Africa and West Asia

12. North Africa—UAR (Egypt), Ethiopia, Sudan, Morocco, Algeria, Tunisia, Libya
13. West Central Africa—Nigeria, Congo (Leopoldville), Ghana, Angola, Cameroon, Ivory Coast, Guinea, Sierra Leone, Togo, Liberia. *Others:* Upper Volta, Mali, Niger, Senegal, Chad, Dahomey, Central African Republic, Congo (Brazzaville), Portuguese West Africa, Mauritania, Gabon, Gambia, Spanish West Africa
14. East Africa—Tanganyika, Federation of Rhodesia and Nyasaland,[2] Kenya, Malagasy Republic. *Others:* Uganda, Mozambique, Rwanda, Burundi, Somali, Mauritius, Reunion, Zanzibar,[3] Seychelles, French Somaliland
15. Southern Africa—Republic of South Africa. *Others:* Basutoland, South-West Africa, Bechuanaland, Swaziland
16. West Asia—Turkey, Iran, Iraq, Syria, Israel, Lebanon, Jordan, Cyprus. *Others:* Saudi Arabia, Yemen, Aden, other Arabian states

[2] Now separate countries; Malawi (Nyasaland), Zambia (Northern Rhodesia), and Rhodesia (Southern Rhodesia).
[3] Now united with Tanganyika into Tanzania.

Far East

17. India
18. Other South Asia—Pakistan, Ceylon. *Others:* Afghanistan, Nepal, Bhutan, Sikkim
19. Japan
20. Other East Asia—Indonesia, Philippines, Thailand, Burma, Taiwan, Malaya.[4] *Others:* South Korea, South Vietnam, Cambodia, Hong Kong, Laos, Singapore, Sarawak, Sabah, Brunei, Melanesia, Micronesia, Polynesia, Ryukyu Islands
21. Communist Asia—Mainland China. *Others:* North Vietnam, North Korea, Mongolia
22. Oceania—Australia, New Zealand

---

[4] Now combined with Sarawak and Sabah to form Malaysia.

Appendix B

Definition of Food Groups

Wheat is shown as grain; trade includes the wheat equivalent of flour.

Rice is shown as paddy or rough rice.

Other grains include corn, barley, oats, rye, millet, and sorghum, as well as minor products such as buckwheat, quinoa, spelt, and teff. Trade generally includes edible products but not mixed feeds or byproducts.

Other starchy crops include potatoes, sweet potatoes, yams, cassava, and similar tropical roots. For European countries, exports generally and imports occasionally include the potato equivalent of starch. In some cases the exports also include the potato equivalent of starch products.

This group of commodities also includes bananas and plantains in countries which produce such crops abundantly, since these fruits provide cheap calories. However, in countries which import bananas, these fruits are classed with other fruits. Consequently, trade figures for these groups of commodities are out of balance to an unusual degree.

Pulses and nuts include beans, peas, lentils, chickpeas, and similar dry leguminous seeds. It also includes peanuts and soybeans in countries where they are used for food (thus excluding soybeans in the United States). Edible tree nuts, including coconuts, are classified in this group.

Sugar is basically raw cane and beet sugar, but honey, maple sugar, edible molasses, syrup, and palm sugar are also included for some countries.

Vegetables and fruits exclude commodities classified as other starchy crops. Trade statistics are generally on a product-weight basis, but for European countries they are mostly on a fresh equivalent basis. For most of the diet deficit areas, basic statistics are incomplete and the data used here are only approximate.

Fats and oils include butter (fat content), edible animal fats, marine oils, and vegetable oils which may be used for food. Oilseeds are not included in production or export data, but for several European countries the imports include the oil equivalent of edible oilseeds. U. S. exports of soybean oil, but not soybeans, are included. As a consequence, imports and exports are unbalanced. For Finland and the United Kingdom, margarine and shortening are included along with their constituent oils, thus causing some double counting in production.

Meat, fish, and eggs include poultry and game, in addition to other kinds of meat. Production of meat is generally on a carcass-weight basis. Production of fish is generally on a landed-weight basis, but for several European countries production is fillet-weight. Trade is usually in product-weight, except trade in egg products has usually been converted to shell-egg equivalent. Estimates of production and consumption of this group of commodities are necessarily only approximate.

Milk products include milk and milk products other than butter. Production refers to whole milk from cows, buffaloes, sheep, and goats. Nonfood use includes milk used for butter and whole milk fed to animals. Exports include the whole-milk equivalent of cheese, canned milk, and dried whole milk but no allowance for skim milk in any form, since the whole milk used for making skim milk was a part of the whole milk already allowed for making butter. The imports, on the other hand, include the whole-milk calorie equivalent of imported skim milk.

Index

Index

malnutrition (malnourishment) (*cont.*)
Western attitudes on, 63
see also diet; hunger
Malthus, Thomas Robert, 59
Malthusian theory of food-population
relationship, 59–60, 62, 65
management skills, agriculture and,
197–98, 199–201
Mann, Jitendar S., 137n
manpower, *see* labor; personnel, technical
market
agricultural development and organization of, 244, 292–95, 301
economic development and free,
304
export, 267–74
for natural products, technological
advances and, 268, 270–71
operation of national grain, 226–
27
for surplus agricultural products,
216–18, 225–27
see also trade
Marshall Plan, 123
Matusow, Allen J., 123n
Mauritania, 133
medicine, advances in, 63, 64
Mellor, John, 248
Metiner, T., 115n
Mexico
agricultural assistance of Rockefeller Foundation, 173, 220
agricultural production, 20, 21, 25:
increases, 67, 128
gross national product, 7, 9:
growth, 8
Middle East
family planning in, 114
see also specific country
milk production, World Food Program and, 131–32
Miro, C. A., 116n
mixed-capitalistic economic policy
model, 163–67, 209
development policies, 222–28
organizational examples, 213–20
relationships to farmers, 220–22
requirements for organizations,
209–13

Morocco, family planning in, 115
mortality, *see* death rate
Mosher, A. T., 185
Myrdal, Gunnar, 64, 179n, 233n;
quoted, 282–83

Nair, Kusum, 236; quoted, 189–92,
194–96
Nasser, Gamal Abdel, 114
National Advisory Commission on
Food and Fiber recommendations on research institutions,
172
Near East
gross national product growth, 8
post-World War II food shortages,
123
see also specific country
Nepal, birth control program in, 110
Nicholls, William H., 231n, 235n
nutrition, *see* diet; food; malnutrition
(malnourishment)
nutritional deficiency diseases, 48–49
nuts, consumption of, 40, 41

Oceania, economic assistance to, 151
Office for Economic Cooperation
and Development (OECD),
150n; *Aid to Agriculture in Developing Countries* report, 176n
oils, consumption of, 40, 41
organization(s)
actions of, 203–4
agricultural development: examples, 213–20; farm input provisioning, 211; farm-related, 210–
11; marketing, 244; progress-
oriented government as, 204–8;
relationships to farmers, 220–22;
requirements for, 209–13
concepts of, 203
development policies, 222–28
private foundations and development assistance, 166–67, 275
see also international organizations;
and specific organization
output, agricultural, *see* agricultural
production
Oxford Committee for Famine Relief, 132

undernourishment (*cont.*)
world incidence, 49, 71, 75
see also diet; hunger; malnutrition (malnourishment)
Union of Soviet Socialist Republics, see Soviet Union
United Arab Republic (UAR)
agriculture in, 180
family planning in, 114
U.S. food aid programs in, 134
United Kingdom
economic assistance by, 151, 152
food aid to, 123
Irish potato famine, 62
population cycle, 60, 61
tariffs, 273n
United Nations (UN)
development assistance and, 275–76, 277
international marketing and, 269
World Food Program, 129–34, 146, 147
see also Food and Agriculture Organization (FAO); World Bank
United Nations Conference on Food and Agriculture, 4
United Nations Conference on Trade and Development (1968), 280
United States
agricultural production yield, 31, 32
economic assistance programs, 92–93, 151, 152, 155–61, 259–60, 262: in agriculture, 168–74; attitudes on economic assistance, 258–59; technical assistance program, 262, 265, 266, 267
food exports vs. food aid shipments, 135
foreign food aid, 122–28, 239, 242: evaluation of, 136; impact on recipients, 136–39; magnitude of, 134–36; responsibilities in food aid, 146–47
standard of living and GNP growth in, 11

United States (*cont.*)
surpluses in, 124, 128
tariffs, 273n
World Food Program and, 130
urban areas, consumer expectations in, 6

vegetables, consumption of, 40, 41
Venezuela
agricultural production, 20
population growth, 17

wages
policy on, 287–90: agricultural development and, 202
resource allocation and income production and, 287–88, 289
weather, crop production fluctuations and, 76–77
welfare payments, 241
West, see developed nations; and under specific country
Witt, Lawrence W., 136n
Woods, George G., 154
workers, see labor; personnel, technical
World Bank
appraisals of development process, 174n
coordinated program for economic development, 94–96
development assistance and, 275–76
on economic assistance, 154
World Food Program (FAO), 129–34, 146, 147
evaluation of, 133–34
projects, 131–33
resources, 130–31
World Plan for Agriculture (FAO), 91n, 97, 174n

Yugoslavia
agricultural production, 20, 31
U.S. food aid programs in, 134